FUNDAMENTALS OF

CARPENTRY

Volume I

TOOLS • MATERIALS • PRACTICE

WALTER E. DURBAHN, B.S., M.A.

Formerly Chairman of Vocational Department
Highland Park High School

Highland Park, Illinois

Member of American Vocational Association

Collaborator
(Third Edition)

NICHOLAS M. VAN LOON

Carpentry Department
Apprentice Training School
Detroit

Illustrated

AMERICAN TECHNICAL SOCIETY

CHICAGO · U.S.A.

PREFACE

A NYONE who at one time or another has worked with wood—or has hankered to—will find this volume indispensable. The fundamentals it presents are important not only for the conventional applications of carpentry to home building, but also for the applications of carpentry to the many closely related trades such as boat building, millwrighting, insulating, composition floor laying, and dock, and bridge construction. Each of these occupations shares a common denominator with carpentry, since many of the tools, materials and methods are common to all.

Fundamentals of Carpentry, Volume I—Tools, Materials, Practice is as broad in its scope as its title implies. For the layman it unfolds the fundamentals of carpentry in simple terms. For the apprentice who wants to become a skilled craftsman it offers clear cut instruction in one-two-three order. For the master carpenter it combines a diversity of coverage with detailed accuracy to provide a valuable reference work.

For the reader of this book, each fundamental process in carpentry is presented in concise and simple terms. Although the book has been organized primarily for class or shop instruction, it is also an efficient self-learning tool, particularly adaptable for home-study purposes. To motivate the student or apprentice, each chapter begins with a set of "Questions This Chapter Will Answer," and ends with a set of review questions "Checking on Your Knowledge." Precise instructive illustrations are employed throughout.

Primarily this volume aims to provide the reader with the basic knowledge that a good carpenter must have. It includes a descriptive discussion of "Principal Woods, Their Uses, Grades, and Classifications," which furnishes the reader with a knowledge of lumber and its proper application. Two important chapters, especially helpful to the apprentice and student, deal with "Wood Fastenings" (considerably expanded in the Third Edition) and "The Framing Square." Con-

PREFACE

structive and mechanical skill in carpentry depends to a large extent upon a knowledge of these fundamentals.

Such other chapters in the book as those upon "Modern Carpentry Tools" (revised and expanded in the Third Edition), "Power Tools" (new to the Third Edition), "Insulation," and "Blueprint Reading" emphasize the twofold purpose of the text—to increase the reader's fund of knowledge, and at the same time to develop his practical skill.

Tables in the Appendix and an extensive "Dictionary of Carpentry Terms" enhance the value of this volume as a ready reference book for the layman, for the hobbyist, for the vocational learner, for the apprentice, and for the carpenter tradesman.

The fundamental carpentry principles introduced in this volume are applied to the actual construction of a house in a companion volume, *Fundamentals of Carpentry Volume II—Practical Construction.*

THE PUBLISHERS

ACKNOWLEDGMENTS

The author gratefully acknowledges the wholehearted co-operation of the many manufacturers and organizations listed herewith.

Organizations, Associations, and Bureaus

American Forest Products Industries, Inc.
American Forestry Association
American Society of Heating and Ventilating Engineers
American Walnut Manufacturers Association
Bureau of Aeronautics, United States Navy
California Redwood Association
Mahogany Association, Inc.
National Lumberman's Association
Red Cedar Shingle Bureau
Southern Pine Association
United States Bureau of Labor Statistics
United States Forest Products Laboratory
United States Forest Service—Division of Information and Education
West Coast Lumbermen's Association

Manufacturers

Alfol Insulation Company, Inc.
American Floor Surfacing Machine Co., Inc.
Appalachian Hardwood Manufacturers, Inc.
Armstrong Cork Company
Continental Steel Corporation
DeWalt Products Corporation
Disston, Henry & Sons, Inc.
Duro Metal Products Co.
Flinkote Company
Gateway Engineering Company
Independent Nail & Packing Co.
Insulite Division, M. & O. Paper Company
Johns Manville
Morse Twist Drill & Machine Co.
Owens-Corning Fiberglas Corporation
Owens-Illinois Glass Company
Skil Corporation
Sprayo-Flake Company
Stanley Works, The
Star Expansion Co.
Starrett, L. S. Co., The (Tools)
United States Gypsum Co.
Yale & Towne Mfg. Company

Books and Periodicals

American Builder, Simmons-Boardman Publishing Co.
American Forests, American Forestry Association
American Lumberman, American Lumberman, Inc.
American Nature Magazine, American Nature Association
Better Homes & Gardens, Meredith Publishing Company
Wood Handbook, United States Department of Agriculture

CONTENTS

CONTENTS

"AMERICA'S FUTURE WILL BE DETERMINED BY THE HOME AND THE SCHOOL"—*Jane Addams*
Photograph by Haskell, Courtesy of United States Gypsum Co.

Carpentry as a Trade

1. *What is carpentry?* 2. *How old is carpentry, as a craft?* 3. *How does the modern carpenter enter the trade?* 4. *What about present-day opportunities?* 5. *How may an apprentice advance?*

INTRODUCTION TO CHAPTER I

If you enjoy handling tools, and you like to build; You will probably experience a genuine satisfaction in seeing a job well done, whether it is a properly constructed workbench, a comfortable animal shelter, or a well-equipped home. If carpentry appeals to you, you will be interested in this book which was carefully planned to meet your needs.

In the first chapter of this book, the author tells you about the work of the carpenter. He tells you interesting facts which should make you take pride in this work, and he also tells how, if you are ambitious, you may prepare for advancement in this field.

CARPENTRY AS AN ANCIENT CRAFT

Carpentry is the art of working with wood, in the construction of buildings in which men live or work, the making of furniture, and many other devices of wood, to help man adapt himself to his environment. The art of carpentry is thousands of years old. We might say that carpentry began when man first left the caves in which he had lived until then; driven out perhaps by hunger and the need to seek better hunting grounds, he made for himself crude shelters of branches which he covered with leaves and grass.

However, this early ancestor had no tools, as we know them today, and since tools are so vital a part of carpentry, it would perhaps be more correct to say that carpentry began when men first fashioned crude tools from bronze and iron. With these tools, wood that was used for building and making could be cut instead of broken. Men then began to shape wood into useful objects and to improve the shelters which protected them from their enemies and the weather.

THE MODERN CARPENTER

At one time the carpenter's work was almost entirely with wood. However, in recent years many substitutes for wood have been put on the market, and, in order to protect his interests, the carpenter has claimed the right to work in many of the newer materials, on the basis that such work requires the use of carpentry tools.

When a jurisdictional dispute arises among the different trades as to which trade is to do certain work, each trade in question selects a representative to present its case, and these representatives jointly select a neutral judge or referee who analyzes with care the facts presented to him, and then renders a decision in favor of one trade or the other.

Through jurisdictional award, the following work has been adjudged to be carpentry: the erecting and insulating of metal trim, such as bucks, jambs, doors, transoms, casings, metal medicine cabinets, metal weather stripping, and other similar work; the laying of plain and ornamental cork and rubber-tile flooring, baseboards, or wainscoting, whether laid or set in composition or glue, and where brads or nails are used; the erecting and applying of all composition materials, such as Zenitherm, Sheetrock, Celotex, Nu Wood, Beaverboard, Compo Board, Transit Asbestos Wood, and other rigid-board substitutes; assembling and setting of all seats in theaters, schools, halls, and similar buildings; all millwright work, such as setting of engines, and installing of all types of machinery in factories and mills.

However, the carpenter's work is not confined to the erection of buildings; this is only one phase of carpentry. Carpenters are employed in the building of bridges, piers, docks, and wharfs. A large number of men are employed as boat or ship carpenters, work requiring training which is different from that for building and construction work.

In the metropolitan areas where labor is more highly organized, the work of the various trades must be carefully defined. In small communities, a carpenter is likely to be called upon to do work which in a city would be done by another tradesman.

Though persons unfamiliar with trade classifications are apt to assume that everyone who works in wood is a carpenter, this is not so. There was a time when the carpenter not only built the house, but also made the trim, the built-in cabinet work, and even in some cases, the furniture. However, today, a builder of furniture is a cabinetmaker, while the man who makes the interior trim and builds stairs is a millman. In general, millmen and cabinetmakers, together with similar woodworking craftsmen, belong to the large group of men who work in factories; whereas the carpenter is employed on what is known as *outside work*.

Training. The practical way of entering the trade is through an apprenticeship or as a helper. In either case one requisite is a background of experience with tools, through training obtained in the industrial arts programs and the vocational training courses that are offered in most modern schools.

A student interested in carpentry should take all the work offered in the industrial arts and drawing classes, both in elementary school and the first year of high school. If this training is then followed by two or three years of vocational trade training and an apprenticeship after graduation, the young carpenter should be well qualified as a journeyman.

A carpenter should be familiar, at least to some extent, with the work of the other building trades. Therefore, it is recommended that his vocational study in high school include general trades training. He should take the various courses offered in bricklaying, concrete work, plumbing, sheet-metal work, painting, and electrical wiring. This training should be secured while the student is still in school because he will probably not have an opportunity for training in these fields after he has indentured himself as a carpenter's apprentice. The value of experience in other trades can scarcely be overemphasized; this is especially true if he wishes to advance to the position of foreman. As a foreman, he must assume some of the responsibility for the work of other trades on the building, for often the workmen in other trades will come to the foreman for information regarding procedure in their work.

The Carpenter Apprentice. The apprentice should have a good high school education. The age of carpentry apprentices varies from seventeen to twenty-five. In order to become an apprentice a written indentureship agreement must be signed with an employer. The employer must be one who regularly maintains a force of qualified carpenters. The agreement must be approved by the state or by a trade

organization. In accordance with the indenture, the apprentice agrees
to work at and to learn the carpentry trade, while his employer agrees
to teach him the trade. The employer also agrees to send the apprentice to school to receive technical instruction in the trade and related
subjects. The frequency of his attendance varies in different areas; it
may for instance be, as it currently is in the Detroit area, one full day
every two weeks. This training is usually provided by the local Board
of Education or the public school system.

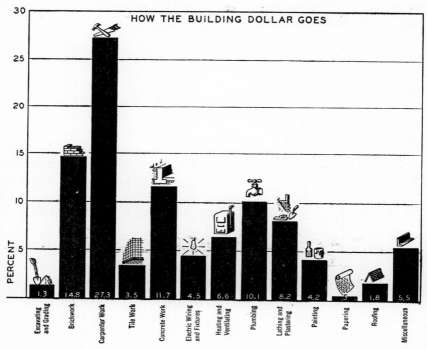

Fig. 1. Diagram Showing Percentage Cost of Each Class of Work in the
Total Cost of a Residential Building, an Average of Fifteen
Cities in the United States
United States Bureau of Labor Statistics

Wages for the apprentice vary in different parts of the country.
They are gradually increased in increments, every four-month period
after the first eight months of apprenticeship. For instance, in the
Detroit area in 1959, for the first eight months they were 60 per cent of
the journeyman's hourly rate. For the third four-month period they

were 65 per cent of the journeyman's rate; for the fourth four-month period, 68 per cent; for the fifth four-month period, 71 per cent; for the sixth four-month period, 74 per cent, and so on until at the end of four years, the apprentice receives 90 per cent of the journeyman's hourly rate. In 1959, in the Detroit Metropolitan area, the journeyman's hourly rate was $3.55, plus fringe benefits.

When the apprentice completes this training period and passes an examination satisfactorily, he becomes a journeyman carpenter. He can then work anywhere he wishes, and it is assumed that his qualifications entitle him to journeyman's wages.

The trade offers an ambitious young man many opportunities for advancement. Progress is usually achieved by supplementary practical experience on the job, with evening school courses or correspondence courses, by reading books and trade journals, and by contact with skilled craftsmen. Those adept at the trade become foremen in due course, then perhaps carpentry contractors, or general contractors. Others may continue their training to become architects.

Building Trades Wage Rates. The hourly wage rates of union building tradesmen are possibly the highest of any group in the mechanical trades. The wage rates in effect in the Detroit area at the end of 1960 are given below; all of these rates include fringe benefits.

Trade	Hourly Wage	Trade	Hourly Wage
Bricklayers	$3.98	Painters	$3.50
Carpenters	3.63	Plasterers	3.90
Electricians	4.00	Plumbers	3.90
Glaziers	3.47	Resilient floor	
Iron workers	4.00	decorators	3.50
Metal lathers	3.65	Sheet metal workers	3.90
Millwrights	3.61	Steamfitters	3.90

The hourly wage rate, of course, is not the only measure by which to judge or select a trade. Work in the trades having higher hourly rates may not be as desirable nor as steady as in other trades having a lower hourly wage scale. For instance, by far the bulk of construction is in residential building, and in this field the carpenters do approximately 27 per cent of the total work as shown in Fig. 1. Thus about

27 cents out of every dollar paid for residential construction goes for carpentry work. Therefore, even though his hourly wage rate is not so high as some of the other trades, the carpenter is apt to be more steadily employed and his yearly income may be higher than the yearly income of other tradesmen with a higher hourly wage rate.

The Building Industry. The building industry is one of the largest industries in the country. Housing is a basic need, and the continuously increasing number and expanding activities of the industrial and business world also make steady demands on construction. Repairs and alterations, too, play an important part in the building field.

CHECKING ON YOUR KNOWLEDGE

The following questions give you the opportunity to check up on yourself. If you have read the chapter carefully, you should be able to answer the questions. If you have any difficulty, read the chapter over once more so that you have the information well in mind before you read on.

DO YOU KNOW

1. What carpentry is?
2. When carpentry first began?
3. What work has been adjudged to be carpentry?
4. What a millman is?
5. What a cabinetmaker does?
6. What is required of a man who wishes to become a carpenter?
7. How a man becomes an apprentice in this work?
8. How a man becomes a journeyman carpenter?
9. Why a carpenter's yearly wage is likely to be higher than that of other tradesmen?
10. What statistics show about the future needs for building in the United States?

CHAPTER II

Tools of the Carpentry Trade—
Hand Tools

QUESTIONS THIS CHAPTER WILL ANSWER

1. *How does the size of a modern toolbox compare with those formerly used by carpenters?* 2. *What primary tools should be in the kit of every carpenter's apprentice? Name ten secondary tools needed when he has completed his training.* 3. *What is the carpenter's most important measuring tool?* 4. *Of all carpentry tools which one is used the most?* 5. *Why does the carpenter usually make for himself such devices as: the sawhorse, workbench, stepladder, miter box, straightedge, door jack, and his various toolboxes? Why is it important for an apprentice to learn how to make a first-rate sawhorse?*

INTRODUCTION TO CHAPTER II

In this chapter you are told how to select your carpentry tools. Because the choice of tools is extremely important to any workman, this chapter deserves careful reading and special study. As a carpenter, your future success depends upon your ability to use tools effectively and skilfully. You must learn to look upon your tools as a true craftsman does; you should examine them in detail and learn to appreciate valuable, efficient tools. The development of a sense of appreciation of a superior tool will give you great satisfaction and pleasure.

The numerous illustrations in this chapter will help you to understand the value and use of each tool. As you read the author's description of each of the various tools illustrated, look closely at the picture. If possible have the same tool or a similar one in your hand as you read the description of it. For example, it will be helpful to have a framing square in your hand as you read about it, and compare the one you are holding with the illustration given in the textbook. Do the same with the saw and plane, and as you read about these tools, compare the one in your hand with the illustration and the author's description of it.

If you study this chapter carefully you will learn many interesting facts regarding tools. You will learn that there are many different types of saws, instead of just one or two with which you are familiar. You will learn also about the various types of planes a carpenter uses in the process of constructing a new building. As you acquire this and other valuable information you will become aware of the fact that carpentry is really a science worthy of careful study and consideration as a lifetime occupation.

You will find the study of carpentry tools fascinating for another reason also. You are now to begin the actual work of making some of the essential equipment used by every carpenter. Observe carefully the minute details given in the instructions for building a sawhorse, a saw vise, a workbench, and other devices used by a carpenter on every construction job.

As you begin to apply the knowledge of tools acquired by the study of this chapter, you are also beginning to acquire valuable practical experience in the use of carpentry tools. Be sure to put forth your best efforts on every object you build. Careless work is never excusable in any trade; from the beginning do your best on even the most simple device you make. An apprentice on a new job is often judged by the kind of sawhorse he builds, hence it is important that as an apprentice you learn to build well. A carpenter enjoys the advantage of doing creative work; whether he constructs buildings or equipment, he takes justifiable pride in a job well done.

A CARPENTER AND HIS TOOLS

A few years ago a carpenter was compelled to own so many tools and devices that his equipment looked like a thriving hardware store. He came on the job with a large toolbox three or four feet long, two feet high, and about two feet deep. All the tools which he might need to complete the job were kept in his toolbox. He needed many different kinds of tools because he not only did all of the rough and finished carpenter work but also made the trim, built the stairs, the cabinets, and the cupboards. Today, after the rough work is done, the carpenter merely fits into place the trim, cabinets, and stairs which have been made in a mill or factory. Trade rules now compel contractors to furnish much of the larger and more expensive equipment. In recent years tools have been improved so much that it is possible for a man with one tool to do the work once requiring several tools; one example is the universal plane. This plane has replaced approximately two dozen matching and molding planes formerly required to do the work. Together with the shifting of much of the work from the job to the mill, these improved tools have reduced the number of tools required by the present-day mechanic.

The carpenter comes onto the job today with a small hand or shoulder box in which he carries two-thirds of his tools. Others that he might need on the job are left in the trunk of his car.

APPRENTICE TOOL KIT

The beginner's or apprentice's *tool kit* usually is limited to tools for rough work; as his training program takes him into finer work the need of other tools must be met. However, it is well for the beginner to exercise considerable care in the selection of these tools so that he may gradually build up a kit of tools of high quality and durability.

To begin with, the tools which the carpenter's apprentice will need are listed under *Primary Tools*. These are the tools used for rough work; named in probable order of purchase, however, this order depends to a great extent upon the nature of the apprentice's work. The *Secondary Tools* are desirable but usually can wait until the training and the nature of the apprentice's work demands their purchase. To buy a complete set of tools would mean a considerable outlay of money at the start and would be inadvisable until he has had at least one year of trade experience which will help him to select the necessary and most desirable tools.

PRIMARY TOOLS	SECONDARY TOOLS
1. Rule	1. Block plane
2. Hammer (curved claw)	2. Ripsaw, $5\frac{1}{2}$- or 6-point
3. Hand ax, or hatchet	3. Crosscut saw, 10-point
4. Crosscut saw, 8-point	4. Compass saw
5. Pinch bar	5. Coping saw
6. Try square	6. Hack saw
7. Roughing chisel	7. Dividers
8. Cold chisel	8. Brace
9. Framing chisel	9. Set of auger bits
10. Screw driver	10. Finish chisel, $\frac{3}{8}''$, $\frac{3}{4}''$, $1\frac{1}{2}''$
11. Framing square	11. Hand drill
12. Level	12. Set of drill points
13. Jack plane	13. Scribers

As an aid to the beginner, a brief description of various common tools is given in this text, together with a more detailed explanation of some of the important tools. However, the list is not complete, as space will not permit showing all the tools which are used by a carpenter.

TOOL CLASSIFICATION

Carpenter tools may be classified into several groups by the usual order of their use.

1. Layout and measuring tools

2. Saws

3. Paring and shaving tools
4. Boring tools
5. Tools for supporting and holding work
6. Abrading and scraping tools
7. Percussion, or pounding, and impelling tools

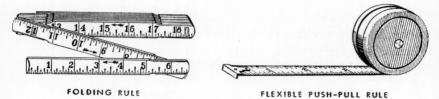

FOLDING RULE   FLEXIBLE PUSH-PULL RULE

Fig. 1.   Two Types of Expanding Rule

Fig. 2.   Steel Tape Available in Various Lengths

1. Layout and Measuring Tools.   The ease and accuracy with which a craftsman lays out his work depend not only upon his skill and training but also to a great extent upon the kind of tools he has available.

A *six-foot zig-zag ruler* (Fig. 1), is the first measuring tool which the carpenter will find that he needs.   There are several grades of ruler available; and it is a wise investment to get one of good quality.   A drop of fine machine oil in each joint of a new ruler will make its operation smoother and its life longer.   A measure of care should be exercised when opening and closing the wood zig-zag ruler.

The *pull-push metal ruler* (Fig. 1), can occasionally be used to advantage.   It is available in both six and twelve foot lengths, and is half an inch wide.   Oil should be applied sparingly to this ruler, for

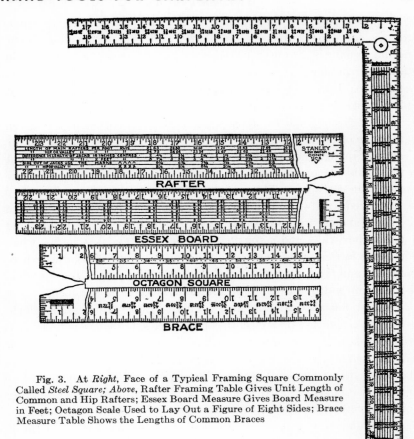

Fig. 3. At *Right*, Face of a Typical Framing Square Commonly Called *Steel Square; Above*, Rafter Framing Table Gives Unit Length of Common and Hip Rafters; Essex Board Measure Gives Board Measure in Feet; Octagon Scale Used to Lay Out a Figure of Eight Sides; Brace Measure Table Shows the Lengths of Common Braces

the oil will collect dirt which in turn will damage the numbers and divisions as well as impair the action of the rule.

The *steel tape* (Fig. 2), is an important tool for layout work; the measurement of rafter lengths, room lengths and diagonals. The measuring of wall diagonals is an aid to insuring that walls are square for framing. Steel tapes are available in lengths from twenty-five feet to one hundred feet. Oil should be applied sparingly as for the pull-push metal ruler.

The *framing square* (Fig. 3), as its name implies finds its main use in the various framing operations performed by the carpenter. Some of the operations are the framing of a house, the spacing of studs, framing for doors, windows, fireplaces, and similar openings. The framing square is also used in the layout of stringers and carriages in stair construction; rafter framing tables for all pitches are found on the square. In fact the uses of the square are so many and varied that entire books have been written on this tool alone.

Although only a brief description of the framing square is given here, some of its many uses are further explained in the chapter on the Framing Square, and elsewhere in this book in connection with layout work. This instrument should be treated with care, and cleaned at the end of each day's use. The readability of the engraved numbers may be improved with white paint wiped off immediately after application.

The standard framing square has a *blade,* or *body,* 24 inches long and 2 inches wide, and a *tongue* 16 inches long and 1½ inches wide. The blade forms a right angle with the tongue. The outer corner where the blade and tongue meet is called the *heel.* The *face* of the square is the side on which the name of the manufacturer is stamped.

On a standard square the inch is divided into various graduations, usually into eighths and sixteenths on the face side; on the outside edge of the back, or reverse side, the inch is divided into twelfths, useful in making scaled layouts; the inside edge is divided into thirty-seconds and one-tenths. On some squares the division of one inch into hundredths is stamped on at the heel, to help the estimator when making quick conversion of decimals into fractions with a pair of dividers.

A framing square made of stainless steel will not rust, an item of great importance when selecting any tool. Galvanized, copper- or nickel-plated squares are also rust resistant; however, the plating on these squares is apt to wear off in the course of time. A copper-plated square has the advantage of white figures, and the division marks can be read more easily than similar marks on the stainless-steel square.

In addition to the convenient division marks and the rust-resistant material, it is advisable to select a square which has useful tables stamped on it; for example, the *rafter-framing table, Essex board measure, octagon scale,* and *brace measure,* Fig. 3. Rafter-framing tables vary with different makes of squares. Some are unit-length tables while others are total-length tables for the most common roof

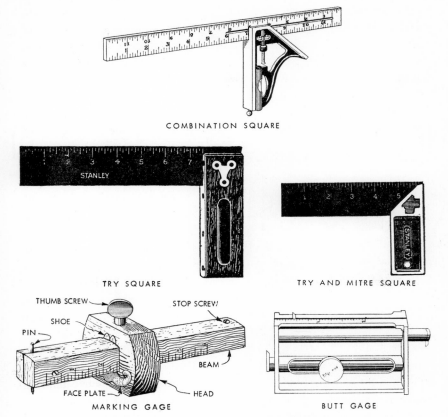

Fig. 4. Selection of Measuring and Layout Tools
Try Square, and Try and Mitre Square Courtesy Stanley Tools

pitches. Although these tables are not always used, it is convenient to have them at hand when the need for them arises. After a workman thoroughly understands the rafter-framing tables, he uses them more frequently. A book of instruction usually accompanies each square and in this book the manufacturer has explained the various tables and how to use them. See also the chapter on the Framing Square in this text.

The *combination square* (Fig. 4), is a steel tool, twelve inches long, with a 4½ inch handle. The blade is either slotted or grooved.

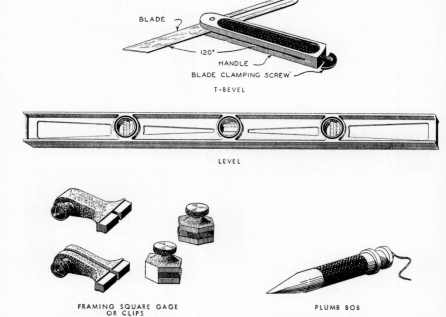

BLADE

120°

HANDLE

BLADE CLAMPING SCREW

T-BEVEL

LEVEL

FRAMING SQUARE GAGE
OR CLIPS

PLUMB BOB

Fig. 5.   Selection of Layout and Leveling Tools, Including Stair Framing Square
Gages, Used in Stair Construction

The handle and the blade are so joined as to allow measurement, on a
go or no go basis, of both 45 degree and 90 degree angles.   It is useful
for short markings, and because of its size it can be carried in the hip
pocket.   Combination squares are sometimes made with a spirit level
built into the handle.   This tool should receive the same care as a
framing square.

The *try and mitre square* (Fig. 4), has a blade ranging from 6
inches to 10 inches in length, with a 4 inch to 6 inch handle.   Angles of
45 degrees and 90 degrees can be checked with the handle, but unlike
the combination square, no adjustment can be made.

The blade of the *try square* (Fig. 4), is between 6 inches and 12
inches long, with a 4⅜ inch to 8 inch handle.   This tool has been almost completely superseded by the combination square which is more
versatile.

The *butt gage* (Fig. 4), is used to lay out hinges on doors and door

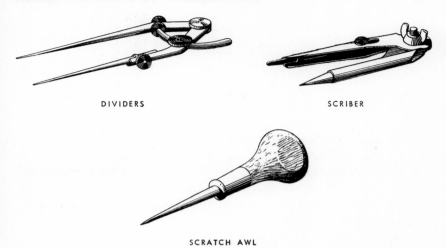

DIVIDERS   SCRIBER

SCRATCH AWL

Fig. 6.   Layout Tools Including a Scratch Awl Used for Marking in Layout Work

jambs. It has three marking knives which can be set from $\frac{1}{16}$ of an inch to 2 inches. It should be kept free from dirt and lightly oiled.

Stair framing square gages (Fig. 5), come in pairs and are used on the framing square to mark off different rises and runs for stringers, in stair construction, and also for rafter layout. They are available in two different styles. The set screw should be oiled regularly.

The *level* (Fig. 5), is a tool used by the carpenter to plumb and level building members. The 24 or 28-inch level is the most commonly used in the carpenter trade. Particular care should be taken not to drop the level, since the glass containing the fluid may shatter, and the level be distorted.

The *plumb bob* (Fig. 5), is a weighted tool, from $2\frac{3}{4}$ ounces to 16 ounces in weight, and ranging in length from 4 inches to 6 inches. It is commonly used in form construction, to ensure that the form is vertical. It is also used in conjunction with a transit (the tool that the carpenter uses in the plotting of a building).

The *T Bevel* (Fig. 5), has a blade which ranges in size from 6 inches to 12 inches, and is adjustable in length. Since the angle of the blade to the handle may be adjusted as well as its length this tool is used a great deal in angular work. When two pieces of wood are to fit together at an angle, the **T** bevel is used to measure that angle, and by

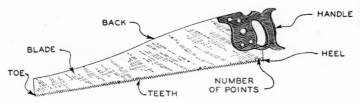

Fig. 7.   Curved or Skew-Back Hand Saw

bisecting it, the cutting line necessary for a perfect fit is obtained.

Wing type dividers (Fig. 6), are available in lengths from 6 inches to 8 inches. This tool is used to check layout work, by stepping off the hypotenuse of the rise and run on both rafters and stringers for stair construction. Both points should be periodically sharpened and the vertex oiled for accurate work.

A *scriber* (Fig. 6), is a small marking tool, usually in the form of a compass, with a metal point at one end and a pencil fixed to the other. The scriber is used when fitting cabinets against walls or other surfaces and for the laying out of coped joints.

The *scratch awl* (Fig. 6). The scratch awl is a handy implement much used by carpenters and other woodworkers for locating positions and starting screws and nails for fastening small hardware, such as hinges on doors and windows. The blade varies in length from 2¾ inches to 3½ inches. Many carpenters also use the scratch awl for marking guide lines in layout work, and hence its classification as a layout tool.

2. Saws. The principal types of saws used in the carpentry trade are: *handsaws* (both *ripsaw* and *crosscut*); the *keyhole* or *compass saws, coping saw, backsaw,* and *hack saw.* Tools not commonly used by the carpenter include other types of saws, such as the turning saw and tenon saw. Most manufacturers make saws in various grades, of either hard or soft steel, and as either regular or lightweight models to suit individual needs.

HANDSAWS. Handsaws are available with either a curved (or skew) back, Fig. 7, or a straight back. The straight edge, which may be used for drawing lines before sawing, is an advantage of the straight-back saw. The better grades of handsaws are taper ground; that is, the blade is thinner along the back than it is along the cutting or toothed edge; such saws need little *set*. Usually prices are governed by quality.

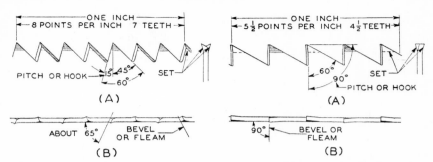

Fig. 8. Crosscut Saw Teeth Which Cut   Fig. 9. Ripsaw Teeth Which Cut Like a
Like Two Rows of Knife Points   Gang of Chisels in a Row

The greatest satisfaction ordinarily is obtained from the use of a relatively high-priced tool of superior quality.

a) Crosscut Saw. This saw is designed to cut across the grain of the wood; therefore, its teeth must be sharpened like a knife so they will cut the fibers of the wood on each side of the saw cut, or kerf, Fig. 8. The blade is from 7 to 11 inches long, and has from 7 to 11 points to the inch. The more teeth that there are to the inch, the finer the cut will be. The 8 point saw is most commonly used in rough construction, and the 10 and 11 point saw for finished carpentry work. The shape of the teeth of the crosscut saw depends upon the nature of the work the saw is intended to perform and also upon the hardness of the wood which is to be cut. For general work, the front face of the tooth should have a *pitch*, commonly called *hook*, of 15 degrees, see (*A*), Fig. 8; and a *bevel* of about 65 degrees, see (*B*), Fig. 8; each tooth should be sharpened with the file held in a horizontal position. For hardwood the tooth is filed with the same pitch and bevel, but the file is not held in a horizontal position; the handle must be held lower than the tip of the file. This will produce a bevel on the front of the tooth while the back of the tooth will remain straight. To produce a smooth cut in softwood, the pitch of the tooth should be about 20 to 25 degrees and the bevel about 45 degrees, with the handle of the file held lower than the tip. The point of the tooth will then be long and sharp and will be more apt to cut the soft fibers instead of tearing them.

A dull saw will not cut rapidly. It will tear the fibers of the wood instead of cutting them; these torn fibers will hang into the saw cut and cause the saw to bind. Dull teeth will reflect light and will appear as bright spots, whereas the tip of a sharp tooth will not be visible. The tip of the tooth is *set;* that is, it is *bent* toward the side of the point of the tooth to give it the clearance which is essential in wet or green wood.

b) Ripsaw. The ripsaw is used to cut wood with the grain, and has a 26 inch blade and in most cases 5½ or less points per inch. The teeth of this saw must be filed chisel-like to cut the wood fibers in the bottom of the saw cut instead of at the side, Fig. 9. The front of the tooth is at right angles, or 90 degrees, to the line of the teeth, see (*A*), Fig. 9; that is, the front of the tooth has no bevel, see (*B*), Fig. 9. Some mechanics prefer to file the ripsaw with a slight bevel. This makes it possible, when desirable, to use the ripsaw as a crosscut saw for cutting heavy timbers. The teeth of the ripsaw must have *set;* that is, the teeth must be *bent* to give them proper clearance. It will be observed that only the tip half of the tooth is set, not the whole tooth.

A carpenter should have no less than three handsaws: a 7- or 8-point 26-inch crosscut saw for rough work, a 10-point 24-inch crosscut saw for finish work, and a 5½- or 6-point 26-inch ripsaw. An old 7- or 8-point crosscut saw which has been worn down to a point makes a useful extra tool, as it is convenient for sawing into tight places, and can be used where there is danger of cutting into nails.

The *coping saw* (Fig. 10), has a 6⅜ inch long blade which is ⅛ inch wide. This saw is used for coping joints. When it is necessary to join two intricate moldings at right angles, the joint is usually coped. This entails first cutting one piece of stock away to receive the molded surface of the other piece, at an angle of 45 degrees to the stock. The blade of the coping saw can be turned as desired, for cutting sharp angles. The teeth of the coping saw blade should always point towards the handle. When many joints have to be coped, a saddle will make the task a very much easier one.

The *keyhole saw* (Fig. 10), is 10 or 12 inches long, with 10 points to the inch. Its main application used to be the making of keyholes in doors, although modern practice employs a lock or latch jig, and a brace and bit. The keyhole saw is still used however to cut openings in plaster board for electrical outlets, where a power tool would be too large.

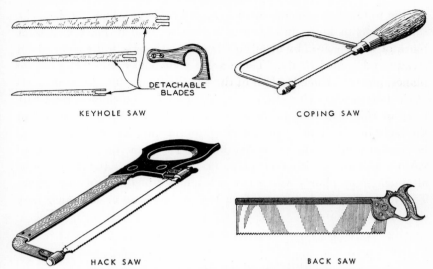

KEYHOLE SAW   COPING SAW

DETACHABLE
BLADES

HACK SAW   BACK SAW

Fig. 10. Selection of Saws Commonly Used by the Carpenter

The *backsaw* (Fig. 10), is used in a miter box. It ranges in size from 10 inches to 28 inches long and has between 11 and 13 points to the inch, which makes a very fine and finished cut.

The *hack saw* (Fig. 10), whose blade is between 10 inches and 12 inches long, has 14 to 32 points to the inch, and is used to cut metal such as nails and bolts. In form work it is used to cut such material as dovetail slot anchors, and is finding increasing use with the growing popularity of metal trim.

3. Paring and Shaving Tools. The paring and shaving tools include those which have knife edges, such as the plane and chisel, the two most important of the group.

PLANES. Together with the hammer, saw, square, and chisel, the *plane* is one of the principal tools used by the carpenter. When timber comes from the mills, it is rough from the saw. Before the rough-sawn timbers or boards can be used for any finished work they must be prepared to receive paint or any other kinds of finish. This preparation consists in smoothing or planing which can be carried to any extent, and may include sandpapering or even polishing. The instrument used for the rougher part of this work is called a *plane,* which consists of a sharp blade, or knife, in the form of a chisel held in place in a large block of wood or iron by means of clamps, so that the knife can be kept steady and guided easily.   There are a great many different kinds of planes, but the principle of all of them is the same.   The knife projects at the bottom through a slot and takes off a shaving which is relatively thick or thin according to the distance which the knife projects below the body of the plane.   Any imperfection in the edge of the knife will be repeated on the surface of the wood.   The plane family consists of various members, with each plane designed for a particular purpose, although some planes will perform a number of different operations. The following list is suggested in the probable order in which they should be bought:

1. Jack plane	7. Spokeshave
2. Block plane	8. Router plane
3. Rabbet plane	9. Scraper plane
4. Scrub plane	10. Universal plane
5. Jointer plane	11. Weatherstrip plane
6. Smooth plane	12. Bullnose plane

The wooden plane, though light and easy to operate, has been replaced to a considerable extent by the metal plane.   The steel-bottom plane, invented some time ago but not extensively used until recent years, is now rapidly becoming the choice of mechanics; it will withstand greater abuse than one of cast iron, and will not break as easily when dropped.

The various parts of the Stanley smooth plane, a development of the original Bailey plane, are shown in Fig. 11.   However, this plane is only one of several different makes available to the mechanic today. To describe in detail all the different planes on the market would require more space than is available for that purpose in this book. Hence, only a few types are given special mention: (*a*) the jack plane; (*b*) the smooth plane; (*c*) the jointer plane; and (*d*) the fore plane.

a) Jack Plane.   A plane for all-around work is the *jack plane* shown in Fig. 12.   This plane is used for rough work and to give preliminary smoothing to lumber coming directly from the mill.   Although the jack plane is manufactured in various sizes, the 14-inch length with

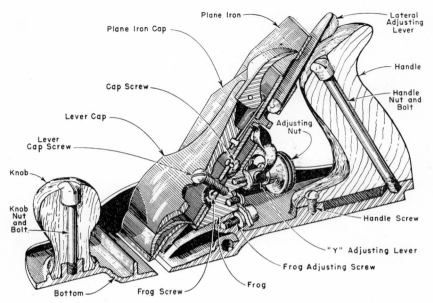

Fig. 11. The Stanley Smooth Plane

a 2-inch *cutter* or *blade* is most commonly used. The craftsman who uses the 14-inch length jack plane is able not only to smooth and joint a board but, also, to do other all-around work with this tool.

b) Smooth, or Smoothing, Plane. The *smooth plane*, though similar in construction to the jack plane, is usually much smaller. Since it is not expected to take off as much material as the jack plane, it does not require as great a force to operate the smoothing plane. This is a short, finely set plane, and may be made of either iron or wood; being light in weight it is easy to operate and will produce a smooth (though not true) surface, quickly, Fig. 13. A smoothing plane 8 inches long with a 1¾-inch cutter is recommended.

c) Jointer Plane. The largest of the planes is the jointer, Fig. 14. The *jointer planes* vary in size from 20 to 24 inches in length. When it is necessary to smooth a large surface, or to make the edge of a board absolutely true so that two such surfaces, when finished, will fit together closely, this plane is used following the preliminary smoothing by the jack plane. The jointer plane is made long and heavy because it is intended for use on long boards and for obtaining a true surface

Fig. 12.   Jack Plane Used for Rough Work and Preliminary Smoothing

Fig. 13.   Smooth Plane, Usually Smaller than the Jack Plane

Fig. 14.   Jointer Plane, Largest of the Carpenter's Planes is Intended for Use on the Work Bench

Fig. 15.   Low-Angled Steel-Block Plane Operated with One Hand

Fig. 16.   Rabbet Plane for Planing into Corners

Fig. 17.   Scrub Plane Used to Hollow Out Trim Members or to Give an Adzed Effect

Fig. 18.   Scraper Plane for Smoothing Large Surfaces

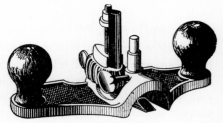

Fig. 19.   Router Plane Used for Surfacing Grooves

when joining two boards. The carpenter finds the jointer plane indispensable in fitting doors, and making the edges straight and true.

d) Fore Plane. Between the jack plane and the jointer is a tool called the *fore plane.* Some carpenters prefer an 18-inch fore plane to a 22-inch jointer since the smaller plane reduces the weight of the tools a carpenter must carry around with him. However, the long length of the jointer usually insures a truer-planed surface than is obtained with the fore plane which is shorter in length.

Other Planes. A few of the other planes which might prove desirable to own are illustrated and explained in Figs. 15 to 22. When working on a scaffold, a desirable plane for fitting is the low-angled steel block plane which can be operated with one hand, leaving the other hand free for holding the work, Fig. 15. A desirable plane for planing into corners or against perpendicular surfaces is the *rabbet plane* with its 1¼-inch cutter. This plane is also convenient in size as it measures only 8 inches in length, Fig. 16. The *scrub plane* with its rounded blade makes it possible to quickly and easily bring the boards down to rough dimension, to hollow out trim members, or to give timbers the adzed effect. The size recommended for a scrub plane is 9½ inches in length with a 1¼-inch cutter, Fig. 17. Where large surfaces are to be smoothed or floors are to be hand scraped, the *scraper plane* is indispensable, Fig. 18. The *router plane* is used for surfacing the bottom of grooves or other depressions parallel with the surface of the wood, Fig. 19. When it is inconvenient or expensive to go to the mill, the *Stanley "Fifty-Five,"* or *universal plane,* is a desirable tool to use to make various moldings, Fig. 20. The *bull-nose plane* will work close into corners or other places hard to reach, Fig. 21. The *grooving* or *plow plane* is used in applying weather strips, Fig. 22. Tool catalogues should be consulted when special work demands the use of additional planes.

OTHER PARING AND SHAVING TOOLS—CHISELS. *Wood chisels* (Fig. 23), are used to make holes or cut away wood to receive hardware, or to accept another piece of wood. They are available in widths from ⅛ of an inch to 2 inches. Short (9½ inch), or long (15 inch) blades can be obtained. Their sharpening is accomplished in an identical manner to the sharpening of the plane iron.

Cold chisels (Fig. 23), are available with blades from ¼ inch to 1¼

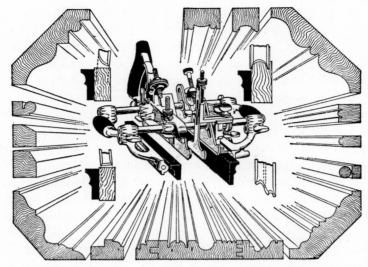

Fig. 20.   Stanley "Fifty-Five," or Universal Plane, Useful for Making Moldings

Fig. 21.   Bull-Nose Plane Works Close into Corners

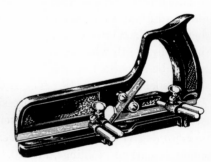

Fig. 22.   Grooving Plow Plane Used in Applying Weather Strips

inches wide and from 5 inches to 18 inches in length. They are made to cut metal such as nails, and dovetail anchor slots.

The *floor chisel* (Fig. **23**), is an all-metal chisel designed for hard usage, and when there is a possibility that the wood contains nails and other obstructions. Since it is also used as a tool for framing work, it must be designed to withstand a great deal of hard pounding.

4. Boring Tools. *Auger bits* (Fig. **24**), are used to bore holes in wood. They come in sizes from $\frac{3}{16}$ of an inch to $3\frac{1}{8}$ inches. Larger holes in wood are made with an *expansive bit* (Fig. **24**). These bits are available with a choice of two adjustable cutters, the smaller of which

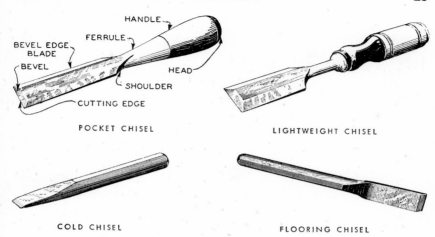

BEVEL EDGE
BLADE

BEVEL

HANDLE

FERRULE

HEAD

SHOULDER

CUTTING EDGE

POCKET CHISEL

LIGHTWEIGHT CHISEL

COLD CHISEL

FLOORING CHISEL

Fig. 23. Selection of Chisels Used by the Carpenter

is used for holes between $\frac{7}{8}$ of an inch and $1\frac{1}{2}$ inches. The larger cutter is used for holes up to $3\frac{1}{8}$ inches. *Lock bits* are used with a lock jig to make holes for the installation of cylindrical locks. The selection of auger bits usually carried by the carpenter runs from $\frac{1}{4}$ inch to 1 inch and is called a *set*.

Bit extensions (Fig. 24), will add to the length of the standard bit. They are obtainable in 18 to 24 inch lengths. The bit extension is used in form construction where two holes have to be lined up at a distance to receive the wall tie, and also when a hole is needed in a surface which cannot be reached with the standard bit.

Drills (Fig. 24), are used to make holes, not only in wood, but in metal, fiber, plastic, and other materials.

The *push drill* (Fig. 24), is a very useful tool for the installation of small builder's hardware. It operates semi-automatically and can be used in one hand, so that the work piece may be held in place with the other hand. As the handle is pushed in, it rotates the drill, and a spring in the handle causes it to return to its original position when the pressure is released. A set of drill bits ranging from $\frac{1}{16}$ inch to $1\frac{1}{16}$ of an inch is stored in the handle.

The *hand drill* (Fig. 24), is used to make holes from $\frac{1}{4}$ inch to $\frac{3}{8}$ of an inch in diameter. It is operated by the turning of a handle which is geared to the chuck.

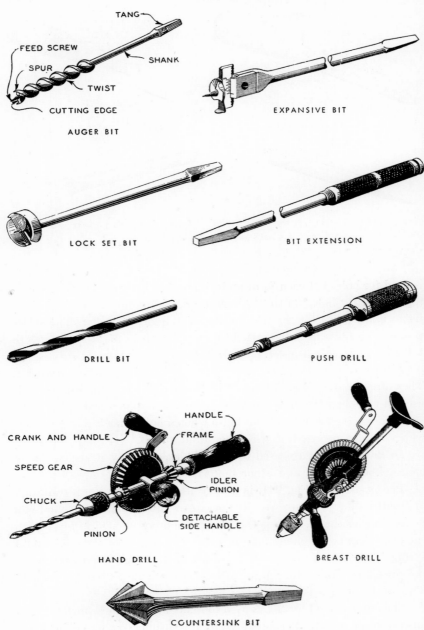

Fig. 24.   Boring Tools Used by the Carpenter

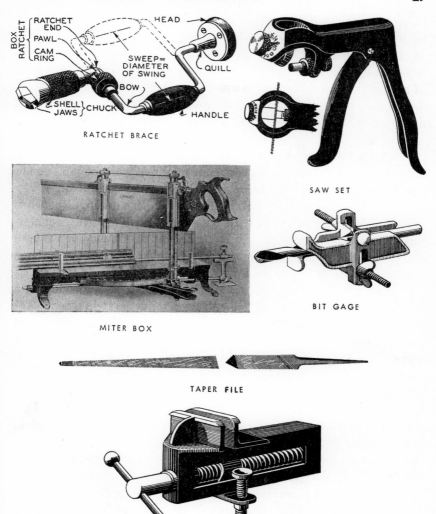

RATCHET BRACE

SAW SET

MITER BOX

BIT GAGE

TAPER FILE

PORTABLE VISE

Fig. 25. Other Important Tools and Accessories Used for Supporting and Holding Work
Miter Box Courtesy Stanley Tools

The *breast drill* (Fig. 24), is similar in appearance to the hand drill, except that it is a heavier tool and is used for making larger holes.

Greater pressure can be applied while drilling than with the hand drill, by applying the chest or shoulder to the breast plate.

The *countersink bit* (Fig. 24), is not actually a drill, but is used to increase the diameter of the top of a drilled hole to receive the head of a screw. The countersink is usually conical in shape; therefore the deeper the countersink is allowed to penetrate the greater will be the diameter of the hole, up to a maximum of ¾ of an inch.

5. Tools for Supporting and Holding Work. In this group are tools or devices, some of which the carpenter may make on the job. A few can be bought, while others are furnished by the contractor.

The *ratchet brace* (Fig. 25), is classified in this group, although it is only a tool-holding device. It is used to hold bits, drills, countersinks and screwdriver bits. The larger the circle of sweep of the handle, the greater the turning power exerted on the bit, and the easier it is to turn. Ratchet braces are available with an 8 inch to 14 inch sweep.

The *miter box* (Fig. 25), is a precision device used for guiding a backsaw at the proper angle for cutting a miter joint in wood. The carpenter usually makes his own miter box on the job, but more accurate manufactured boxes can be obtained. The standard miter box will cut wood up to 4 inches in thickness, and up to 8 inches in width if the cut is at right angles. The quadrant is graduated in degrees.

The *portable vise* (Fig. 25), which is clamped onto a sawhorse or work bench can easily be carried in the carpenter's tool kit, and receives heavy use. A typical vise of this type will clamp on a bench or saw horse up to 2½ inches in thickness. The L-shaped jaws are designed to hold work both horizontally and vertically, and open up to 3½ inches. This type of vise when clamped onto a sawhorse makes an excellent holding device for doors during the application of hardware. The *vise* used by carpenters is too bulky to be easily carried around, and is therefore usually furnished by the contractor.

The *saw set* (Fig. 25), is a tool used in the maintenance of crosscut hand saws and ripsaws. It is used to bend the teeth to alternate sides, so as to provide clearance for the blade while cutting. The teeth are bent alternately to the right and to the left, to an angle determined by the setting of the saw set.

Tapered files (Fig. 25), are available in regular, slim, extra slim and double extra slim styles; 6, 7, 8 and 10 inches in length. The carpenter uses these files for sharpening his saws and auger bits.

The *bit gage* (Fig. 25), is used as an attachment to a drill bit, to make a hole of a specific depth. It acts as a stop, and when the required depth is reached, prevents the drill from penetrating the material any further.

6. Abrading and Scraping Tools.

All implements, used for wearing down material by friction or rubbing, are known as *abrading tools*. Among others these include whetstones, grindstones, and files, as well as the abrasive papers, such as sandpaper and emery papers. If these tools are examined under a microscope it will be found that all of them have sharp edges or teeth which do the cutting.

ABRASIVE TOOLS. Different minerals are used as cutting agents for making abrasive tools. Three of these used in their natural state are: garnet, emery, and quartz which is commonly called *flint*. Examples of abrasives manufactured by an electric-furnace process are silicon carbide, trade-marked *Carborundum*, and aluminum oxide. The abrasive minerals are shaped and bonded to form abrasive tools, such as whetstones and grindstones.

ABRASIVE PAPERS. The abrasive minerals are crushed and graded for making abrasive papers. To make sandpaper or the emery papers, a paper backing is coated with some kind of adhesive substance, such as glue; then the crushed mineral is powdered over the paper. The same method is used in making abrasive cloth. Abrasive papers come in sheets 9x11 inches or in rolls measuring from 1 inch to 27 inches in width and 50 yards in length. The 27-inch width is used principally on machines and on belt or drum sanders. The abrasive paper also comes in open coat where the abrasive particles are separated and cover only about 50 to 70 per cent of the surface. The closed coat has the abrasive particles close together covering the entire surface of the paper or cloth backing. Since flint paper has a weaker structure, and does not have the sharpness of garnet, it is not desirable for production work. However, it does serve a useful purpose in sanding down painted or varnished surfaces.

The comparative grit numbers for various abrasive papers are shown in Table I. To remove tool marks, by hand sanding on bare wood, use garnet paper ranging from *medium,* No. ½ and 0 to *fine,* No. 3/0 or 4/0, for the finished surface.

TABLE I. APPROXIMATE COMPARISON OF GRIT NUMBERS

ARTIFICIAL*	GARNET	FLINT	GRADE
400–10/0	——	——	
360	——	——	
320–9/0	——	7/0	
280–8/0	8/0	6/0	Very fine
240–7/0	7/0	5/0	
220–6/0	6/0	4/0	
——	——	3/0	
180–5/0	5/0	——	
150–4/0	4/0	——	
——	——	2/0	Fine
120–3/0	3/0	——	
——	——	0	
100–2/0	2/0	——	
——	——	½	
80–0	0	——	
——	——	1	Medium
60–½	½	——	
50–1	1	1½	
——	——	2	
40–1½	1½	——	
——	——	2½	Coarse
36–2	2	——	
30–2½	2½	3	
24–3	3	——	
20–3½	3½	——	Very Coarse
16–4	——	——	
12–4½	——	——	

* Includes *silicon carbide* and *aluminum oxide.*

As used by the carpenter, abrasive papers (sandpapers) or cloths are made of four different materials; two of them are natural and two are manufactured. The two natural minerals are *quartz,* commonly called *flint,* and *garnet.* Flint, which was originally used for sandpaper, is still in use today. It makes a softer abrasive which will crumble quickly. This quality makes it more suitable for sanding paint surfaces as the abrasive will crumble off the surface and will not gum up the sandpaper. Garnet does not crumble as easily as flint. Since it is also sharper it will stand up better for sanding wood surfaces. Therefore, though more expensive than flint, garnet is more economical in the long run.

Silicon carbide, an artificial abrasive, is made of silicon and coke, a product of an electric furnace operated at extremely high temperature. This abrasive is used for sanding floors. Another artificial abrasive, *aluminum oxide,* is also the result of fusing in an electric furnace. It has as its base *bauxite,* a natural mineral. This abrasive is used for hand sanding of wood.

The coarseness of sandpaper originally was designated as #3 for very coarse to 7/0 for very fine. This designation of abrasives is still in practice today. However, the more modern method is to designate the coarseness by the size of the screen through which the abrasive must pass in the manufacturing process. When a screen with 280 openings per square inch is used, the paper is designated as 280.

Due to difference in hardness of some of the abrasives, it will be noted that a coarser grade of flint paper is used to bring about the same results as with garnet or artificial papers. For example, an 8/0 garnet paper is the same in coarseness as 280–8/0 artificial paper, but it would require a 6/0 flint paper to give the same results. In the list of abrasive papers and cloth, shown in Table I, the various abrasive agents are arranged according to their degree of coarseness. The higher a material stands in the scale, the finer it is.

SCRAPING TOOLS. Woodworkers use scrapers made of flat plates of tool steel to smooth wood surfaces. The scraping tools include various types depending upon the particular use for which the implement is designed; for example, the *molding scraper* is specially designed to fit into the curves or depressions of a molding surface.

OTHER ABRADING AND SCRAPING TOOLS. In order to do satisfactory work, a carpenter must keep his tools sharp. The sharpening is done with a tool grinder and a whetstone. Contractors usually furnish the grinder but each mechanic is expected to provide his own whetstone. A combination whetstone, with both a medium and fine surface, takes care of the usual tool-sharpening job. Size 2x6x1 inch is recommended.

It is difficult to smooth the surface of wood which contains knots or has an interwoven grain. However, such a surface can be worked

BURNISHER   SCRAPER HOLDER

Fig. 26.   One Type of Scraper Holder, *Right*, and a Burnisher Used to Dress the Scraper
Edge, *Left*

smooth with a *scraper*.   The scraper usually consists of a piece of tough
steel sharpened with a file and whetstone with the edges turned under
by a *burnisher*, Fig. 26.   For heavy work the blade of a scraper is supported by a *scraper holder*.   Many different types of holders are available.   One type is shown in Fig. 26.

Although *goggles* are not exactly tools, they should be found in
every carpenter's tool kit, and should be used to protect the eyes whenever there is a danger of getting flying particles of metal, dust and dirt
in the eyes.   Goggles are particularly necessary when working with
scraping and abrading tools, and that is why they are mentioned in
connection with this section on abrading tools.

7. Percussion, or Pounding, and Impelling Tools.

THE HAMMER.   Of all carpentry tools, the most used is the hammer, Fig. 27.   Its weight should be about 16 ounces, for general all-
around work.   The steel in the head must be of such a quality that its
face will withstand contact with hard surfaces without marring or
chipping.   The claw must retain sufficient sharpness for pulling nails
without heads.   The handle is made of wood to absorb some of the
shock instead of transmitting all of it to the worker's arm.   This prevents the arm tiring quickly.   The distance between the handle and
the tip of the claw, also the distance between the handle and the face,
should be great enough to fit over the flat side of a 2x4 piece of lumber,
thus enabling the carpenter to pull up a nailed 2x4 and to drive a nail
home over it.   For rough work the carpenter frequently has a straight
claw hammer, slightly heavier than the regular hammer, with which he
can split pieces of wood as well as drive and pull nails.

The *sledge hammer* (Fig. 27), weighs between 2 pounds and 20
pounds and is used by the carpenter for driving layout stakes and batter boards in the laying out of a building.   *Two-pound* hammers are

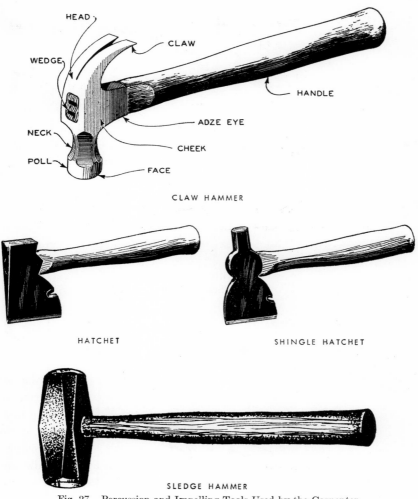

HEAD

CLAW

WEDGE

HANDLE

NECK

ADZE EYE

POLL

CHEEK

FACE

CLAW HAMMER

HATCHET

SHINGLE HATCHET

SLEDGE HAMMER

Fig. 27. Percussion and Impelling Tools Used by the Carpenter

used in timber construction when the wood is 3 or more inches thick, as in the construction of roofs.

The width of *hatchets* (Fig. 27), varies from $2\frac{1}{8}$ inches to 4 inches, this measurement indicating the length of cut that the hatchet will make. They are used to make stakes, and for the rough work, in the construction of forms.

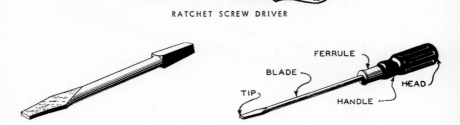

RATCHET SCREW DRIVER

SCREW DRIVER BIT

SCREW DRIVER

SPIRAL RACHET SCREW DRIVER

Fig. 28(*A*). Types of Screwdriver in Common Use

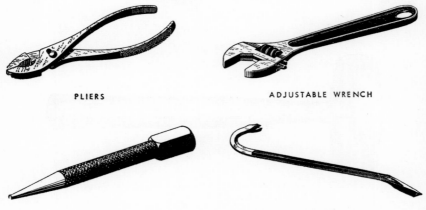

PLIERS

ADJUSTABLE WRENCH

NAIL SET

PINCH, OR WRECKING, BAR

Fig. 28(*B*). Impelling Tools Used in the Carpentry Trade

The *shingle hatchet* (Fig. 27), is used in the application of cedar shingle roofs; it has a sharp cutting blade useful in splitting the shingles to any desired width, and a head suitable for driving shingle nails.

Screw drivers (Fig. 28A), are available with shanks from $1\frac{1}{4}$ inch to 12 inches in length. The blades also vary in size so that they may be matched to the screw being used. The blade should fit snugly into the slot of the head, and should not be any wider than the diameter of the head, or else it will damage the material surrounding the head.

Spiral ratchet screw drivers (Fig. 28A), are generally available with three different size screw bits, and as additional accessories, a phillips screw driver bit and a countersink may be obtained. The spiral ratchet screw driver is most useful for the rapid tightening of screws. It is especially practical where many screws are to be used at one time, as in the application of butts to doors. It can be steadied by holding the revolving chuck sleeve with the free hand. Screws can also be removed by changing the ratchet shift to the opposite direction.

The *ratchet screw driver* (Fig. 28A), has a blade from 1 to 8 inches long, and operates on the same principle as the spiral groove ratchet screw driver, except that it has no spiral and consequently must be turned by hand.

The *screw driver bit* (Fig. 28A), is mainly used with large screws and is held in a ratchet brace.

The *adjustable wrench* (Fig. 28B), is available in lengths from 4 to 18 inches and will open from $\frac{1}{2}$ inch to $2\frac{1}{16}$ inches. This tool is used to tighten nuts and bolts in construction. Typical applications being the bolting of plates to a foundation wall, and the bolting of stanchions to beams.

Pliers (Fig. 28B), are available in lengths from 8 inches to 10 inches. They are used to tighten or hold small nuts that are found on stove bolts as well as machine and carriage bolts. Another common use for pliers is the removal of stubborn nails that resist extraction with a carpenter's hammer.

Nail set (Fig. 28B). This tool is used to sink the head of a nail below the surface of the wood in finish work. The resulting cavity is filled. The tip of the nail set ranges from $\frac{1}{32}$ of an inch to $\frac{1}{8}$ of an inch in diameter, and the tool itself is usually $3\frac{3}{8}$ inches long.

The *wrecking bar* (Fig. 28B), varies in length from 12 to 36 inches and is made from $\frac{1}{2}$ to $\frac{7}{8}$ inch stock steel. It is used to strip down forms and wood scaffolding, as well as a pry to tighten wood braces.

DEVICES MADE ON THE JOB

To simplify the making of this equipment, drawings and instructions suggest materials commonly found on the construction job or obtainable at any lumberyard. Detailed instructions have been worked out as an aid to the beginner or apprentice, on *how to make* the following devices:

Sawhorse	Stepladder
Saw vise	Miter box
Workbench	Straightedge

Lumber used in construction is designated or spoken of in *lumberyard sizes,* rather than the exact dimensions. For example, a piece of lumber 1⅝x3⅝ exact size is called a *2x4;* a board 25/32x9½ is called a *1x10.* However, it does not necessarily follow that a 1x10 will be exactly 25/32x9½ inches; nor a 2x4 exactly 1⅝x3⅝ inches; the exact size depends somewhat upon the moisture content. Lumber will swell in wet weather and shrink in dry weather, but when the 1x10 board was kiln dried and planed at the planing mill it was exactly 25/32x9½ inches. This information is given as a precaution and to encourage the beginner to measure his materials when exact sizes are demanded.

HOW TO MAKE A SAWHORSE

The sawhorse is an essential part of the carpenter's equipment, Fig. 29. It serves as a workbench and supports his tools. It also serves as a scaffold to stand on while working. A great many times a carpenter's mechanical ability is tested by the kind of sawhorse he can build when he starts out on a new job. The length and height of the sawhorse will depend somewhat upon the carpenter's individual needs and the type of work for which the sawhorse is intended to be used. The dimensions given in this instruction unit will serve the average person and job. It is advisable to make the sawhorse out of soft and lightweight material, such as No. 1 spruce or white pine.

MATERIALS

Top:	one piece 2x4 by 3'8"
Legs:	one piece 1x4 by 9'0"
Ends and tray:	one piece 1x10 by 5'6"
Reinforcements:	one piece 1x2 by 9'0"

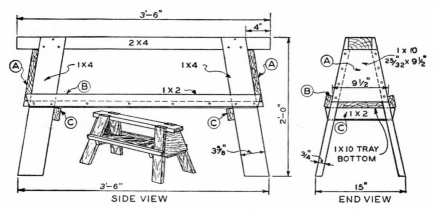

Fig. 29. A Sawhorse, an Essential Part of a Carpenter's Equipment

1. Legs. Select a straight and smooth piece of soft 1x4 for the legs.

a) Lay the framing square on the 4-inch face of this board, as shown in Fig. 30, taking *4* inches on the tongue and *24* inches on the blade of the square. Draw the line *1*, along the tongue. This will be the line for the bottom cut of the leg. *Note:* The square is held so that the figures on both tongue and blade are along the same edge of the board.

b) Measure 24⅝ inches from this line along the same edge of the board and make a check mark. Reverse the square, as shown in Fig. 31, and hold it at the same figures as before (*4* and *24* inches). Draw the line *2* along the tongue through the check mark. This will be the line for the top cut of the leg. *Note:* The lines *1* and *2*, for the top and bottom cuts, should be parallel to each other.

c) Turn the board on edge and lay out the side cuts, *3* and *4*, Fig. 32, by holding the framing square to the figures 5¼ inches on the tongue and *24* inches on the blade; the tongue of the square should touch the line *1*, the bottom cut. Draw the line *3* along the tongue.

d) Reverse the square and draw the top side cut *4*, Fig. 32. *Note:* The lines *3* and *4* should be parallel to each other.

e) With a crosscut saw, cut to the lines, sawing on the waste side of the line.

f) With a block plane, smooth up the cuts to the lines.

g) Using this one leg as a pattern, lay out and cut the other three legs.

2. Top. Select a straight, smooth, and soft piece of 2x4 for the top member of the sawhorse. Cut it to the required length.

a) Lay out the gain joints, Fig. 33, which will receive the legs. *Note:* In studying the side view in Fig. 29, it will be observed that the legs of the sawhorse are set at an angle of 4 inches to the 24 inches of height. Although the legs are back 4 inches at the top, at the bottom they are in line with the end of the top piece.

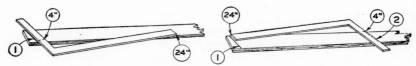

Fig. 30. Leg Layout—Bottom Cut   Fig. 31. Leg Layout—Top Cut

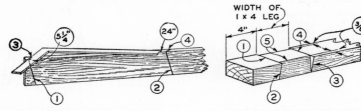

Fig. 32. Layout for Side Cuts of Leg   Fig. 33. Gain Joint for Receiving Leg

b) Measure 4 inches in from the end of the top piece, as shown in Fig. 33. Use the square as a guide and draw line *1* across the top.

c) Turn the top piece on one side and lay the framing square on the edge, holding the square to the 4-inch mark on the tongue and the *24*-inch mark on the blade; the tongue of the square should touch line *1*. Draw line *2* along the tongue. *Caution:* Be sure to have the angle in the right direction; i.e., angling outward toward the end of the 2x4.

d) Draw line *3*, Fig. 33, using the leg pattern to get the exact width of the gain joint.

e) Square line *4* across the top edge.

f) Draw the gain joint on the opposite edge by setting a **T** bevel to the angle formed by line *2*, Fig. 33.

g) For the depth of the joint, set the marking gauge to $\frac{3}{8}$ inch and gauge and draw lines *5*. *Note:* The depth of the gain joint is from $\frac{3}{8}$ inch at the top to nothing at the bottom; this will give the desired angle to the legs, as shown in the end view, Fig. 29.

h) Lay out the two gain joints on the other end of the top piece.

i) Before cutting out the joint, check the layout for the following points:

(1) The lines of each joint on the edge of the top member must angle outward at the bottom.

(2) The lines of each joint must be parallel to each other.

(3) The width of the joint should not exceed the width of the leg.

j) Cut out the gain joint with saw and chisel. Be sure to cut on the waste side of line, leaving just the line, to insure a tight fit for the leg.

k) Nail each leg to the top member with three 8-penny coated box nails.

3. *Ends.* Lay out the two end pieces (*A*), Fig. 29, on a piece of 1x10. Be sure to have the grain run from one leg of the horse to the other leg. The end pieces are wedge-shaped. The angle can be obtained by taking $5\frac{1}{4}$ inches on the tongue of the framing square and *24* inches on the blade, marking along the tongue. The length of this piece, on the long edge, is equal to the width of the tray, $9\frac{1}{2}$ inches. Lay off this distance and draw the other angle. Cut

and nail the two end pieces in place with 8-penny coated nails, nailing them tightly up under the top member.

4. *Tray.* Select a 1x10 board for the tray bottom. Its width is determined by the width of the bottom or widest part of the end piece (*A*), Fig. 29, the length is equal to the length of the sawhorse measuring from the outside of the end pieces marked (*A*). Lay out the tray bottom and cut the notches for the legs. Fit the piece in place, nailing it tightly against the end pieces. Plane off any excess stock from the edges of the tray bottom. *Note:* The tray bottom must fit closely around the legs; therefore, when cutting out the notches for the legs do not cut to the layout lines, but leave sufficient stock to make a tight fit. To insure a good fit, remove excess stock carefully with a chisel, little by little.

5. *Reinforcements.* In order to make sure the sawhorse is properly built and strong enough to serve the purpose for which it is intended, some reinforcement is advisable.

a) The sides of the tray are formed by the two pieces marked (*B*), Fig. 29. The sides are made from a piece of 1x2, which should extend past the legs far enough to support the end pieces marked (*A*). Saw the side pieces to the proper length and nail them into place with 8-penny coated box nails. This will make the tray tight and firm enough to provide a place for a workman to stand.

b) The pieces indicated by (*C*), Fig. 29, are additional supports and reinforcements for both bottom and sides of the tray.

c) Finally, test the completed sawhorse by placing it on a true surface or level plane. If constructed according to the instructions given in this unit, the sawhorse should be firm and solid when standing on a true surface.

HOW TO MAKE A SAW VISE

Several kinds of metal saw vises are available on the market. However, Fig. 34 shows a saw vise which can be made by the carpenter on the job. Such a vise has the advantage of having its jaws at a convenient height for filing. The correct height is about 4 inches below the arm pits of the workman who does the filing.

MATERIALS

Legs:	softwood, two pieces 2x4 by 4'4"
Jaws and braces:	softwood, one piece 1x4 by 9'6"
Tightener:	hardwood, one piece 1x2 by 1'6"
Hardware:	flat-head screws, eight No. 10x1½"
	carriage bolts, two ⅜"x4"

PROCEDURE

1. *Legs.* Select two straight pieces of softwood for the legs shown in Fig. 34.

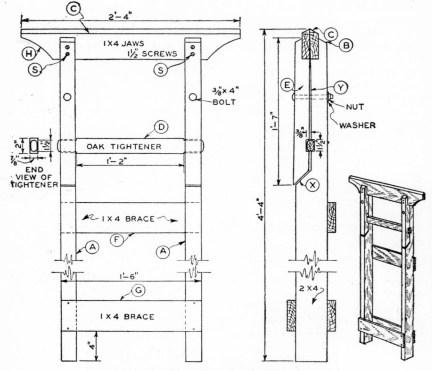

Fig. 34. A Saw Vise Which Can Be Made on the Job

a) Cut two pieces of 2x4 as shown at (*A*), to the desired length to suit the height requirements of the user.

b) Bevel the top as illustrated at (*B*).

c) Bore two ⅜″ holes for the 4″ bolts.

d) To make the arms, lay out lines (*X*) and (*Y*) and cut along these lines.

e) Lay out and cut the notches to hold the jaws shown at (*C*). *Note:* The jaws are tilted slightly to insure a tight grip of the saw on the top edge.

f) Lay out and cut two notches ⅜″x1½″ to receive the oak tightener (hardwood) shown at (*D*).

2. *Jaws.* Take two pieces of softwood board 1x4x28 inches, lay out the jaws and cut them off square; then bevel the top edges shown at (*C*), and cut and smooth the edges of the curved portion, as shown at (*H*) in the illustration, Fig. 72.

3. *Braces.* Take three pieces of softwood board 1x4x18 inches, lay out and cut off square for the braces shown at (*F*) and (*G*), Fig. 34.

4. *Tightener.* For the tightener use hardwood, such as oak.

a) Lay out and cut a piece ⅞x2x18 inches as shown at (*D*), Fig. 34.

b) Lay off 2 inches at each end and cut to an oval shape, smooth with sandpaper. See illustration Fig. 34.

5. Assembly. Before beginning to assemble the various parts for the saw vise, check each part carefully to make sure it has been prepared according to instructions.

a) Nail the two lower braces (*G*) into place with 8-penny coated nails.

b) Fasten one jaw to the legs marked (*A*) with four No. 10x1½" screws, like those shown at (*S*), Fig. 34.

c) Lay the tightener in place. Then place the arms (*E*) in position, slip the two bolts into place and fasten with washers and nuts, shown in Fig. 34.

d) Fasten the other jaw to the two arms with screws, shown at (*S*).

e) Nail the third brace (*F*) into place. The position of this brace is governed by the height of the knee of the operator when he has one foot on brace (*G*).

f) Lastly, test the vise to make sure it will hold a saw in a tight grip. This may save delay in work at a later time.

HOW TO MAKE A WORKBENCH

A workbench designed similar to the one shown in Fig. 35 makes it possible for the carpenter to carry the bench to his work instead of carrying his work to the bench. Such a workbench is a great con-

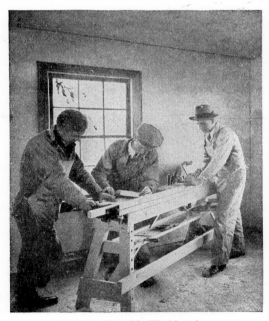

Fig. 35. Portable Workbench

venience, especially in finishing work, such as fitting doors and windows. A portable vise fastened to one end of the workbench will hold the work while it is being planed and fitted. The movable ledge on the front of the bench can be adjusted to accommodate large doors, sash, or cabinet doors while fitting and applying hardware, such as hinges.

MATERIALS

Legs (four):	one piece 2x4 by 12'0"
Top:	one piece 2x12 by 6'0"
Movable ledge:	one piece 2x4 by 6'0"
Braces and cleats:	one piece 1x6 by 12'0"
Shelf:	one piece 1x8 by 5'0"
Angle braces:	one piece 1x4 by 6'6"
Shelf back and supports:	one piece 1x2 by 8'0"
Hardware:	two bolts ⅜"x6"

PROCEDURE

1. Legs. For the legs, select a 2x4 of softwood. Cut the piece into four lengths for the legs of the workbench shown in the thumbnail sketch, Fig. 36.

a) Cut off two pieces from the 2x4 for the front legs 2' 8¼" in length. Both ends of these legs should be cut square.

b) Lay out and bore (at the angle shown, about 15°) the ½-inch holes, 3 inches O.C. (on center). The bolts which hold the movable ledge are inserted in these holes.

c) The top and bottom of the rear legs are cut at an angle. See Fig. 36, end view at left. To obtain the correct angle for cutting these legs, hold the framing square to the figures 3½ inches on the tongue and 12 inches on the blade. Mark along the tongue; that is, the 3½-inch side of the square. The length of the rear legs is 2' 9½" with end cuts parallel to each other. See layout for legs of the sawhorse, Figs. 30 and 31.

2. Braces A and B. Lay out and cut braces (*A*) and (*B*) for both ends of the workbench.

a) Take a piece of board 1x6 and cut off two pieces 19½ inches in length for the two lower braces.

b) For the two top braces cut off two pieces from the 1x6 board, 12 inches in length. Each brace should be cut square on one end with the other end cut at an angle. The angles for both top and bottom braces should be cut in the same way the angles were cut for the top and bottom of the rear legs.

c) Nail the braces in place as shown in Fig. 36.

3. Top. Lay out and cut a piece of 2x12 plank to a length of 6 feet. Nail the plank to the top of the legs, keeping the legs back 6 inches from each end of the top piece, as shown in Fig. 36, illustration at right.

4. Brace C. For this brace use a 1x6 board cut to a length of 5 feet.

a) Square the board at each end and nail it to the rear legs of the bench under the top piece as shown in Fig. 36, illustration at top right.

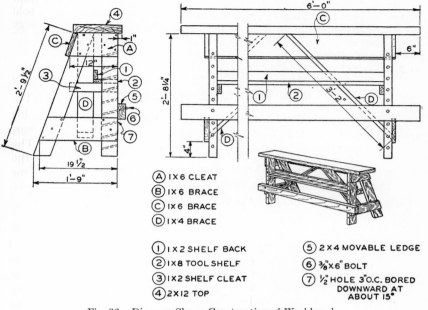

(A) I X 6 CLEAT
(B) I X 6 BRACE
(C) I X 6 BRACE
(D) I X 4 BRACE

(1) I X 2 SHELF BACK
(2) I X 8 TOOL SHELF
(3) I X 2 SHELF CLEAT
(4) 2 X 12 TOP

(5) 2 X 4 MOVABLE LEDGE
(6) ⅜" X 6" BOLT
(7) ½" HOLE 3" O.C. BORED DOWNWARD AT ABOUT 15°

Fig. 36. Diagram Shows Construction of Workbench

b) Before nailing the brace in place, check the spread of the legs at the bottom, making the spread the same as at the top.

c) Nail a piece of 1x2 across the bottom of the legs to hold them in place until all the braces have been securely fastened.

5. *Braces D.* These braces should be cut from a piece of 1x4. Each brace is 3'2" in length and is cut at an angle of 45 degrees.

a) The framing square can be used to lay out the angles at each end of the board. A 45-degree angle can be laid out by holding the square on the edge of the board to the same figure on both the tongue and blade. For example, 10 inches on the tongue and 10 inches on the blade; or 6 inches on the tongue and 6 inches on the blade.

b) After the angle cuts have been made, nail the braces into place as shown in the illustration, Fig. 36.

6. *Shelf.* First, cut two pieces of 1x2 to a length of 12 inches for *supports* for the shelf.

a) Nail these pieces to the inside of the legs 12 inches down from the top piece.

b) For the shelf take a piece of 1x8 measuring 5 feet in length. Cut, fit, and nail this into place on the two supports.

c) After the shelf is in place, cut a piece of 1x2 to the length of 5 feet and nail it into position as a back for the shelf.

7. *Movable Ledge.* Use a piece of 2x4 for the movable ledge.

a) Cut the 2x4 to a length of 6 feet.

b) Hold the piece in position against the front legs and mark the center of two bolt holes on the ledge, one hole at each end.

c) Bore two 5/16-inch holes at the same angle as the holes in the front legs. Then drive two ⅜-inch carriage bolts, 6 inches long, into place to hold the ledge in position. See thumbnail sketch, Fig. 36, which shows the ledge in place.

HOW TO BUILD A STEPLADDER

The ordinary folding stepladder is not strong enough to withstand the rough usage of a construction job. Therefore, it is necessary for the carpenter to build his own stepladder which is more suitable for his particular type of work. A stepladder with housed steps, 1x4 rigid legs, and thorough bracing is a sturdy piece of equipment, Fig. 37. The most convenient height is about 4 feet and 6 inches. However, the height can be altered to meet the individual needs of the workman for whom the ladder is designed.

MATERIALS

Legs, steps, and rear brace:	three pieces 1x4 by 10'0"
Top:	one piece 1x8 by 2'0"
Braces:	one piece 1x2 by 14'0"

PROCEDURE

1. Legs. For laying out the legs with a framing square, follow the method used when laying out the legs of the sawhorse, Figs. 30 and 31.

a) On a piece of 1x4 lay out the length of the front legs each *4* feet 7½ inches as shown at (*A*), Fig. 37. The cutting lines, for the top and bottom of the legs, must be parallel to each other. The correct line for the angle cut can be obtained by placing the framing square on the board in a position similar to that for the legs of the sawhorse, as shown in Fig. 30. However, to find the guide line for the angle cut for the top and bottom of the front legs of the stepladder, hold the square to the figures *3*⅝ inches on the tongue and *12* inches on the body, or blade. Draw a guide line along the tongue of the square and cut on this line.

b) Beginning at the bottom of each of the front legs, space lines for the steps along the front edges of these legs, 11¼ inches apart, and lay off the width of the steps, as shown in Fig. 37. Draw lines on the side of the legs and gauge the depth of the cutouts equal to the thickness of the steps. Cut on the waste side of the lines and chisel out each notch, little by little, to the gauge marks shown in Fig. 37.

c) On a piece of 1x4, lay out the rear legs shown at (*B*), Fig. 37, the length of each of the rear legs being 4 feet 5¼ inches. The angle cut for the top and bottom can be obtained by placing the framing square on the board

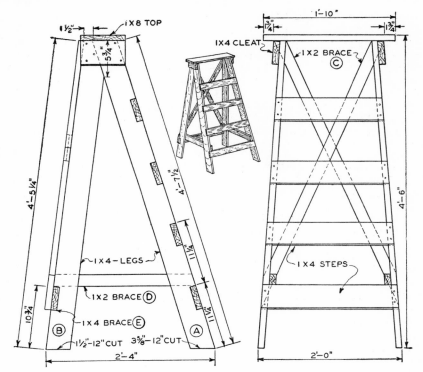

Fig. 37. Stepladder; Diagram Shows Construction and Thumbnail Sketch

in a position similar to that shown in Fig. 30, holding the square to the figures
1½ on the tongue and *12* on the blade. Draw a guide line on the 1½-inch
side; that is, along the tongue of the square, as shown in Fig. 30.

d) The top of the rear legs has an additional angle cut for fitting against
the front legs. Cut this angle according to the measurements given in Fig. 37.

e) Lay out and cut the notch for the 1x4 brace (*E*) near the bottom of
the rear legs.

f) Lay out and cut two 1x4 cleats 7½ inches long. Tie the front and
rear legs together at the top with these cleats, as shown in Fig. 37.

g) Nail the cleats to the legs at the top, holding the cleats flush with the
top of the legs and spreading the legs to 2 feet 4 inches at the bottom. Use
6-penny coated nails and clinch them on the inside.

2. Top Piece. The top is an important feature of the stepladder. It is
not only important as the highest step of the ladder but also serves as a
finishing member. Nailing should be done carefully to avoid splitting of the
top piece.

a) On a piece of 1x8, lay off the top, 1 foot 10 inches in length. Cut off
square on both ends.

b) Nail the top in place with 8-penny coated nails. The legs are set back 1¾ inches from the ends of the top piece, as shown in illustration at right, Fig. 37.

3. Steps. Study the front view of the ladder, Fig. 37. The length of the top piece is 22 inches and the legs are set in at the top 1¾ inches from each end. At the bottom the legs are spread to a measure of 2 feet. This difference in the spread of the legs at top and bottom makes it necessary to cut the four steps different lengths so they will conform to the shape of the ladder.

a) Set the legs to a spread of 2 feet at the bottom. Lay a piece of 1x4 in the notches cut for the lowest step. Mark the cutting lines for both ends of the step flush on the outside of the legs. This will insure the proper fit of the step to conform to the shape of the ladder. Cut off the length of the step along the marks and nail it into place with one nail to each leg.

b) Using the same method, cut and fit each of the other steps into place, nailing them with one nail in each leg.

c) Cut the rear brace (*E*) the same length as the lowest step of the ladder and nail the brace in place with one nail in each rear leg.

d) After all the steps are in place, the stand of the ladder should be checked to make sure it stands plumb, not lopsided. Then nail all steps and the rear brace (*E*) securely, using 8-penny coated nails.

4. Braces. There are five braces used in this type of stepladder, two at the back which are crossed as shown at (*C*), Fig. 37, one at the bottom and rear, brace (*E*), and two side braces near bottom, as shown at (*D*), Fig. 37.

a) Cut and fit the 1x2 (*C*) braces and nail them in place as shown in the diagram, Fig. 37.

b) Before cutting and nailing the 1x2 (*D*) braces, check the leg spread at the bottom. This spread should be 2 feet 4 inches.

HOW TO MAKE A STRAIGHTEDGE

The *straightedge*, a simple yet necessary device, is used in connection with a level for plumbing door jambs and corner posts, or for leveling work when spans greater than the length of the level are encountered, Fig. 38. Northern white pine, *Pinus strobus,* is a desirable wood to use for this purpose. When properly seasoned, white pine will not warp.

Accuracy in construction is all-essential. The edge (*1*) must be straight, true, and square with the surface. Edge (*2*) must be parallel with edge (*1*). Blocks (*A*) must be of the same thickness. These blocks can be glued onto the main section or cut out from the main board, as desired. However, when finished, the ends of the straightedge must be *exactly* the same width. The *handhole* makes it convenient to grasp the device firmly while plumbing. There is on the market a two-glass leveling device which can be screwed to the face of the

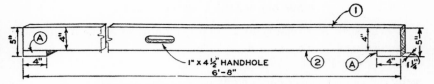

Fig. 38. Straightedge for Plumbing Door Jambs and Corner Posts

straightedge; this device does away with the need of the regular level.

The size of the straightedge varies with the needs of the job, but the dimensions shown in the diagram, Fig. 38, usually are accepted for average work. A makeshift emergency straightedge can be made quickly by using a straight piece of 2x4 with blocks ⅞ of an inch in thickness nailed on each end similar to those shown in Fig. 38.

HOW TO MAKE A MITER BOX

It is difficult to make a perfect joint between two pieces which come together at an angle of ninety degrees to form a corner. There are a number of different methods of cutting these pieces to make such a joint. The simplest method is to cut off each piece at a bevel of forty-five degrees, so that the pieces will fit together at an angle of ninety degrees. A *miter box* is a convenient device used by carpenters for cutting pieces at the exact angle desired when mitering joints, Fig. 39. To miter moldings, the carpenter usually constructs a device on the job by nailing together lengthwise two pieces of 2x6, two or three feet in length. The desired angle cuts are laid out on this device, and saw cuts are made to serve as guides for cutting the angles on moldings.

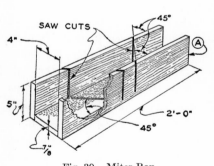

Fig. 39. Miter Box

A better looking and more permanent piece of equipment can be made by using hardwood boards, maple or birch, ⅞ of an inch in thickness with the sides glued or screwed on the bottom. Many woodworkers prefer a two-sided miter box which can be made easily by adding a second side as shown at (A), Fig. 39. For a simple miter box omit the side (A).

HOW TO MAKE A DOOR JACK

Whenever it is necessary to fit a large number of doors, a carpenter finds it advisable to make a *door jack* to hold the doors while planing the edges and fitting the hinges. The door jack can be constructed easily out of materials found on any construction job. For the base use a 2x6 if available. However, a piece of 1x6 or even a 1x4 can be used for the base piece, shown at (*A*), Fig. 40. The 2x4 crosspiece (*B*), two feet in length, is nailed at right angles to (*A*), about 12 inches from one end of the base, which should be 6 feet long, see Fig. 40. The 1x6 piece (*C*), with a **V** cut in the upper end, holds any thickness of door and should be set at an angle great enough so that the **V** cut will be above the center of the door. Two 1x4 braces are required, one on each side of the **V** cut as indicated by (*D*) in Fig. 40. Though not essential the 1x6 shelf (*E*) is desirable as it provides additional stiffness to the jack and is also convenient for holding the plane when not in use. Note the 1x2 braces supporting the shelf, also the 1x2 brace on end of base. The crosspiece (*B*) is supported at each end by a 2x4 block. The distance between the upper end of the (*C*) piece and the base is 2 feet.

HOW TO MAKE A SHOULDER BOX

The man who is skilful in the use of tools appreciates their value and takes good care of them. He has a place for every tool and keeps every tool in its place when it is not in use. Any boy who hopes to become a skilled mechanic should form this habit early, and when he buys tools he should also provide a place where they can be kept. The mechanic who works in a shop keeps his tools on the workbench, in the drawers of the bench, or in a cabinet above the bench. However, the mechanic who moves about from job to job must provide himself with devices in which he can keep his tools. For this purpose he should have tool boxes which are convenient in size, and light enough in weight to carry around easily.

Every carpenter should provide himself with two toolboxes, a *shoulder box* and a *tool case*. The tool case will house the finer trim tools and keep them under lock and key. The shoulder box is for the framing or rough tools. Since it is not so large, it is more convenient to carry around on ladders or scaffolds while preparing the framework of a building.

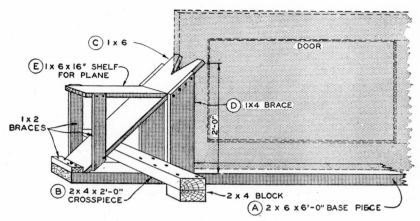

Fig. 40. Door Jack for Holding Door While Fitting It

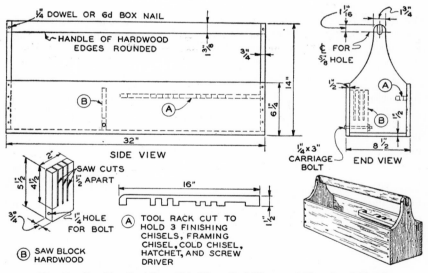

Fig. 41. Shoulder Tool Box; Side View; End View; and Thumbnail Sketch

The shoulder box should be made from materials which are light in weight but strong enough to withstand hard wear, Fig. 41. *Note:* Although not so specified here, the sides may be made of ¼-inch plywood; if available; however, the ends and bottom should be of solid boards which have better nail-holding qualities.

MATERIALS

Ends:	#1 soft lightweight wood, one piece 1"x8" by 2'6"
Bottom and sides:	soft lightweight wood, one piece ½"x8" by 8'6"
Handle and tool rack:	oak, birch, or maple, one piece ¾"x1½" by 5'6"
Saw rack:	oak, birch, or maple, once piece ¾"x2" by 6"
Hardware:	two #8x1½" flathead screws; one ¼x3" carriage bolt

PROCEDURE

1. End Pieces. It is assumed that the reader knows how to use the most important of the simple tools.

a) Saw the board intended for the end pieces into two equal lengths. Then square each board to ¾"x7½"x13½". To square up a board it must first be cut to the correct length, width, and thickness; all faces should be planed smooth, true, and square with adjacent faces. The accuracy required depends upon where and how the board is to be used. For achieving a high degree of accuracy, the plane plays an important part; in less exacting cases, a good square cut with the saw might be sufficient.

b) For each end piece, measure off with the framing square 6¼ inches from one end. From this point draw a line square across the board, then lay out the curves for the upper part which receives the handle, as illustrated in the end view, Fig. 41. Cut out the curves with a coping, or compass, saw. Smooth the edges with a spokeshave or woodfile, and finish with sandpaper. When finished, the width of the end piece at the top should be 1¾ inches.

c) Lay out the slot, ⅝"x1⅜" to receive the handle. Bore a ⅝-inch hole 1¹⁄₁₆ inches down from the top edge of the end piece, and cut out the remaining portion of wood with the saw, cutting on the waste side of the lines and leaving the bottom of the slot round in shape.

2. Bottom. Square up a piece of ½-inch lumber to ½"x7½"x32" for the bottom. Nail the bottom into place with four 6-penny coated nails on each end.

3. Sides. Square up two pieces to ½"x6¼"x32" for the sides and nail into place with four 6-penny coated nails on each end. *Note:* Quarter-inch fir or pine plywood, if available, is equally as strong as ½-inch solid wood and is lighter in weight.

4. The Handle. For the handle, select a piece of hardwood free from defects. Oak, birch, or maple will serve the purpose. The piece should be long enough to extend from outside to outside of the finished toolbox, as shown in Fig. 41.

a) Square up the handle piece to the required size—⅝"x1⅜"x32"—so it will fit tightly into the slots prepared for it in the two end pieces.

b) Chamfer the edges about ⅛ inch or just enough to give the handle a rounded shape.

c) Place the handle in position and bore a ¼-inch hole in each end for the *dowel pins,* or nail the handle in place with 6-penny box nails, Fig. 41.

5. Tool Rack for Holding Small Tools. The tool rack, indicated at (*A*), Fig. 41, should be cut from hardwood—oak, birch, or maple.

a) Square up this piece of hardwood to ¾"x1½"x16".

b) Select the tools which are to be kept in this rack and arrange them in order on the bench. Hold the board for the rack over the tools and mark the sides of the *cutouts*.

c) To make sure each tool will fit tightly into its place, indicate the depth of each cutout on the board with a marking gauge. *Note:* Both faces of the board should be so marked.

d) Make the cutouts with the saw and chisel, then remove the wood on the waste side, little by little.

e) Fasten the rack into place with two #8x1½-inch flathead screws. These should be screwed into the piece from the outside of the toolbox. *Note:* Bore pilot holes for the screws to prevent splitting of the wood.

6. *Saw Block for Holding the Saws.* The saw block, indicated at *B,* Fig. 41, should be made out of hardwood.

a) Square up a piece of hardwood to ¾"x2"x5½".

b) Lay out three *saw cuts.* The spaces between the cuts should be ½ inch in width. Saw on the lines indicated to within 1 inch from the other end of the block *(B),* Fig. 41.

c) Bore a ¼-inch hole through the block to receive a bolt.

d) Fasten the block into place in the box with a carriage bolt (¼x3 inches), as shown at *(B),* Fig. 41.

7. *Painting.* Two coats of paint on the outside of the box will help to preserve the wood and make the toolbox more durable. The paint will also improve the appearance of the box.

8. *Tool Protection.* Tools are exposed frequently to rain and snow. However, the tools can be protected to some extent by a piece of lightweight canvas 2'x2'8" spread over the shoulder box and tacked to the handle.

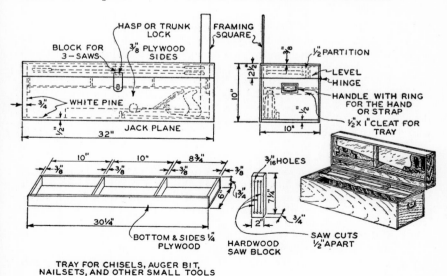

Fig. 42. Tool Case; Diagram Showing Construction and Thumbnail Sketch

HOW TO MAKE A TOOL CASE

Most mechanics favor a tool case which is not too heavy, yet is large enough to hold his most expensive equipment, Fig. 42. Such a case can be carried around by the mechanic while working, if it is suspended from his shoulder by a rope inserted through a short piece of garden hose and fastened to the two handles of the tool case. However, this case has the disadvantage of being too small to house the framing square which, therefore, must extend out through a hole in the cover, as shown in the side view of Fig. 42.

MATERIALS

Ends:	soft lightweight wood, one piece 1x10 by 1'8"
Bottom and partitions:	soft lightweight wood, two pieces ½"x10" by 2'9"
Top:	plywood, one piece ⅜"x10" by 2'8"
Sides:	plywood, two pieces ⅜"x9⅝" by 2'8"
Tray sides and bottom:	plywood, one piece ¼"x10" by 2'8"
Saw block:	oak, birch, or maple, one piece ¾"x2" by 7¼"
Hardware:	three hinges, one hasp, or trunk lock, and two handles

PROCEDURE

1. Ends of the Tool Case. When a box has a cover similar to that shown in Fig. 42, a better and easier fit of the cover can be obtained by building the box as a single unit, then making a saw cut through the box on a line 2½ inches below the top; the smaller piece becomes the cover.

a) Square up two pieces of pine, spruce, or other soft lightweight wood to ¾"x9⅛"x9¼". *Note:* The grain of the wood should run with the 9¼-inch dimension as shown by the finished box in Fig. 42.

2. Bottom. Square up a piece of soft lightweight wood ½"x9¼"x32" for the bottom. Apply waterproof glue to the edges and nail onto the end pieces with 6-penny coated nails.

3. Sides. Square up two pieces of plywood to ⅜"x9⅝"x32". Glue and nail into place with 6-penny nails.

4. Top. Square up a piece of plywood to ⅜"x10"x32" for the top. After the bottom and side pieces have been nailed in position, apply waterproof glue to the edge of the top piece and nail it onto the two end pieces with 6-penny coated nails. Finally, apply waterproof glue to all the joints of the tool case.

5. Cover. In addition to serving its primary purpose as a cover, space is provided here for three saws and a level.

a) With a marking gauge, draw a line around the sides and ends of the box, 2½ inches down from the top and carefully saw the box apart along this line.

b) Fit the cover to the box by smoothing the sawed edges.

c) Prepare a piece of soft lightweight wood for the partition. Saw a piece ½"x10"x33" lengthwise into four strips ½"x2½"x33". Square one piece to ½"x2¼"x30¼". Fit, glue, and nail the partition into place in the cover which will then hold the level and three saws. The size of the level governs the position of the partition. Two turn buttons fastened to this partition will hold the level in place.

d) Prepare a block to hold the saws and fasten it into place. The saw block should be made from a piece of hardwood which has been squared to ¾"x2"x7¼". Cut openings for the saws ³⁄₁₆ of an inch in width and spaced ½ inch apart as shown in Fig. 42.

e) Cut a slot in the front right-hand corner of the cover for the tongue of the framing square, as shown in Fig. 42.

6. *Finish.* The tool case should be finished by smoothing the surface with sandpaper and applying paint. Finally, the hinges are added and the trunk lock, or hasp, is put in place to provide protection for the tools.

a) Sandpaper the entire box to a smooth surface, rounding the edges slightly.

b) Apply two coats of paint. The paint serves a twofold purpose, it improves the appearance of the box and also helps preserve the wood, hence prolonging the life of the box.

c) Fasten the cover to the box with three hinges. Then fasten in place the hasp or trunk lock. *Note:* It is advisable to use flathead brass screws which can be cut off and riveted on the inside. Use flathead screws also for fastening the handles in place. See finished tool case at right in Fig. 42.

7. *Inside Fittings.* An important feature of the tool case is the inside tray. Tools that are used frequently can be kept in separate compartments. If kept in proper order these tools can be picked up easily when needed.

a) A tray of a size and arrangement that will carry chisels, bits, nail sets, and other small tools is shown in Fig. 42. The bottom and sides of such a tray can be made of ¼-inch plywood. However, it is advisable to use solid wood for the ends and partitions. The size and number of compartments should be arranged to suit the individual needs of the mechanic for whom the case is made. In the illustration given here, there are three compartments—one of 8¾ inches in length and the other two, each 10 inches long. The piece of plywood provided for the tray is 10 inches wide. This should be sawed into three lengthwise strips, one of which is 6 inches wide, the other two, each 2 inches wide. The 6-inch piece serves as the bottom of the tray, and the narrower pieces are for the sides. For the bottom, square a piece of plywood to ¼"x6"x30¼". The side pieces should be squared to ¼"x1½"x30¼". The end pieces and partitions, of soft lightweight wood, should be squared to ⅜"x1½"x5½". Fit and nail the sides and bottom piece to the two end pieces, then nail in the two partitions. The tray rests on two ½x1-inch cleats fastened to the ends of the tool case, as shown in finished box at right, Fig. 42.

b) To protect the cutter of the jack plane, place a small block under the *toe* or *heel* of the plane. A partition one inch high will keep the plane in position. See side view at top, left, Fig. 42.

c) The balance of the storage space in the tool case may be occupied by other tools which are laid in without any special order or arrangement.

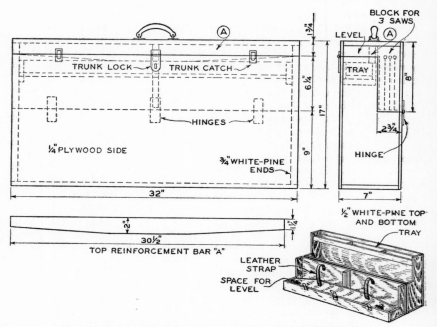

Fig. 43. Suitcase Tool Box—Construction and Thumbnail Sketch

HOW TO MAKE A SUITCASE TOOL BOX

The suitcase toolbox, shown in Fig. 43, is preferred by many carpenters because its height is sufficient to completely house the framing square, and the tool capacity of this type of toolbox is considerably larger than that of the tool case shown in Fig. 42.

MATERIALS

Ends:	soft lightweight wood, one piece 1x8 by 4'0"
Reinforcing bar:	soft lightweight wood, one piece 1x2 by 2'8"
Top and bottom:	soft lightweight wood, two pieces ½"x8" by 2'9"
Sides:	plywood, two pieces ¼"x18" by 2'9"
Tray:	plywood, one piece ¼"x8" by 2'8"
Saw block:	hardwood, one piece ¾"x2" by 0'6"
Strap:	leather, one piece 24"
Hardware:	three hinges, one hasp or trunk lock, two catches, and one suitcase handle

The peculiar L-shaped cover of the suitcase toolbox requires building the cover separate from the main part of the box. Otherwise the construction is similar to the case shown in Fig. 42.

1. Bottom or Lower Section. For the outside of this type of toolbox use lightweight wood and plywood.

a) Ends. Square up two pieces of white-pine boards to ¾"x6½"x14¾". *Note:* The grain of the wood should run up and down on the ends of the suitcase toolbox, as shown in thumbnail sketch at right.

b) Cutout. Lay out on the two end pieces the 2¾x6¼-inch cutout for the cover as shown in Fig. 43. Cut out this portion of each end piece and smooth the edges where the cut is made.

c) Bottom Piece. For the bottom piece square up a piece of white-pine board to ½"x6½"x32". At the ends of this piece apply waterproof glue where the bottom and end pieces meet. Then nail the bottom to the end pieces already prepared. Use 6-penny coated nails for this purpose.

d) Sides. For the side pieces square up two pieces of ¼-inch plywood. One piece should measure ¼"x9"x32"; the other piece should measure ¼"x15¼"x32". Apply waterproof glue where the sides meet the end pieces and the bottom piece. Then nail each side piece to the bottom and the end pieces with 6-penny coated nails.

2. Cover or Upper Section. For the outside of the cover use lightweight wood and plywood the same as that used for the lower section of the toolbox.

a) Ends. Square up two pieces of white-pine boards to ¾"x6½"x7½". The grain of the wood should run up and down.

b) Cutout. Lay out on the two end pieces of the cover the 3¾x6¼-inch cutout. This portion should be cut out so the cover will fit into the bottom section of the end pieces. See Fig. 43. Smooth edges of cut.

c) Top. Square up a piece of white-pine board to ½"x6½"x32". Apply waterproof glue to the outer edges of the ends. Then nail to the end pieces with 6-penny coated nails.

d) Sides. Square up two pieces of plywood for the two sides. One piece should measure 8x32 inches; the other piece should measure 1¾x32 inches. Apply waterproof glue where the sides meet the top and end pieces. Nail the sides into place with 6-penny coated nails.

3. Inside Fittings. The inside fittings of the suitcase toolbox include the reinforcing bar and saw block in the cover, and the small-tool tray fitted into the lower section.

a) Reinforcing Bar. For the reinforcing bar shown at *A* in Fig. 43, use lightweight wood. Square up and shape the bar as illustrated from ¾-inch material. The bar should measure 1¼ inches in width at the two ends and 2 inches in width at the center. The bar extends the full length of the toolbox or 32 inches. Apply waterproof glue to the bar where it meets the cover. Nail the bar into the middle of the cover as shown in Fig. 43. The purpose of the bar is to reinforce the cover and provide a place to fasten the handle.

b) Saw Block. Use a piece of hardwood for the saw block. Prepare the block similar to that shown in the illustration. The piece should measure ¾"x2"x6". Apply waterproof glue to the block where it meets the cover and nail in place with 6-penny coated nails. To hold the saws in place nail two leather straps to the cover and reinforcing bar as shown in the illustration, Fig. 81. The straps should be about 12 inches in length.

  c) Tray. Construct a tray from a piece of plywood. The measurements of the tray should be 3¾ inches in width and 30¼ inches in length. The height should be about 1¾ inches. For illustration see Fig. 43. If desired another tray of the same dimensions can be made to fit below the top tray. The tray can be divided into sections according to individual needs, by fitting in partitions.

  4. Finish. After the box has been painted, the three hinges, lock, and catches can be fastened in place.

  a) Sandpaper the entire box on the outside, and round the edges slightly.

  b) Apply two coats of paint to the outside of the box.

  c) After the paint has dried, fasten the hinges, lock, and catches in place with flat-headed brass screws. The screws can then be cut off and riveted on the inside. Finally, fasten the handle on securely with ⅛-inch bolts passed through the top and reinforcing bar.

SAFETY AND FIRST AID

A carpenter's equipment is not complete without a few essential first-aid supplies. These supplies should include at least antiseptics, bandages, and first aid for burns. Such provisions will help to prevent infection after minor skin injuries, bruises, and burns. Provision should be made also to avoid excessive loss of blood, heat exhaustion, and eye injuries. A minimum supply of first-aid provisions should include the following materials:

Antiseptic. A small bottle of an antiseptic with applicator of either mercurochrome or metaphan.

Bandages. Four compresses, three inches square, sealed in wax paper; a small roll of 1-inch gauze; a five-yard roll of ½-inch adhesive tape; and a package of band aids.

First Aid for Burns. One tube of Butesin Picrate or Sulfa Diazine.

Heat Exhaustion. One bottle of 50 sodium chloride (common table salt) tablets. There are two kinds of sodium chloride tablets—the plain and the enteric coated. The enteric coated do not dissolve until they reach the intestines. This avoids stomach disturbances.

Eye Protection. Every tool kit should contain a good pair of goggles for eye protection when drilling holes or when using abrasive tools or papers.

Instruction. The physical well-being of the mechanic is of equal or greater importance than his skill or knowledge of the trade. The mechanic must be physically fit in order to do his work properly. He must not only keep himself physically fit but he must be safety conscious also in order to protect himself and his fellow workers against accidents and the consequent loss of time on the job. Although the carpenter may be safety conscious and take every precaution possible to prevent accidents, nevertheless, he should be able to administer simple first aid to an injured worker when accidents occur. A reliable instruction book on first aid should have a place in his tool kit.[1]

---

[1] American Red Cross First Aid Textbook.

Accidents are frequent in the construction industry, yet the severity of these accidents is not as great as in many other industries. Large construction organizations have their safety engineers, doctors, nurses, and hospital facilities. However, the smaller organizations, unfortunately, cannot provide these aids. Therefore, the mechanic in the small organization must be his own safety engineer and be prepared to administer first aid to an injured worker. It is of prime importance then that every mechanic become safety conscious, thinking in terms of safety for himself and others while performing every operation in the process of erecting a building. Since safety instruction becomes most effective when given as the situation or need arises, such instruction is given throughout this book in connection with the various construction operations.

It is not within the scope of this text to deal with first aid, hence this information must be obtained from another source such as the textbook issued by the American Red Cross. However, a few suggestions are advisable here.

1. The mechanic should develop safety consciousness, since "an ounce of prevention is worth a pound of cure."

2. He should protect his eyes with goggles when working near flying objects.

3. Slight cuts, bruises, or skin breaks should be treated immediately with an antiseptic and protected with a bandage to prevent infection. *Note:* Never put adhesive tape directly on a wound.

4. Air, dust, and dirt should be excluded from burns with butesin picrate or sulfa diazine, then covered with a bandage immediately.

5. To avoid heat exhaustion, a construction worker should drink plenty of water and take salt tables to replace the salt lost from the body through perspiration.

6. Before moving an injured worker, always examine him for broken bones. This precaution may prevent compound fractures.

7. In case of serious injuries, always call or see a doctor as quickly as possible.

CHECKING ON YOUR KNOWLEDGE

The following questions give you the opportunity to check up on yourself. If you have read the chapter carefully, you should be able to answer the questions. If you have any difficulty, read the chapter over once more so that you have the information well in mind before you go on with your reading.

DO YOU KNOW

1. What tools the apprentice carpenter should have in his tool kit, and what tools he should add as he advances to more complicated construction work?

2. How carpentry tools are classified?

3. How the framing square can help you in the solution of various difficult problems of construction?

4. What are some of the important percussion and impelling tools?

5. In what order of importance the various types of planes should be bought?

6. What are the important boring tools? Cutting tools? Measuring tools?

7. What are the important abrading and scraping tools?

8. Why contractors furnish much of the larger and more expensive equipment?

9. Into how many groups tools may be classified?

10. What useful tables are found on the face and back of a standard steel framing square?

11. In addition to the framing square, what are some of the other important layout and measuring tools?

12. Why the handle of a hammer should be made of wood?

13. What the difference is between a crosscut saw and a rip saw?

14. What types of planes are listed in this chapter?

15. Three minerals used as abrasive agents?

16. What materials are needed for making a sawhorse?

17. What materials are needed for making a workbench which the carpenter can easily carry about?

18. Why it is necessary for the carpenter to build his own stepladder on a construction job?

19. How a straightedge is used?

20. How a door jack is used?

21. What different types of toolboxes are described in this chapter?

22. What advantage is provided by a suitcase toolbox?

23. Why a carpenter should carry his tools in two toolboxes; that is, a *shoulder box* and a *tool case?*

24. What precaution should be taken to protect the cutter of the jack plane in the toolbox?

25. What first-aid supplies a carpenter should include in his equipment?

Tools of the Carpentry Trade—
Power Tools

QUESTIONS THIS CHAPTER WILL ANSWER

1. *What safety factors are incorporated in modern power tools?* 2. *What the difference is between jointing and facing?* 3. *Which power tool should be used for sharpening drill bits?* 4. *What abrasive materials are used for making grinding wheels, and what are their respective applications?* 5. *What are the uses of the powder-driven fastener?*

INTRODUCTION TO CHAPTER III

In this chapter we shall deal with the use and care of power tools; with particular emphasis on the safety precautions to be observed. This classification includes both the fixed tools to be found in the shop and those which are transportable to the job site outside the shop. However for the sake of discussion, they will be divided into two groups: shop tools and portable tools.

Today, speed in production often makes the difference between profit and loss. Speed and accuracy are two of the most significant assets of the power tools employed by today's carpenter. It is to be expected, however, that some of these machines are rather complex in their operation, and can be dangerous to the worker if not operated properly. It is for this reason that it is very important for the carpenter to familiarize himself in detail with the various power tools, before attempting to use them. It is also very important that the carpenter consistently take every safety precaution recommended for the particular machine in use; for they will rarely hinder or slow his work, as might be thought.

POWER TOOLS USED IN THE SHOP

The *table saw,* shown in Fig. 1, is one of the most frequently used power tools. This tool employs a circular saw blade, up to 16 inches in diameter, and is equipped with many accessories and safety devices. The axis of the saw can usually be tilted from the vertical so that precision ripping, cross-cutting, dadoing and moulding can be done on a production basis. This feature is known as a tilting arbor, and is adjusted by a graduated hand-wheel on the front of the machine. Another hand-wheel located on the side of the machine raises or lowers the saw blade to give a cut of different depth, or for cutting wood of varying thickness.

The saw blade is protected by a safety blade guard which also in-

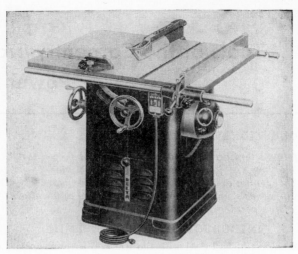

Fig. 1.   Table Saw
Rockwell Manufacturing Co.

corporates anti kick-back fingers to prevent the work being thrown
back at the operator, causing him bodily harm.   Although this guard
can be flipped back or even taken off for making adjustments to the
saw; it should always be in place when the saw is in actual operation.
The controls of the ripping fence are all located forward, near the operator, as a safety precaution.   The ripping fence locks to two guide
bars located at the front and back of the machine; and allows of minute adjustments in position.

The miter gage, fits into the slots on the table top.   There are various circular saw blades available for the table saw; cut-off, rip, combination and hollow ground.   These blades should be frequently inspected for sharpness and damage; and sharpened when necessary.

Another accessory for the table saw is the dado head, which will
cut grooves from $\frac{1}{8}$ of an inch to $1\frac{3}{16}$ of an inch wide in increments of
$\frac{1}{16}$ of an inch.   The blades and chippers are matched in sets to assure
clean, even cuts with or against the grain.   A set consists of two outside blades and four inside cutters.

When using the dado or moulding cutter heads, a cast insert must
be used in the table top, to reduce the size of the saw aperture.   There
are many different styles of knives available in sets, fitting the moulding cutter head, for making moulding of various configurations.

Fig. 2. Band Saw
Rockwell Manufacturing Co.

The main use of the *band saw*, shown in Fig. 2, is the cutting of curved surfaces, or contour cutting as it is sometimes called, although it is equally suitable for straight cutting and resawing. Other applications include: relishing, trimming circles, cutting notches, vertical stop cuts and ripping. The band saw can also be used with a skiptooth blade for cutting plastic, building materials, bakelite, and nonferrous metals such as copper.

Since band saws are manufactured in a great variety of sizes and styles, the length of the band varies to fit the particular machine for which it is intended. The width of a band very rarely exceeds one inch; and it is usually in the order of $\frac{1}{8}$ inch to $\frac{1}{4}$ inch wide. The pitch of the teeth and the cutting speed are largely determined by the material being cut.

The sawing table can be tilted on most machines to the exact angle, with respect to the vertical, at which the cut is desired.

Fig. 3.   Long Bed Jointer
Rockwell Manufacturing Co.

The fence is supported on two guide bars and may be adjusted over a wide range, its exact position with respect to the saw being indicated on a scale calibrated in inches.   The guide bar, and the pivoting work support body are equipped with a scale and pointer, reading through about 120 degrees.   There are usually adjustable positive stops at the 45 degree and the 90 degree positions.

The *jointer*, Fig. 3, is designed for straightening wood by planing the surfaces.   The operation of straightening the face of the board is called *facing*.   The operation of straightening the edge is called *jointing*.   Jointing usually implies that the edge is to be jointed at right angles to the face side.   Other operations that may be performed on the jointer include beveling, chamfering, tapering and rabbeting. Hollow glue joints can also be made.

This power tool usually has a three-knife cutter head of a cylindrical shape with the knives set in it longitudinally; and in a typical operation gives many thousand knife-cuts a minute.   The length of each knife varies from 4 inches to 8 inches.

The fence, may usually be tilted to a maximum of 45 degrees in either direction (from the horizontal plane), with the actual degree of tilt shown on a gage.   Many jointer fences have plunger-type or positive stops at 90 degrees and at 45 degrees for making chamfer and bevel cuts.   A cam-type lock with single lever control locks the fence at

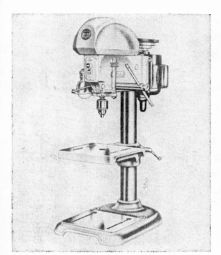

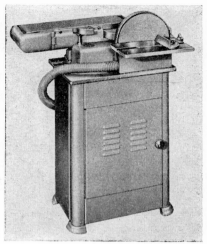

Fig. 4. Drill Press
Rockwell Manufacturing Co.

Fig. 5. Combination Belt and Disc
Sander
Duro Metal Products Co.

any position across the work table. Both front and rear tables, on the machine illustrated, may be raised or lowered, and locked in position on inclined dovetailed ways. And the cutter head guard affords maximum coverage of the cutter knives at all times.

The cutter knives are usually made of properly tempered, high-speed tool steel and should give good service; but they should nevertheless be inspected frequently and sharpened when necessary.

The *drill press*, Fig. 4, is a commonly encountered shop tool, and although it does suffer from a certain immobility, from the carpenter's point of view, it compensates for this characteristic by being adaptable for the jobs of routing, mortising, jointing, shaping, sanding and plug cutting. It is of course the ideal tool for drilling on a production basis.

The drilling table can be raised or lowered and locked in position, and in some models, it can also be tilted in any direction. The speed of the drill may be changed by means of a series of pulleys and belts located in the head of the machine, where the driving motor is usually also located. Various drilling speeds must be used according to the nature of the material being drilled and the drill in use.

The drill itself is lowered to the work by means of a feed pinion usually controlled by a capstan hand-wheel, and returns automatically when the wheel is released. The drill may also be locked in a specific position, or for a specific limit, which is particularly desirable for precision depth and repeat drilling, and for mortising and shaping. In using the drill press the work should be firmly clamped to the table rather than being held in place by hand; otherwise it is likely to break loose and start spinning freely, causing possible harm to both the operator and the press.

There are two kinds of sanders. The *belt sander,* and the *disc sander,* although some models are a combined belt and disc sander in one machine, using a common drive-motor, as is the model illustrated in Fig. 5. These combined machines can usually be employed in either a horizontal or a vertical position. The belt sander in particular gives a uniform cutting speed across the entire surface of the belt which results in a smooth, even cut. Both types of sander can be operated on curved, straight or angular surfaces, and the unsupported side of the belt sander may be used for sanding irregular surfaces.

Either type of sander is usually equipped with an adjustable, tilting table, which, from its normal position at right angles to the sanding surface may be tilted to a maximum of 45 degrees away from the abrasive surface, or 35 degrees towards the abrasive surface. The table is equipped with a slot parallel to the sanding surface for a miter gage which assures accuracy in all sanding operations. If the table is entirely removable, this is an advantage, since it allows long pieces of material to be sanded more conveniently.

The abrasive belts are changed by releasing the belt tensioner, slipping the belt off and replacing it with a new one. Abrasive discs are held to the backing plate by means of an adhesive compound.

Grinders (Fig. 6), are available as either single or double purpose units. However, the double purpose units are now more or less standard. The primary use of the grinder is the maintenance of various cutting and drilling tools used by the carpenter. Many accessories are available for grinders considerably extending their usefulness. Other uses made possible by the application of accessories include polishing and cleaning of various materials and even sanding. The double purpose grinder is usually directly driven by an electric motor, although some are designed to be belt driven. Special models are made with

Fig. 6.   Double-Purpose Bench Grinder
Stanley Electric Tools

"thin" motors to allow the grinding of long pieces of material.   Twin
arbors allow for the mounting of the grinding wheels which are made
in various grades and of various materials depending on or dictated by
their intended use.   The two commonest abrasive materials for this
application are vitrified aluminum oxide, the silicon carbide; the latter
being harder and more durable is consequently more expensive.   For
grinding very hard materials, or for a very fine cut to close tolerances,
diamond wheels are occasionally used.   Accessories which are mounted
in the place of the abrasive wheels include cloth or fiber wheels for
buffing and polishing, and wire wheels of various types, sometimes
known as scratch wheels, which are used for cleaning and finishing
work.

The wheels themselves are always guarded so that only the working
area is exposed.   The shields are sometimes equipped with exhaust
ducts so that the waste may be collected and disposed of conveniently.
Also attached to the shield it is common practice to use a device known
as a spark deflector, which is adjustable and also gives further protection against flying particles, but this is not necessary if an eye shield is
used.   So that these last two devices will operate properly, and also for
correct grinding procedure, a grinder should be equipped with a re-
versing switch, so that it is always possible to grind on the downward
motion of the wheel.

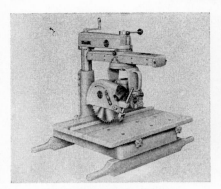

Fig. 7. Portable Radial Saw
Rockwell Manufacturing Co.

Fig. 8. Electric Hand Saw
Porter-Cable Machine Co.

An important accessory designed to further protect the operator is an eye shield which mounts over the working area and is equipped with shatterproof glass. Eye shields are sometimes combined with a lamp, which floods the working area with almost shadowless light. The eye shield is such an important safety measure that it is now standard equipment on many models; and in its absence, goggles should be used.

Apart from a tilting support table, often with a groove for mounting jigs and fixtures, two additional devices are available for use with grinders. They are a plane grinding attachment and a drill grinding attachment. A wheel dresser, often diamond, is used as a maintenance tool to even the surface of abrasive wheels which have become worn or damaged by chipping.

PORTABLE POWER TOOLS

Many portable power tools find frequent use in the shop, but since they were specifically designed to be portable, we will discuss them in this section rather than in the section on shop power tools.

The *portable radial saw*, Fig. 7, is a very versatile power tool which is used in all types of construction, including house construction, form construction, and timber construction. Although it is also used in the shop, whenever the saw has to be moved rather than the work. It may weigh more than 200 pounds, but it is balanced so that it can easily be carried by two men; and it is narrow enough to pass through an ordinary door.

The radial saw has many of the characteristics of the table saw, but differs in one important respect. The material being cut always remains in the same place, while it is the saw itself that moves.

The turret arm to which the saw head is attached allows the saw head to swing in a full circle about the horizontal plane, while keeping the saw over the table. The motor unit, of which the saw is a part, also tilts to any desired angle. This flexibility allows practically any type of cut or dado to be made, including left-hand mitering. The position of the fence is variable, and in the interests of safety, the fence controls are in the front of the machine out of the way of the saw blade. During the making of complicated cuts an advantage is realized with the radial saw, by being able to see the cut at all times, particularly when making dados.

The *electric hand saw*, Fig. 8, is a very powerful portable tool, which finds its main use on construction jobs and in maintenance work. Hand saws are available in sizes to accommodate saw blades from about 6 inches in diameter to about 9 inches in diameter. The diameter of the saw blade controls the maximum depth of cut that may be made with the saw. Electric hand saws are primarily used for cross-cutting and ripping, and accordingly standard models are usually equipped with a combination rip and crosscut blade; although special blades are available.

The base of the saw may be raised or lowered on a calibrated scale to control the depth of the cut, and most electric hand saws will make a bevel cut of up to 45 degrees; the angle of the cut being indicated on a calibrated quadrant.

The blade, and the operator, are protected by a safety blade guard which is pushed back by the work piece and returns automatically when the saw is removed from the work. This safety device is of vital importance and should not be taken off or jammed back.

Two of the accessories available for the hand saw are the ripping fence or guide, which permits the ripping of lumber to a predetermined width, and the saw protractor which enables the operator to make rapid, accurate cuts at any angle up to 90 degrees. The protractor is placed on the board, with the desired angle set, and the saw shoe is advanced along the straight edge in making the cut.

In construction work, sub-floor and roof board may be trimmed

Fig. 9.   Heavy-Duty Jig Saw
Black & Decker Mfg. Co.

Fig. 10.   Portable Power Plane
Black & Decker Mfg. Co.

with the electric hand saw, all at one time, after laying, rather than cutting each length individually before laying. This method results in a better and faster job.

The *jig saw,* Fig. 9, which also goes under the name of *sabre saw* and *recipro saw,* is a relatively new saw with many applications. As one of its names implies, it is a reciprocating-blade saw with a stroke of about one inch. The tip of the blade is pointed and sharp, by which means the saw is able to start its own hole.

The shoe is adjustable so that either left-hand or right-hand bevel cuts may be made. Sharp angles and curves may easily be cut, and a guide fence is available as an accessory.

Many special saw blades may be obtained for cutting wood, metal sheets, rods, tubes, plastics, fibreglass, masonite, leather and other materials.

The *power plane,* Fig. 10 provides fast accurate edging on all types of cabinet work, and in the fitting of doors, drawers, window sash, storm sash, screens, shutters, transoms and inside trim. It is in speed, particularly, that the power plane outdistances the hand plane since it will do a planing job many times faster than a hand plane. Most power planes are equipped with a spiral cutter, which results in a fine smooth finish regardless of the direction of the grain.

Planes are available which will finish surfaces up to about $2\frac{1}{2}$ inches wide, depending on the width of the cutter supplied. A graduated dial on the front of the machine adjusts the front shoe for depth of cut, which may on some models be a maximum of $\frac{3}{16}$ of an inch.

This adjustment may also be made during the planing operation. The angle fence will tilt up to about 15 degrees outboard and about 45 degrees inboard.

The portable router, Fig. 11, is extensively used in the shop and in construction work for fine joinery, inlay work, or decorative wood finishing. Many varieties of cutters and accessories are available for this tool. With the proper choice of cutter and jig, the router will do such diverse jobs as beading, grooving, routing, fluting, template making, mortising and dovetailing. By using two special template jigs, butt mortising and lock mortising may be accomplished on a produc-

Fig. 11. Portable Router
Porter-Cable Machine Co.

Fig. 12. Portable Router Equipped with Combination Straight and Circular Guide
Black & Decker Machine Co.

tion basis at production speed. In fact these two operations can be done fast enough by one man to keep several carpenters busy installing the butts and locks.

Standard equipment for the portable router usually includes a combination straight and circular guide. This device attaches to the router base, and runs on two parallel bars to insure maximum control and accuracy. The use of this guide is illustrated in Fig. 12. Dovetailing requires the use of a special cutter and template.

Three types of *portable sanders* are manufactured. They are the *disc sander,* the *belt sander,* and the *orbital sander.*

Although the *disc sander,* Fig. 13, is used for some of the same purposes as the belt sander and the orbital sander, its main asset is that it can be used to sand uneven and curved surfaces. The disc sander is also slightly more versatile than the other two types of portable sanders in that it can be used with a number of accessories in place of the sanding disc. With the use of a wire torque brush, the disc sander can be used for cleaning cracked paint and other deposits. A felt pad used in place of the sanding disc results in a portable buffer for rubbing down lacquered surfaces. Used with a rubber pad and a polishing bonnet, the disc sander makes a versatile portable polisher.

The *belt sander,* Fig. 14, is used for large flat areas, in production work, and in maintenance work such as the removal of old paint and

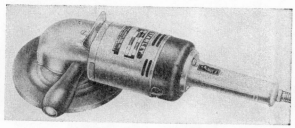

Fig. 13.   Portable Disc Sander
Stanley Electric Tools

varnish, prior to refinishing. Belts are available in three grades, the choice of which is dictated by the nature of the job. Some models of this type of sander are equipped with their own integral dust bags to collect the dust produced by the sanding operation.

The *orbital sander,* Fig. 15, is used in smaller and less accessible areas than the belt sander, and for finer work. It is not restricted to a limited number of abrasive surfaces since it uses standard sheet abrasive paper and cloth. The abrasive paper is cut to size and applied to the sander by means of clips at each end of the base-plate. As implied by its name, the base of the sander oscillates in an orbital pattern. So that even pressure can be applied to the work surface, a rubber or felt pad is used between the oscillating base-plate and the abrasive paper. This pad extends beyond the base-plate, permitting the sanding of corners and sanding in other close quarters such as right up to the riser of a stair tread.

The *portable electric drill,* Fig. 16, is an important and frequently

Fig. 14. Portable Belt Sander
Porter-Cable Machine Co.

Fig. 15. Portable Orbital Sander
Porter-Cable Machine Co.

Fig. 16. Portable Electric Drill
Skil Corporation

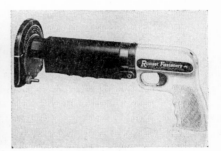

Fig. 17. Powder-Driven Fastener
Ramset Fasteners Inc.

used item in the carpenter's tool kit, since, apart from precision, it adds speed to his work.

Portable drills are available in the size range of ¼ inch to about 1¼ inches, this dimension being the maximum size of drill that the particular model will accommodate. This however, is not the final limitation, for some large drill bits and auger bits are available with reduction shanks. The largest portable drill used by the carpenter is probably the ¾ inch drill, and he uses this size for making holes for carriage and machine bolts in truss construction. This size of drill is also used with a special cutting tool for making grooves for split rings used in large trusses.

The *powder driven fastener*, Fig. 17, is a tool that fires a specially designed cartridge which provides the power to sink fasteners into a wide variety of construction materials. The depth of penetration can be controlled to a fine degree, by a combination of adjustment and the use of charges of different power. Interchangeable barrels are used for different sizes of fastener. The powder actuated fastener is particularly suitable for securing fasteners in concrete and steel, and can penetrate up to an inch of steel.

CHECKING ON YOUR KNOWLEDGE

The following questions give you the opportunity to check up on yourself. If you have read the chapter carefully, you should be able to answer the questions. If you have any difficulty, read the chapter over once more so that you have the information well in mind before you go on with your reading.

DO YOU KNOW

1. Into what two groups power tools are generally classified?
2. What additional accessory must be used on a table saw when a dado head is used?
3. What different types of circular saw blades are available for the table saw?
4. What kind of saw blade is used on a band saw for cutting plastic?
5. What the main use of the band saw is considered to be?
6. The term used to describe the operation of straightening the edge of a board?
7. What the term facing means?
8. The number of knives usually found on the cutting head of a jointer?
9. How many types of shop sander are available, what they are called and what their respective uses are?
10. What the main use of the grinder is considered to be?
11. Why some grinders are designed with "thin" motor units?
12. What two uses of the grinder are, when special accessories are used?
13. The names of the two commonest abrasive materials used for making grinding wheels?
14. What maintenance measure is required for grinding wheels?
15. In what important respect the radial saw differs from the table saw?
16. What advantage is realized by the use of the radial saw over the table saw in making complicated cuts?
17. The primary use of the electric hand saw?
18. How the electric hand saw is used in the laying of sub-flooring?
19. How the power plane differs from the hand plane as far as the grain of the wood is concerned?
20. The special characteristics of the electric jig saw?
21. Two uses of the portable router?
22. Which type of portable electric sander is used for the sanding of corners not otherwise easily accessible?
23. Which power tool uses a hole saw as one of its accessories?
24. How the depth of penetration of a powder-driven fastener can be altered?
25. How different sizes of fastener are accommodated in a powder driven fastener?

The Framing Square

QUESTIONS THIS CHAPTER WILL ANSWER

1. *Can you find the center of a circle by use of the framing square?* 2. *Is it possible to figure wages with a framing square?* 3. *Where is the Essex Board Measure located on the framing square?* 4. *In what way are the tables, stamped on the face of the square, especially useful to a carpenter?* 5. *What simple method can a carpenter use to test the accuracy of the right angle, at the heel, of his framing square?*

INTRODUCTION TO CHAPTER IV

The development of new carpentry tools and the improvement of old ones are noteworthy achievements of our age. Improved equipment makes possible increased skill and greater efficiency on the part of any workman. Unfortunately, however, the carpenter often fails to fully appreciate the opportunities afforded him by his improved equipment. He may continue on the job year after year without taking advantage of the time-saving devices which have been developed by skilled tradesmen, after much thought and many years of experience.

The framing square provides an excellent illustration of the foregoing statement. On the face and back of the framing square you will find tables and scales which, when properly applied, are remarkable devices for saving time. These devices have been prepared by men who have had many years of experience in the trade. Yet, many carpenters never take the trouble to learn how to use these valuable timesavers.

The purpose of this chapter is merely to introduce you, the beginning carpentry student, to the various uses of the framing square. It is not expected that the average student will be able to put all of this information to immediate practical use. However, the numerous and carefully prepared illustrations will help you to become familiar with the various scales and uses of the framing square, for which you will find uses as you progress in your study of carpentry.

The chapter has been divided into two parts: Part I and Part II. In Part I you will find a description of the applications of the framing square which you will need to know in your study of this book. The contents of Part II are of more than passing interest, but you may not find need for them until you have progressed somewhat further in your study of carpentry.

Study all the examples carefully. If possible, have a framing square at hand as you work through the problems. Follow step-by-step, the methods of procedure given in the text.

PART I

FRAMING SQUARE—SOME OF ITS USES

Without a framing square in his tool kit, the present-day carpenter would be seriously handicapped in his work. To a skilled craftsman in the trade, the square is almost as indispensable as the hammer, saw, or plane. To the inexperienced the square may be merely a tool for use in drawing lines at right angles, or for testing a board to determine whether or not it is straight and true. However, in the hands of a skilled workman who understands how to use the scales and tables on the framing square, it is a highly valuable tool and an essential part of his equipment. Therefore, it is advisable for the mechanic not only to acquaint himself with the fundamental operations performed with the square but also to become familiar with a few of the special layouts where the square is useful for solving common construction problems. The framing square serves the carpenter not only as an efficient tool but also as a handbook and instructor. The use of scales and tables given on the framing square avoids complicated mathematical computations which would consume much of the carpenter's valuable time. Information regarding lines and angles presented by means of scales and tables on the square is simple, practical, and condensed. In this chapter, the laying out of the various cuts is illustrated in a step-by-step method which makes some of the most difficult operations seem easy.

There are many different makes of framing squares and various finishes are applied to different makes as explained in the chapter on Modern Carpentry Tools. The scales and tables vary with the cost and make. When buying a framing square, it is advisable for a mechanic to spend enough money to secure one with complete tables and scales because they supply information particularly valuable on the job, making the square comparable to an engineer's handbook.

The chief difference in the tables of the various kinds of framing squares is found in the rafter table, as some tables are based upon *unit length* and others upon *total length*. Since space will not permit description of all of the tables, the one most frequently used—the unit length table—is the only one explained in detail in this book. The locations of the various tables and different graduations, or scales, are shown in Fig. 1.

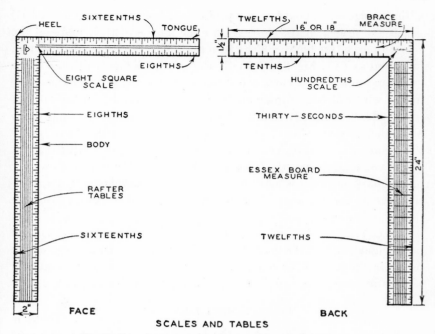

Fig. 1. Locations of Scales and Tables on Framing Square

TESTING A FRAMING SQUARE

Smooth up one side of a wide four-foot board. Dress one edge of the board until it is a true straight edge. Then lay the prepared board on the workbench with the straight edge turned toward you and the smoothed face turned upward. Place the square on top of the board with the blade, or body, extending to the left and the tongue at right angles to the straight edge of the board. Hold the square firmly in position with the entire length of the blade aligning perfectly with the straight edge of the board. The tongue will then be extending away from you across the board,

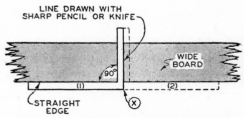

Fig. 2. Testing Framing Square for Accuracy

as shown at (1), Fig. 2. While still holding the square exactly in line with the edge of the board, take a penknife or a sharp-pointed, hard-lead pencil and draw a mark close against the tongue of the square on the smooth face of the board. Then turn the square over, keeping the heel, indicated as (*X*), Fig. 2, at exactly the same point but with the blade extending to the right along the straight edge of the board and exactly in line with this edge throughout the entire length of the blade of the square, as shown at (*2*), Fig. 2. Always hold the square firmly in place along the edge of the board and keep the heel exactly where it was before the square was turned over, then compare the position with the mark which you made across the board. If the edge of the tongue is exactly on the mark, or if a new mark made with the penknife or pencil against the edge of the tongue, in its new position, coincides exactly with the first mark drawn, then the square is truly *square*.

If the angle of the square is found to be less than 90 degrees it can be brought back to the correct position by careful hammering of the metal in the heel. The hammering of the metal stretches it at this point, throwing the end of the tongue outward.

ESSEX BOARD MEASURE

A series of figures known as the *Essex Board Measure* appears on the back of the blade of the framing square. These figures provide a means for the rapid calculation of *board feet,* the unit of measure for lumber. A piece of board one foot square and one inch thick contains one board foot. A piece of board 1 foot long, 1 inch thick, and only 6 inches wide contains ½ foot board measure. Another piece 2 feet long, 1 foot wide, and 1 inch thick contains 2 feet board measure (f.b.m.). We use the term *feet board measure* when referring to quantities of lumber and when determining buying or selling prices of lumber or timber.

You can find the feet board measure for any size of board or timber by arithmetic, but the process can be simplified greatly and much time saved by turning directly to the back of the blade of your framing square. When holding the blade in your right hand and the tongue in your left hand with the heel pointing outward, that is, away from your body, you will be looking at the back of the blade of the square. With the square held in this position, you can observe the inch divisions *1, 2, 3, 4, 5,* and so on, along the outside edge of the square, Fig. 3.

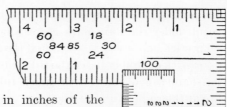

Fig. 3. Essex Board Measure Table
on Back of Framing Square

These figures show the width in inches of the stick of timber or board to be measured. Under each of these widths seven other figures appear. These figures give directly in feet (to the left of the vertical line) and in twelfths of a foot (to the right of the vertical line) the feet board measure, in boards of that particular width one inch thick, of seven different lengths. These lengths beginning at the top edge of the blade under the *12*-inch mark and reading downward are: *8, 9, 10, 11, 13, 14,* and *15* feet. The Essex board measure gives the number of board feet of practically all the sizes of boards or timber in common use. To find feet board measure the inch graduations, along the outer edge of the back of the blade of the square, are used in combination with the values given along the seven parallel lines.

The figure *12* at the outer edge of the back of the square represents a board **12** inches wide and one inch thick, Fig. 3. This is the starting point for all calculations. The numbers in the column directly under the *12*-inch mark indicate the lengths of a piece of board in feet. The regular inch divisions of the square on each side of the *12*-inch mark represent the widths of the boards in inches. The figures under each of these inch division marks represent the number of board feet and the twelfths of a board foot.

When you wish to find the feet board measure of a particular piece of lumber, first find under the *12*-inch mark the figure corresponding to the length (in feet) of your stick of timber. Then follow along

the horizontal line under this figure to the left until you come to the
point under the inch mark corresponding to the width (in inches) of
your stick, and there you will find the figure which gives the contents of
your stick of timber in feet board measure. The figure appearing at the
left-hand side of the vertical line is full feet board measure and the figure at the right of the vertical line is twelfths of a foot board measure.

EXAMPLE

Find the feet board measure in a board 1 inch thick, 10 feet long,
and 9 inches wide.

PROCEDURE

a) First, look in the column of figures underneath the *12*-inch mark on
the outside edge of the back of the blade of the square and near the middle of
the back of the blade you will find the number *10*.

b) Follow along the horizontal line underneath this number and to the
left of it, until you come to the column of figures underneath the 9-inch mark
at the edge of the blade.   There you will find the numbers 7|6, which stands for
seven and six twelfths feet board measure, which is the feet board measure of
your board. If the board were more than 1 inch thick, you would find the
feet board measure by multiplying the figure just found by the thickness of
the timber in inches. If the piece were more than 12 inches wide, you would
follow the horizontal line underneath the figure *10* in the *12*-inch column to the
right instead of to the left.

A length of 15 feet is the longest timber indicated in the column of figures
underneath the *12*-inch mark on the outer edge of the back of the blade of the
square. If the feet board measure is required for a stick longer than 15 feet, it
can be found by following the directions given in the preceding example, but
using only one half of the actual length, then doubling the results, since it is
evident that doubling the length of a piece of timber doubles the contents in
feet board measure. In order to show how to deal with a larger and longer
piece of timber than provided for in the Essex board measure, another example
follows.

EXAMPLE

Find the feet board measure in a timber 10 inches wide, 16 inches
thick, and 23 feet in length.

PROCEDURE

a) Divide the length of 23 feet into two parts of 10 and 13 feet. Let the
10-inch dimension be taken as the width and consider the timber to be made
up of 16 separate boards each one inch thick and 10 inches wide.

b) Find the feet board measure for each of the two pieces of board. Then add the results and multiply the sum by 16 to find the entire feet board measure of the whole stick of timber.

c) Following the procedure used in the foregoing example and referring to Fig. 3, we find a 1-inch board 10 feet long and 10 inches wide contains $8\frac{4}{12}$ feet board measure.

d) Following the same procedure for finding the number of board feet in a board 13 feet long, 10 inches wide, and 1 inch thick, we find this board would contain $10\frac{10}{12}$ feet board measure. Adding the contents of the two boards together gives $19\frac{2}{12}$ feet board measure. Multiplying this sum by 16 gives $306\frac{8}{12}$ feet board measure, the entire contents in board feet of the 23-foot stick of timber.

USING THE OCTAGON SCALE

You will find the octagon scale on the face of the tongue of the framing square, Fig. 4. This scale, sometimes known as the *eight-square scale*, consists of a series of divisions in the shape of dots marked off along the middle of the tongue of the square. Starting nearly under the *2*-inch mark on the outside edge near the heel, the dots continue almost to the other end of the tongue. There are 65 of these dots on a square having a 16-inch tongue. Every fifth dot is numbered, thus you find on the square: *5, 10, 15, 20* and so on up to *65*. The octagon scale is used for laying out figures with 8 equal sides.

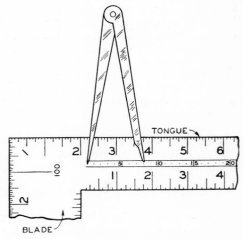

Fig. 4. Octagon Scale on Face of Tongue of Framing Square

Sometimes it becomes necessary for a carpenter to transform a square stick of timber into an eight-sided stick, for example, an octagonal newel post for a stairway. To do this, it is necessary to lay out an eight-square or octagon on the end of a square stick of timber. The method for doing this follows.

PROCEDURE

a) In laying out an octagon it is necessary first to square the stick to the

desired size, for example, 8 inches. Then cut the end of the stick square with
the sides, in this case making the end an 8-inch square. Locate the center
of each side as shown at (A), (B), (C), and (D) in Fig. 5. Then draw the
intersecting lines (AB) and (CD).

b) With dividers or a ruler, measure off on the octagon or eight-square
scale, on the tongue of the square the length of 8 spaces, since the timber is
8 inches square, Fig. 4. If the timber should be 10 inches square, the length
of 10 spaces should be measured off, if the timber should be 12 inches square,
the length of 12 spaces should be measured off, and so on.

c) After measuring off the length of 8 spaces on the octagon scale apply
this measurement to each side of the square timber on both sides of the center
points, (A), (B), (C), and (D), as (Aa), (Ab), (Bf), (Be), (Ch), (Cg),
(Dc), (Dd), Fig. 5. Joining the points (ah), (bc), (de), and (fg), will out-

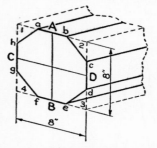

Fig. 5. Method of Laying Out
an Octagon on End of
Square Stick

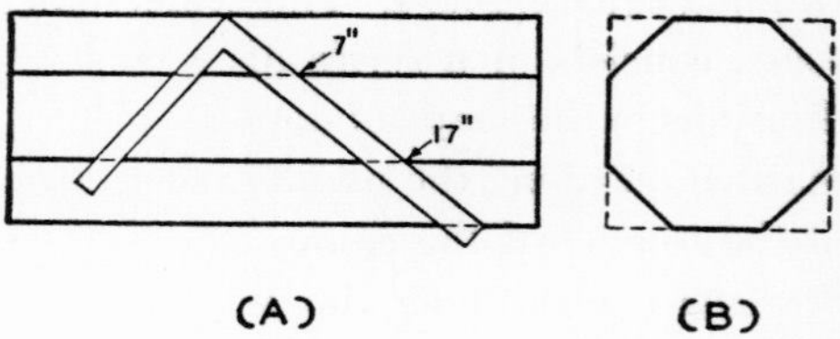

Fig. 6. Laying Out an Octagon on Square Stick
of Timber

line on the end of the stick a figure having 8 equal sides. Then with this as a
guide the entire stick can be shaped to this form by cutting off the solid triangular pieces from each of the four corners.

CONVERTING A TIMBER FROM SQUARE TO OCTAGON

Any square stick, or timber, can be laid out also for an octagon
timber with the framing square by using the following method.

PROCEDURE

a) Lay the framing square on the face of the timber to be cut, with the
heel of the square on one side of the timber and the tip of the blade, that is,
the 24-inch mark, on the other edge of the timber as shown at (A), Fig. 6.

b) Holding the square firmly in this position, mark points on the timber
at the inch divisions *7* and *17*. Through each of these points draw a line
parallel to the edges of the timber.

c) Proceeding in the same manner, draw corresponding lines on the other
three sides of the timber. These lines are used as cutting lines and indicate the
amount of wood that must be removed to change the timber from a square to
an octagon. The end of the octagon timber is shown at (B), Fig. 6.

CALCULATING PROPORTIONS WITH FRAMING SQUARE

1. Proportions. The inside edge of the back of the tongue on a framing square can be used to figure many problems involving costs, wages, etc., where a definite rate is established. The method is shown in the following example.

EXAMPLE

1. If clay soil, to be used as a fill, costs $9.00 for an 8 cubic yard load, how much would $3\frac{1}{4}$ cubic yards cost?

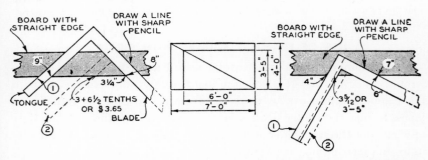

Fig. 7.   Calculating Costs with Framing Square

Fig. 8.   Calculating Proportions with Framing Square

PROCEDURE

a) Lay the square on a board with a straight and smooth edge as shown in position (*1*), Fig. 7. Hold the square to the proper figures so that these figures are over the edge of the board as shown in Fig. 7. In this case, the figure *8* (cu. yds.) on the inside of the blade and the figure *9* ($9.00 for 8 yards) on the inside of the tongue. Draw a line with a sharp pencil along the edge of the blade. Then slide the square to the right, along this line, until the figure *3¼* on the inside of the blade touches the edge of the board, as shown in position (*2*), Fig. 7. Read the figure on the inside of the tongue and you will find it to be *3* and *6½/10ths,* or $3.65, the cost of 3¼ yards.

2. Reductions of Enlargements. The framing square can be used for calculating proportions for finding reductions or enlargements. For example, correct proportions in reducing or enlarging a rectangular figure can be quickly obtained by means of sliding the framing square. The need for such calculations may arise when paneling a wall to keep small panels to the same proportions as larger panels. A similar need arises when making enlargements in photography. The following example gives the method of procedure when making reductions or enlargements.

EXAMPLE

2. What should be the width of a small panel 6 feet in length in order to retain the same proportions as a larger panel measuring 4′0″x7′0″?

PROCEDURE

a) Lay the framing square (with the 12th scale upward) to *4″* on the tongue and *7″* on the blade as in position *(1)*, Fig. 8.

b) Draw a line with a sharp pencil along the blade of the square.

c) Slide the square to the right, along this line, to the position shown at *(2)*, Fig. 8, with the figure *6* on the blade touching the edge of the board. The figure on the tongue will then be *3⁵⁄₁₂ths*, or 3 feet and 5 inches, the correct width of the rectangle that has a length of 6 feet.

USE OF FRAMING SQUARE WITH CIRCLES

The framing square is especially useful when finding the circumferences of circles and also when finding the centers of circles. Likewise, the framing square can be used to advantage to find the capacity of pipes, to find the center of arcs, and the size of an elliptical hole in a pitched roof through which a pipe is to be passed. Read carefully the following instructions for finding:

1. Circumference of a circle.

2. Capacities of round pipes.

3. Center of a circle.

4. Center of an arc.

5. Layout of an ellipse.

1. Finding the Circumference of a Circle. The circumference of a circle can be found with the framing square by the following method.

PROCEDURE

a) Lay the square along the edge of a straight smooth board, as shown at *(1)*, Fig. 22, to the figures *12″* on the blade and *3⅝″* on the tongue.

b) Draw a line along the blade with a sharp pencil.

c) Slide the square to the left to position *(2)*, Fig. 9, holding the blade along this line to the figure which is equal to three times the diameter of the circle. Make a check mark on the tongue as at *(B)*, Fig. 9.

d) Measure the bridge, or distance, between the points *(A)* and *(B)*, Fig. 9; this figure is the approximate circumference of the circle.

2. Finding the Capacities of Round Pipes. The size of a round pipe, required to carry the capacity of two or more other round pipes, can be found with the framing square, using the following method.

a) Lay the framing square along the edge of a straight stick, as shown in Fig. 10, with the size of one pipe (its diameter) on the tongue and the size of the other pipe on the blade.

b) Mark with a sharp pencil along the tongue and the blade.

c) Measure the bridge, or distance, between the two points at the edge of the board. This distance is the diameter of a pipe which will be large enough to carry the capacity of the two smaller pipes.

When three pipes are to be joined and their contents emptied into a fourth pipe the capacity of this pipe is found by the following method. First find

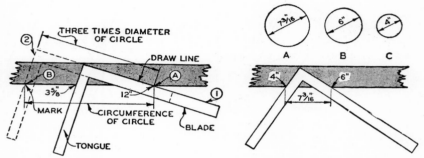

Fig. 9. Finding Circumference of Circle with Framing Square   Fig. 10. Pipe (*A*) Has Same Capacity as Pipe (*B*) Plus Pipe (*C*)

the diameter required for a pipe to carry the capacity of two of the smaller pipes as in the foregoing paragraphs. Take this figure on one side of the square and the diameter of the third pipe on the other side of the square. The bridge, or distance, between these two points will be the diameter required for a round pipe which is to carry the capacity of the other three pipes. This same procedure can be followed for joining any desired number of pipes whose combined contents are to be emptied into another pipe.

3. Finding the Center of a Circle. The center of a circle can be found by means of the framing square, using the following method.

a) Lay the square in the position shown at (*1*), Fig. 11, with the point of the heel touching the circumference, using the same figure on both the tongue and blade of the square.

b) Make check marks at the points where the tongue and blade touch the circumference.

c) Draw line (*A*) through these two points, as shown in Fig. 11.

d) Move the square to the position (*2*), Fig. 11, and hold the square in the same position as in position (*1*), Fig. 11.

e) Make check marks on the circumference at the points where the tongue and blade touch the circle.

f) Draw line (*B*) through these two points, as shown in Fig. 11. The point where the lines (*A*) and (*B*) intersect is the center of the circle.

4. Finding the Center of an Arc. Sometimes a carpenter must find the center of an arc or part of a circle which will pass through three

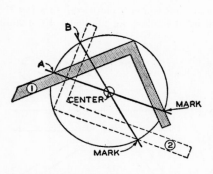

Fig. 11. Finding Center of a Circle with Framing Square   Fig. 12. Locating Center of Arc with Framing Square

points not in a straight line. Circular layout, such as stair work, requires a carpenter to lay out arcs which must pass through certain points.

PROCEDURE

The center of an arc, which must pass through three points not in a straight line, can be found with the framing square by connecting the three points with straight lines, as shown at (*A–B*) and (*B–C*), Fig. 12.

a) Find the centers (*a* and *b*) of the lines (*A–B*) and (*B–C*).

b) Lay the square to these lines with the heel at the point (*a*), position (*1*), Fig. 12; and at the point (*b*), position (*2*), Fig. 12.

c) Draw lines along the blade of the square through the points (*a*) and (*b*), as shown in Fig. 12. The point where these two lines intersect is the *center* of the arc.

5. Layout of an Ellipse for Pipe Passing through Pitched Roof. Passing a pipe through a pitched roof, as shown in Fig. 13, requires the cutting of an elliptical hole for the pipe. The length of the required ellipse, for any given pipe size, and the layout of the elliptical hole on the roof can be found by the following methods.

a) Lay the framing square on a board with a straight edge, taking the unit run (12 inches) on the blade and the unit rise of the roof on the tongue, as shown in Fig. 14.

b) Draw a line, shown as (*1*) in Fig. 14, along the blade. This gives the angle of the roof.

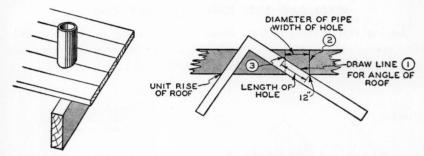

Fig. 13. Round Pipe Pass-   Fig. 14. Finding Length of Elliptical Hole for Pipe
ing through Pitched Roof

c) Lay out and draw, at right angles to the edge of the board, lines (*2*) and (*3*), as shown in Fig. 14. The distance between these two lines should be the same as the diameter, or width, of the pipe; that is, the width of the hole to be cut.

d) Measure the distance between the points where the lines (*2*) and (*3*) cut line (*1*). This gives the length of the ellipse, hence the length of the elliptical hole required for passing the pipe through the roof. After finding the size required for the elliptical hole, it must be laid out on the roof.

e) The elliptical hole for the pipe, shown in Fig. 13, can be laid out on the roof by locating the center of the pipe (*0*), Fig. 15. Draw the center lines; (*AB*) major axis, length of hole, and (*CD*) minor axis, width of hole, of the ellipse, shown at (*A*), Fig. 15.

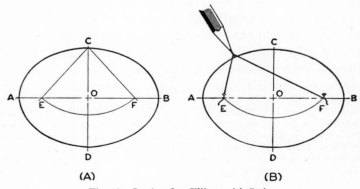

Fig. 15. Laying Out Ellipse with String

f) With (*C*) as a center and (*AO*) as a radius, draw an arc cutting the line (*AB*) at the points (*E*) and (*F*).

g) Drive a nail at each of the points (*C*), (*E*), and (*F*). Then tie an inelastic cord or string tightly around these three nails.

h) Remove the nail at (*C*) and holding a pencil in its place proceed to draw the ellipse, keeping the string taut, as shown at (*B*), Fig. 15.[1]

MITER AND BUTT JOINTS ON POLYGONS

Laying Out Miter and Butt Joints. The framing square is useful when laying out the angle for cuts in joining the pieces which form the sides of objects, such as boxes, plates on buildings, in cabinet construction, and columns which have many sides.

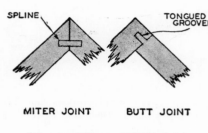

Fig. 16. Miter and Butt Joints
Commonly Used

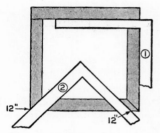

Fig. 17. Layout of Joints for
Square Objects

The two joints commonly used are the miter and the butt joints, shown in Fig. 16. In framing plates of a building, nails are commonly used to hold the joints together. In cabinet construction the joints frequently are made secure by using a spline on miter joints and the tongue and groove for butt joints as shown in Fig. 16.

On square objects the butt joint is an angle of 90 degrees. Such a joint can easily be laid out by holding the framing square as at (*1*), Fig. 17. The miter joint is laid out by taking any figure such as 12 on both the tongue and blade of the square. Lay the square so that these figures are on the edge of the stick, or board, as shown at (*2*), Fig. 17.

---

[1] When laying out the ellipse, extra space should be allowed around the pipe if it is to be the outlet for smoke from a heating plant, or stove. In such a case, the ellipse should be drawn so as to allow a 2-inch air space around the pipe. This precaution is necessary in order to avoid danger from fire. In addition to the air space, other requirements for protection from fire usually are given in building codes. These should be observed carefully.

The layout of miter and butt joints for three common polygons is shown in Fig. 18. Note that the figure on the blade for all of these joints is always 12″ while the figure on the tongue will vary, depending upon the shape of the figure and the joint. By always using the figure 12 on the blade as a constant, then there will be only one figure to remember when laying out the joint. This is an important fact to remember as it will simplify the operation.

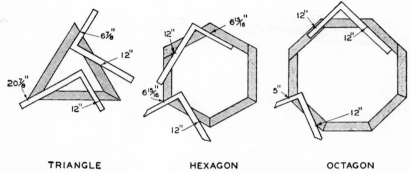

| TRIANGLE | HEXAGON | OCTAGON |

Fig. 18. Layout of Miter and Butt Joints for Three Types of Polygons

The miter cuts for other polygons having from three to twenty sides are shown in Fig. 19. This is a useful table for determining quickly the angle cuts for objects with three to twenty sides. The angle can be laid out with a protractor and **T** bevel or by taking the figure 12 on one side of the square and on the other side the figure indicated for the polygon.

HOPPER JOINTS

Laying Out Hopper Joints. When making a square or rectangular box the four corners form an angle of 90 degrees and the miter joints to 45 degrees. However, the hopper is wider at the top than at the bottom, as shown at (A), Fig. 20. This type of jointing requires a butt joint of more than 90 degrees and a miter cut of more than 45 degrees.

Since the hopper is like a roof turned upside down the principles of roof framing are applied in laying out the cuts. The run, Fig. 20, is the distance the top extends over the bottom, this is the same as the run

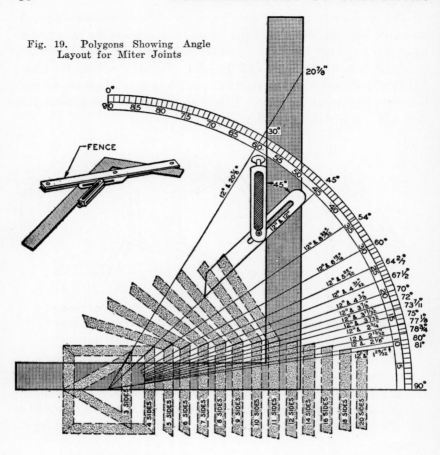

Fig. 19. Polygons Showing Angle
Layout for Miter Joints

LENGTHS OF SIDES WITH A CIRCUMSCRIBED DIAMETER OF ONE FOOT			LENGTHS OF SIDES WITH AN INSCRIBED DIAMETER OF ONE FOOT		
3	sides................10.3923	inches	3	sides................20.7840	inches
4	sides................8.4953	inches	4	sides................12.0000	inches
5	sides................7.0534	inches	5	sides................8.7184	inches
6	sides................6.0000	inches	6	sides................6.9282	inches
7	sides................5.2070	inches	7	sides................5.7795	inches
8	sides................4.5921	inches	8	sides................4.9705	inches
9	sides................4.1042	inches	9	sides................4.3576	inches
10	sides................3.7032	inches	10	sides................3.8990	inches
11	sides................3.3813	inches	11	sides................3.5230	inches
12	sides................3.1058	inches	12	sides................3.2154	inches
14	sides................2.6688	inches	14	sides................2.7373	inches
16	sides................2.3410	inches	16	sides................2.3869	inches
18	sides................2.0888	inches	18	sides................2.1159	inches
20	sides................1.8771	inches	20	sides................1.9005	inches

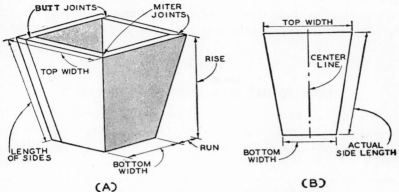

Fig. 20. Layout for Miter and Butt Joints for Hopper

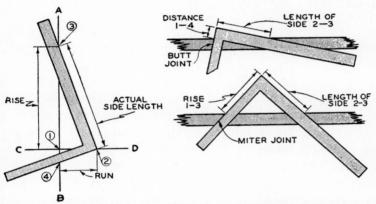

Fig. 21. Method Used to Obtain   Fig. 22. Layout for Obtaining the Angle of
Figures for Miter and Butt   the Miter and Butt Joints
Joints on Hopper   on Hopper

of the common rafter on a roof. The rise is the distance vertically
between the top and the bottom of the hopper. The length of the side
is the same as the length of a common rafter. The butt joint is the same
as the backing of a hip rafter and the miter joint is the reverse of the roof
sheathing cut.

The method of laying out the side of a hopper from a center line
to get true lengths of the joints is shown at (B), Fig. 20. When miter
joints are used on square hoppers, all sides will be the same. When butt
joints are used, two sides are smaller by the thickness of the material
of the other two sides. The layout in Fig. 21 will give all necessary

figures, which are to be used on the framing square, as shown in Fig. 22, for obtaining the angle of the butt and miter joints.

PART II

HOW TO USE UNIT-LENGTH RAFTER TABLES

When laying out rafters for a building, the skilled carpenter uses the unit-length rafter table stamped on the face side of the blade, or body, of the framing square, Fig. 23. This table gives the unit lengths of

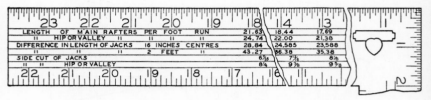

LENGTH OF MAIN RAFTERS PER FOOT RUN		21.63	18.44	17.69
HIP OR VALLEY		24.74	22.00	21.38
DIFFERENCE IN LENGTH OF JACKS 16 INCHES CENTRES		28.84	24.585	23.588
2 FEET		43.27	36.38	35.38
SIDE CUT OF JACKS		6⅜	7½	8½
HIP OR VALLEY		8¼	9⅜	9⅝

Fig. 23.   Unit-Length Rafter Table on Face of Framing Square

common rafters for **17** different rises, ranging from 2 inches to 18 inches. It also gives the unit length for hip rafters, difference in lengths of jack rafters set **16** inches on center (O.C.), jack rafters set **24** inches on center, and the side cuts for jack and hip rafters. When the carpenter once learns how to apply the information given in the tables, on the framing square, he finds them clever expedients as timesavers and quite simple. However, he must first understand the principles of roof framing and the laying out of the various rafters before attempting any short-cut methods, or undertaking to apply the information given in the tables. The following examples show how to find the different rafter lengths by means of the rafter tables given on the framing square.

EXAMPLES

For a building with a span of 10 feet and a unit rise of common rafter of 8 inches, by means of the tables given on the framing square, find:

1. Total length of the common rafter.

2. Total lengths for hip rafters and valley rafters.

3. Side cuts for hip rafters or valley rafters.

4. Common difference of lengths of jack rafters.

5. Side cuts for jack rafters.

1. Total Length of the Common Rafter. A *common rafter* extends from the plate to the ridge; the length of a common rafter is the shortest distance between the outer edge of the plate and a point on the center line of the ridge. The roof frame will not fit tightly together nor the structure be firmly braced unless the rafters are cut to just the right length. To insure correct cutting of rafter lengths by means of the rafter tables, proceed as follows.

PROCEDURE

a) First, find the rafter tables on the face of the blade of the framing square as shown in Fig. 23. Since the unit rise in this problem is 8 inches, locate the *8*-inch mark on the inch line along the outside edge of the rafter tables given on the square. This point is shown in (*A*), Fig. 24.

b) On the first line at the left end of the blade of the square is stamped *Length of main rafters per foot run*, Fig. 23. Follow this line until you come to the *8*-inch mark, shown at (*A*), Fig. 24. Under this mark you will find the number *14.42* on the first line. This means that when the unit rise per foot run is 8 inches the unit length of a main, or common, rafter will be 14.42 inches for every foot of run.

c) Since the span of the building in the example is 10 feet, the run of common rafter will be 5 feet ($\frac{1}{2}$ the width of the building). Multiply 14.42, the number of inches for every foot of run, by 5 feet, the number of feet in the run of the common rafter; this will equal 72.10 inches, or 72$\frac{1}{8}$ inches, equal to 6 feet and $\frac{1}{8}$ inch, the total length of the common rafter, shown at (*B*), Fig. 24. This total length is laid out on the rafter stock from the ridge cut at the top to the building line at the bottom.

2. Total Lengths for Hip Rafters and Valley Rafters. The *hip rafters* are the heavy rafters which slope up and back from the outside corners of a hip-roofed building to the ridge. The *valley rafters* are similar heavy rafters which also slope up from the outside wall to the ridge of the building, but occur at the intersection where adjacent roof slopes meet and form a valley.

PROCEDURE

a) On the second line at the left end of the blade of the square is stamped *Length of hip or valley rafters per foot run*, Fig. 23. Follow this line until you come to the *8*-inch mark shown at (*A*), Fig. 25. Under this mark you will find the number *18.76* on the second line. This means that when the unit rise per foot run is 8 inches, then for every foot of main, or common, rafter run, the length of the hip rafter will be 18.76 inches or 18$\frac{3}{4}$ inches.

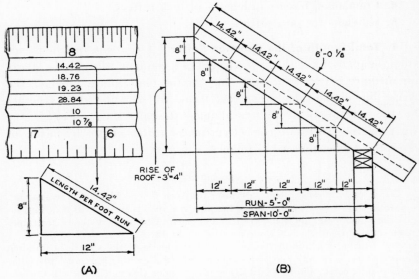

Fig. 24.   Unit Length of Common Rafter for 8-Inch Unit Rise

b) The unit length of hip rafter, 18.76 inches multiplied by the number of feet in the run of common rafter, 5 feet (½ the roof span) equals 93.80 inches or 93¹³⁄₁₆ inches which equals 7.81 feet, or 7 feet 9¹¹⁄₁₆ inches, the total length of the hip rafter or valley rafter (*B*), Fig. 25.

3. Side Cuts for Hip or Valley Rafters.

Both hip and valley rafters must have an angle cut to fit against the ridge or common rafter at the top. You will understand why accuracy is important in side cuts for hip and valley rafters when you begin practical construction work.

PROCEDURE

a) On the sixth line at the left end of the blade of the framing square, on the face side, is stamped *Side cut of hip or valley rafters,* Fig. 23. Follow this line to the 8-inch mark the same as you did in finding the lengths of the common and hip rafters. Under the figure *8* you will find the number *10⅞* on the sixth line of the rafter table, shown at (*A*), Fig. 26.

b) On the rafter stock which is to be cut, lay the square in the position shown at (*B*), Fig 26. Take the *12*-inch mark on the tongue and the *10⅞*-inch mark on the blade and hold the square in the position shown at (*B*), Fig. 26. Mark a line for cutting along the outside of the tongue on the 12-inch side of the square.

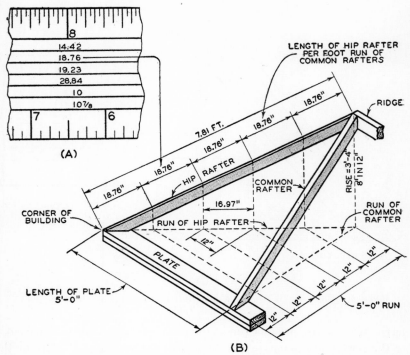

Fig. 25. Unit Length of Hip or Valley Rafter for 8-Inch Unit Rise

4. Common Difference of Lengths of Jack Rafters. In every roof containing a hip or a valley there are some rafters known as *jack rafters* which are common rafters *cut off,* by the intersection of a hip or valley rafter, before reaching the full length from the plate to the ridge. Jack rafters are spaced the same distance apart as the common rafters, usually 12, 16, or 24 inches on center. Because the jack rafters fill a triangular-shaped space in the roof surface these rafters vary in length. Since they rest against the hip or valley rafters, equally spaced, the second jack rafter must be twice as long as the first one, the third jack rafter three times as long as the first one and so on. This establishes a common difference in jack rafters for various pitches. These differences in lengths of jack rafters are given on the third and fourth lines of the rafter table found on the face side of the framing square, Fig. 23. The jack rafters

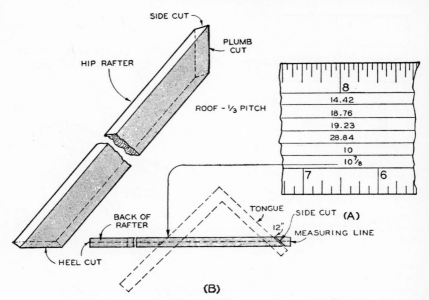

Fig. 26. Side Cuts for Hip and Valley Rafters, Using Figure Shown in Sixth
Line of Table

have the same rise per foot run as the common rafters on the same slope
of the roof, and the cuts where they rest against the wall plate or the
ridge board are obtained in the same way as for common-rafter cuts,
previously explained. Jack rafters differ from common rafters in length
and in the side cut necessary to make them fit against the hip or valley
rafter. When a roof slope has an 8-inch rise per foot run of common
rafter and the jack rafters are spaced 16 inches on center, to find the
common difference in lengths of these rafters proceed as follows.

PROCEDURE

a) On the third line at the left end of the blade of the framing square,
on the face side, is stamped *Difference in length of jacks 16 inches centers.*
Follow this line of the rafter table until you come to the *8*-inch mark. Under
this mark is the number *19.23.* This means that the difference in length of
jack rafters or the length of the first and shortest jack rafter is 19.23 inches.
To find the length of the third jack rafter multiply 19.23 by 3 which gives
57.69 inches, or 4 feet 9⅔ inches. When the spacing between the jack rafters
is more than 24 inches the dimension is given in feet instead of inches.

b) On the fourth line at the left end of the blade of the square, on the
face side, is stamped *Difference in lengths of jacks 2 feet centers,* Fig. 23.
Follow along this line until you come to the *8*-inch mark, Fig. 26. Under this

figure, on the fourth line of the rafter table, you will find the number *28.84*. This means that the difference in length of jack rafters spaced 2 feet on center is 28.84 inches, or 2 feet 4.84 inches.

5. Side Cuts for Jack Rafters. Jack rafters must have an angle or side cut to fit against the hip or valley rafter. The angle of this cut can be found by again making use of the rafter table, on the face side, of the framing square.

PROCEDURE

a) On the fifth line of the rafter table at the left end of the framing square, on the face side, is stamped *Side cut of jacks*. Follow along this line to the *8*-inch mark. Under this figure on the fifth line you will find the number *10*, Fig. 26.

b) On the stock which is to be used for jack rafters, lay the framing square in a position similar to that for side cuts of hip and valley rafters, shown at (*B*), Fig. 26. Since the number in the fifth line of the rafter table, under the 8-inch mark, is *10*, locate this number on the blade of the square and *12* on the tongue of the square. Hold the square firmly in position at these two points while drawing the cutting line along the outside of the tongue of the square as shown at (*B*), Fig. 26. This will give the side cuts for the jack rafters on a roof that has a unit rise of 8 inches per foot of run of common rafter.

Study the diagrams and learn the locations of: *span, run, rise, pitch, common rafters, hip* and *valley rafters, jack rafters, plates,* and *the measuring line of the ridge.* With the illustrations at hand, study the procedures for working the various examples given in this chapter.

RULES

It would be to your advantage later, if you would learn the following rules at this time.

Rule 1. The *total length of a common rafter* (Fig. 23) can be found by multiplying the length given in the rafter table under the figure representing the unit rise of the rafter by the number of feet of run.

Rule 2. The *total length for hip and valley rafters* (Fig. 25) can be found by multiplying the length given in the rafter table under the figure representing the unit rise of the rafter by the number of feet of run of the common rafter.

Rule 3. The *side cut for a hip or a valley rafter* can be found by taking the figure given in the rafter table, under the figure representing the unit rise of the rafter, on the blade of the square, and 12 inches on the tongue. Then draw a line along the tongue. This will give the cutting line for the side cut.

Rule 4. The *length of a jack rafter* can be found by multiplying the value given in the rafter table, under the figure representing the unit rise of the rafter, by the number indicating the position of that particular jack; that is, multiplying by 3 for the third jack.

Rule 5. The *side cuts for jack rafters* can be found by taking the figure shown in the table, under the figure representing the unit rise of the rafter, on the blade of the square and 12 inches on the tongue. Then draw a line along the tongue for the side cut.

BRACE LAYOUT

1. The principles involved in laying out a brace are the same as those for laying out a common rafter. The common rafter represents the hypotenuse of a right triangle, while the run and rise of the rafter represent the other two sides of the triangle, as shown at (*B*), Fig. 25. Likewise, a brace represents the hypotenuse, while the run and rise of the brace represent the other two sides of a right triangle, *1–2–3*, Fig. 27.

Note that when cutting the brace to fit at the top (*1*) and at the bottom (*3*) the method used is the same as that for the common rafter. Also, the length for a long brace is stepped off in the same way as for a common rafter.

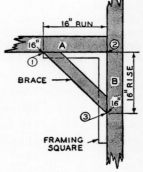

Fig. 27.   Basic Triangle of a Brace

PROCEDURE

a) When the run and rise of a brace are the same length, the brace represents the hypotenuse of a right triangle in which each of the acute angles is 45 degrees. The brace then is a 45-degree brace, Fig. 28.

b) For this type of brace, the angles for the cutting lines are laid out by taking the same figure on both the tongue and blade of the square. For example, if the run and rise are 16 inches or less in length, the brace can be laid out by taking the run on the tongue and the rise on the blade.

c) Draw a line along the tongue for the angle of the cut to fit against the top (*A*), Fig. 27. Another line drawn along the blade will give the angle for the cut to fit against (*B*), Fig. 27.

d) A line connecting points (*1*) and (*3*) will give the length of the outside of the brace as shown in Fig. 27.

e) For long braces, when the run and rise are the same length, the step method can be used to find the total length of the brace, as shown in Fig. 28. Here we assume the run and rise to be 48 inches, or 4 feet.

f) Lay the square in position near the right end of the piece of timber which is to be used for a brace. The 12-inch mark on both the blade and tongue should be exactly on the edge of the timber as shown in Fig. 28.

g) Holding the square firmly in this position, draw lines along the outside edge of both the blade and the tongue.

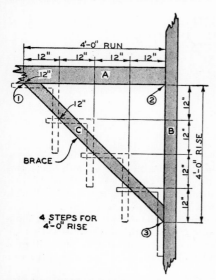

Fig. 28. Method of Stepping Off Length of
Brace Having Equal Run and Rise

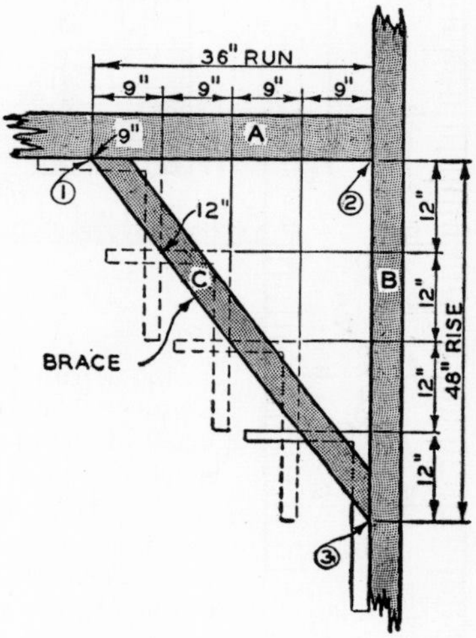

Fig. 29. Stepping Off Length of Brace
with Unequal Run and Rise

h) Next, move the square along the timber toward the left until the 12-inch mark on the blade coincides with the same point where the 12-inch mark of the tongue was in the previous position. Again draw lines along the outside of both blade and tongue. Continue this procedure until the four steps have been completed. The cutting lines of the brace at the points (*1*) and (*3*) will make an angle which fits at top and side. Care should be taken in using this method as a slight error will spoil the angle cut and cause an imperfect fit of the brace.

2. For long braces when the total run is less than the total rise, to find the length of the brace and the angle cuts for the top and side, the total run is divided into as many units as there are feet in the rise. For example, if the total rise is 48 inches and the run 36 inches, since the rise contains four 12-inch units, then the run should be divided into four 9-inch units, as shown in Fig. 29.

PROCEDURE

a) Lay the square in position near the right end of the piece which is to be used for the brace, with the *9*-inch mark of the tongue and the *12*-inch mark of the blade exactly on the edge of the timber as shown in Fig. 29.

Fig. 30.   Brace-Measure Table
on Back of Tongue of
Framing Square

b) Draw lines along the outside edge of both blade and tongue. Then move the square to the left until the 12-inch mark of the blade coincides with the point where the 9-inch mark of the tongue was in the previous position.

c) Again draw lines along the outside edge of the blade and tongue of the square. Repeat this procedure until four positions of the square have been stepped off. This will give the length for a brace when the rise is 48 inches and the run 36 inches.

d) Cutting the timber on the lines indicated at each end will give the correct angle for fitting the brace at the top (*A*), Fig. 29 and at the side (*B*), Fig. 29.

BRACE MEASURE

Along the center of the back of the tongue of the framing square you will find a table which gives the lengths of common braces. This series of figures known as the *brace measure*, or the *brace rule*, is illustrated in Fig. 30.

The use of this table is somewhat limited since it is chiefly for 45-degree braces. For example, the figures of the table show that when the run and rise of the brace are both 36 inches, then the length of the brace will be 50.91 inches; or if the rise and run are both 24 inches, the length of the brace will be 33.94 inches. However, the last set of figures shown at the right end of the tongue is for braces which have the proportion of 18 inches of run to 24 inches of rise, giving a brace of 30 inches in length.

Whenever possible to use it, the brace-measure table is convenient since it gives the total length of a brace, thus making it unnecessary to use the step-off method previously explained. Application of the table is illustrated in Fig. 31. Any multiple of the figures found in this table can also be used.

EXAMPLE

Find the length of a brace with run and rise of 78 inches.

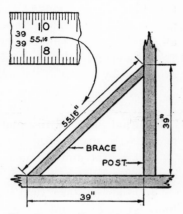

PROCEDURE

a) Since the figure 78 is not given on the table we use the multiple 39 which is one-half of 78. The table shows that when the run and rise of a brace are both 39 inches, then the length of the brace is 55.16 inches.

b) Since 39 inches is one-half of 78 inches, then twice 55.16 inches, or 110.32 inches, is the total length of the brace which has a run and rise of 78 inches.

The foregoing example shows that if you have a brace whose run and rise is longer than any run or rise shown in the brace-measure table, you can find the length of the brace by finding one-half the actual run or rise in the brace

Fig. 31. Application of Brace Measure Found on Framing Square

measure and then doubling the length given for it. Thus for a run and rise of 78 inches, you find $\frac{39}{39}$ *55.16* on the square and the length of the brace will be twice 55.16, which is 110.32 inches, or 9 feet 2.32 inches.

THE 12TH SCALE ON FRAMING SQUARE

The 12th scale, with the inch divided into 12 parts instead of 16, is usually found on the back of the framing square along the outside edge. In this scale an inch represents one foot and each inch is divided into 12 parts; hence, each one of these parts or graduations equals 1 inch on the 12th scale. Thus, the 12th scale makes it possible to reduce layouts to $\frac{1}{12}$th of their regular size while still retaining the same proportions.

The 12th scale on the framing square can be put to many uses in roof framing. This scale is especially useful for solving basic right triangles, without mathematical computation. This scale also enables the workman to make a layout of his work for a building, or any part of it, one-twelfth ($\frac{1}{12}$th) of the regular size. If the layout is carefully made it can be relied upon to give reasonably accurate results. Many carpenters prefer to find rafter lengths by using the 12th scale instead of using the step method or the mathematical method. However, use of the 12th-scale method demands accuracy and unless the work is carefully done errors may occur. Use of the 12th scale is recommended for making an overall check of rafter lengths when rafters are laid out by other methods.

Methods for using the 12th scale, given on the framing square, are explained by means of the following examples.

EXAMPLES

1. Find the total rise and total length of a rafter when total run and unit rise are given.

2. Find the unit rise of a rafter when the total rise and total run are given.

3. Find the theoretical length of a hip or valley rafter when the total run and the unit rise of the common rafter are given.

1. Find the Total Rise and Total Length of a Rafter When Total Run and Unit Rise Are Given. The total run of a rafter is 6 feet 7 inches and the unit rise is 8 inches. To find the total rise and total length.

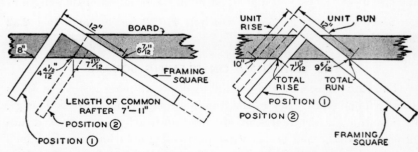

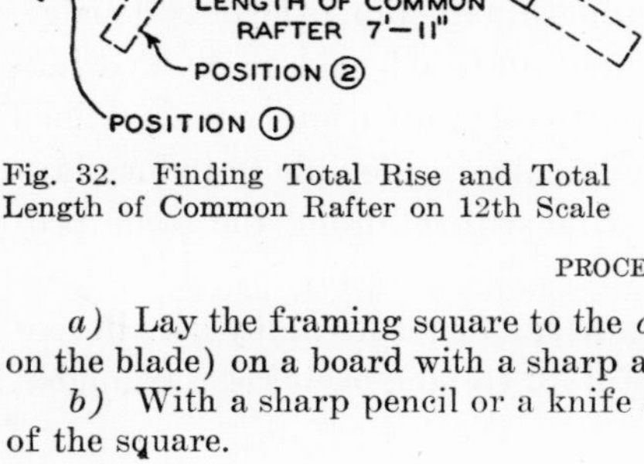

Fig. 32. Finding Total Rise and Total
Length of Common Rafter on 12th Scale

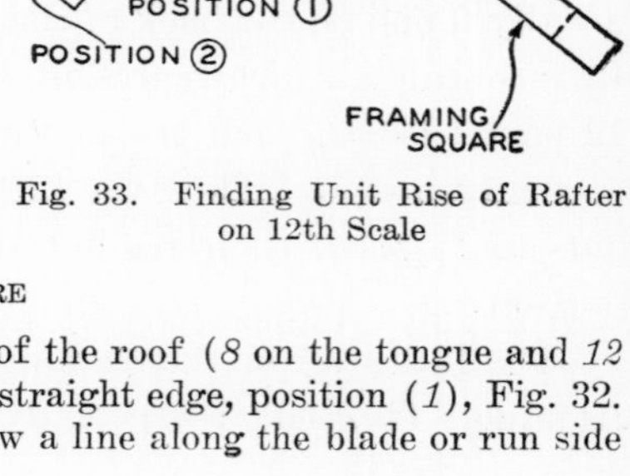

Fig. 33. Finding Unit Rise of Rafter
on 12th Scale

PROCEDURE

a) Lay the framing square to the *cut* of the roof (*8* on the tongue and *12* on the blade) on a board with a sharp and straight edge, position (*1*), Fig. 32.

b) With a sharp pencil or a knife draw a line along the blade or run side of the square.

c) Slide the square, that is, move it to the right along this line until the figures *6⁷⁄12* are directly over the lower edge of the board, position *(2)*.

d) Hold the square to this line with the edge of the blade coinciding with the line and the tongue perpendicular to the line. Then read the figure on the tongue at the edge of the board. This figure should be *4* and *4½/12ths*, or 4 feet and 4½ inches, which will be the total rise of the rafter.

e) While the square is in this position (position *2*), mark the edge of the board on the tongue side of the square, as shown in Fig. 32.

f) Measure along the edge of the board with the 12th scale the distance between the line and the mark just made. This distance should read *7¹¹⁄12ths* or 7 feet and 11 inches, the total length of the rafter.

2. Find the Unit Rise of a Rafter When the Total Rise and Total Run Are Given.

A rafter has a total run of 9 feet 6 inches and a total rise of 7 feet 11 inches. To find the unit rise.

PROCEDURE

a) Place the framing square as before on a board with a straight and smooth edge using *9⁶⁄12ths* inches on the blade and *7¹¹⁄12ths* inches on the tongue, position *(1)*, Fig. 33.

b) Mark along the blade with a sharp pencil or knife.

c) Slide the blade of the square along this line to the left so the figure *12* (unit run) is over the lower edge of the board, position *(2)*, Fig. 33.

d) Read the figure on the tongue directly over the edge of the board. This should read *10* inches. Therefore, 10 inches is the unit rise for a rafter that has a total run of 9 feet 6 inches and a total rise of 7 feet 11 inches.

The 12th scale can also be used to find the theoretical length of the hip or valley rafters, as shown in the following example.

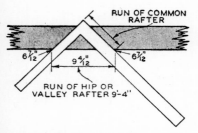

Fig. 34. Finding Total Run of Hip or Valley Rafter on 12th Scale

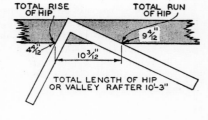

Fig. 35. Method of Finding Theoretical Length of Hip or Valley Rafter on 12th Scale

3. To Find the Theoretical Length of a Hip or Valley Rafter.

The run of the common rafter of a roof is 6 feet 7 inches and the unit rise is 8 inches. Find the theoretical length of the hip or valley rafter.

PROCEDURE

a) Lay the framing square on a board with a straight and smooth edge, in the position shown in Fig. 34.   Then take the figure *6⁷⁄₁₂ths* inches (run of the common rafter) on the blade and the same figures on the tongue.   Make a mark along the blade and the tongue with a sharp pencil, as shown in Fig. 34.

b) The distance between these two marks will be *9⁴⁄₁₂ths* inches.   Therefore, the total run of the hip or valley rafter will be 9 feet and 4 inches.   The total run of the hip and valley rafter is the diagonal of a square whose sides are equal to the common rafter run, in this case 6 feet and 7 inches.

c) Find the total rise, 4 feet and 4 inches, by the method shown in Fig. 32.

d) Lay the square on the edge of the board, as shown in Fig. 35, taking *4⁴⁄₁₂ths* (total rise) on the tongue and 9⁴⁄₁₂ths (total run) on the blade.   Mark with a sharp pencil on both sides of the square.

e) The distance between these two points will measure *10³⁄₁₂ths* inches.   Therefore, the theoretical length of the hip or valley rafter will be 10 feet 3 inches.

CHECKING ON YOUR KNOWLEDGE

If you have read this chapter carefully, you should be able to answer the following questions.   If you have any difficulty, you should read the chapter again, so that you will have the information well in mind before you go on with your reading.

DO YOU KNOW

1. Where the hundredths scale is located on the framing square?

2. How to find the capacity of round pipe using the framing square?

3. Where the Essex Board Measure is located on the framing square?

4. How to find the feet board measure in a board 2 inches thick, 10 feet long, and 9 inches wide, by using the Essex Board Measure found on the framing square?

5. Where to find the octagon scale on the framing square?

6. How to convert a square piece of timber into an octagon?

7. How to lay out an ellipse for a pipe passing through a pitched roof?

8. How to use the framing square to find the center of an arc which passes through three points not in a straight line?

9. What kind of joints are commonly used when constructing hoppers?

10. How to correct the angle of the framing square if it is less than 90 degrees?

Principal Woods, Their Uses, Grades, and Classifications

QUESTIONS THIS CHAPTER WILL ANSWER

1. *How can the approximate age of a tree be determined?* 2. *Upon what does the weight and strength of wood depend?* 3. *What varieties of softwood and hardwood are most commonly used by the carpenter?* 4. *What are some of the common causes of defects and blemishes in wood and lumber?* 5. *How is lumber graded and sold?*

INTRODUCTION TO CHAPTER V

You are going to be fascinated by the study of wood. The average person does not know, as the carpenter *must*, the many varieties and special uses of wood; also the many factors which enter into the proper selection of wood for building and construction purposes.

You will learn many interesting facts about trees, and undoubtedly you will enjoy a considerable sense of satisfaction in this knowledge. When you pick up a piece of lumber you will be able to see certain features and characteristics that the untrained eye would never observe. Behind the board you hold in your hand you will see a whole history of development and growth, indicated by the physical appearance of the board.

A carpenter is more than a man who merely handles tools; he is a man who knows his materials, who can glance at a piece of lumber or hold it in his hands and appreciate its worth. In this chapter you will learn how to detect blemishes and defects in wood and how lumber is graded and prices determined. Such knowledge will give you confidence in yourself and a sense of justifiable pride in your work. Furthermore, it is such knowledge as this that will enable you to advance in the field of carpentry, for the more a man knows about his trade the greater are the opportunities for his advancement.

The author's practical knowledge of this subject will prove of great benefit to you in your work. Read the text carefully and well; remember it is advisable to review the chapter if you find difficulty in answering the questions at the end of it.

GROWTH OF WOOD

Wood is composed essentially of cellulose in minute elongated cells, called *fibers*, firmly cemented together by lignin. The fibers are tapered at the end and run vertically in standing trees. In softwoods the length of the fibers is about ⅛th of an inch and in hardwoods about 1/24th of an inch. The central diameter of a fiber is about 1/100th of the length.

The appearance of different woods varies with the arrangement of the cells or fibers. In addition to the fibers running with the grain there are bands of cells extending radially from the pith or center of the tree across the grain toward the bark. These so-called *wood rays* or *medullary rays* are responsible for the prominent flakey figure in some woods when quartersawed. In most woods these rays are small and inconspicuous.

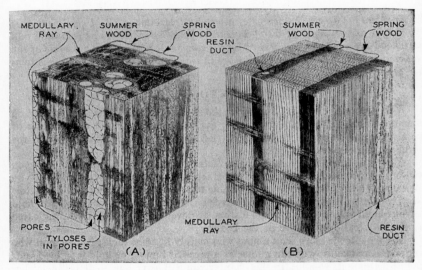

Fig. 1. Magnified Blocks of White Oak *(A)* and Shortleaf Pine *(B)*

The top of each block represents the end—cross, or transverse section. The left side shows a quartersawed section (hardwood) and vertical grain or radial section (softwood). The right side illustrates flat-grain, plain-sawed, or tangential section.

The weight and strength of wood depends upon the thickness of the cell walls. The shape, size, and arrangement of the fibers, the presence of the wood rays, and the layer effect of the springwood and summerwood, Fig. 1, account for the large difference in the properties along and across the grain.

Hardwoods and Softwoods. Trees commonly cut into lumber and timber products are divided into two broad groups: *hardwood* and *softwood*.

The term *softwood* as used in the lumber trade does not necessarily mear a tree whose wood is soft, nor does *hardwood* always indicate one whose wood is hard. In fact, no definite degree of hardness divides the two groups. The custom has developed of calling the coniferous trees *softwood,* and the broad-leaved trees *hardwood.* Coniferous trees are those with needles or scalelike leaves, popularly called *evergreens.* Broad-leaved trees are often termed *deciduous* because most of those in the United States shed their leaves each year.

In general, the woods in the *hardwood* group are harder than those in the *softwood* group. However, a few of the softwoods are harder than many hardwoods. Fir is an example of a hard *softwood,* while some *hardwoods* are among our softest woods, an example being basswood, or poplar.

The commercial softwoods and hardwoods of the United States are:

SOFTWOODS	HARDWOODS	
Cedars and junipers	Alder	Gums
Cypress	Ashes	Hackberry
Douglas fir	Aspen	Hickories
True firs	Basswood	Locust
Hemlocks	Beech	Magnolia
Larch	Birches	Maples
Pines	Buckeye	Oaks
Redwood	Butternut	Sycamore
Spruce	Cherry	Walnut
Tamarack	Chestnut	Willow
Yew	Cottonwoods	Yellow poplar
	Elms	

Lumber suitable for structural purposes may be obtained from two other groups; but for some reason these groups have not been utilized extensively as yet except in the immediate vicinity where they grow. This is especially true of bamboo which grows in abundance in China and the Philippine Islands and is used there extensively for building purposes. Although the wood has certain characteristics which might make it suitable for use in other locations, it has not been introduced into other countries. The tree could be grown probably in any warm climate, such as that of our southern states; of the other group, not used for structural purposes, the palms are the best-known representatives. However, the use of lumber cut from palm trees is extremely limited.

Heartwood and Sapwood. The cross section of a log cut from a tree trunk shows distinct zones of wood. First, there is the *bark* placed like a sheath around the outside of the log; then, a light-colored zone next to it called *sapwood;* and an inner zone, usually darker in the center, called *heartwood.* In the structural center of the log and usually of the heartwood is the *pith,* sometimes termed in the lumber trade as *heart center.* When a piece of lumber contains the pith, it is called *boxed pith;* when it does not, it is termed *side-cut* (pithless). A cross section of a tree trunk is shown in Fig. 2. The outer bark, or corky layer, shown at *(A)*, is composed of dry dead tissue which gives the tree protection against external injuries. The inner bark *(B)* is moist and soft. It carries prepared food from the leaves to all growing parts of the tree. The wood and bark cells are formed in the microscopic cambium layer shown at *(C)*

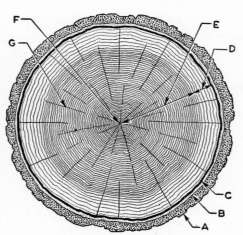

Fig. 2. Cross Section of Tree Trunk Showing Outer *(A)* and Inner *(B)* Bark, Cambium *(C)* Sapwood *(D)*, Heartwood *(E)*, Pith *(F)*, and Wood Rays *(G)*

just inside the inner bark. Immediately beneath the bark is the light-colored wood (D) known as *sapwood.* The sapwood carries sap from the roots to the leaves. The inactive heartwood is shown at *(E)*. This part of a tree is formed by a gradual change in the sapwood and gives the tree strength. The pith *(F)* is the soft tissue about which the first wood growth takes place in the newly formed twigs. The various layers of the tree are connected by wood rays *(G)* which extend from the pith to the bark and provide for the storage and transference of food.

A tree grows by forming new layers of wood at the point where the bark and sapwood meet. *Cambium* is the technical name for this layer of soft cellular tissue from which new bark and new wood originate. The cambium is supplied with nourishment by a fluid known as *sap* which circulates through the wood cells located immediately underneath the bark. These wood cells make up the living, active portion of the tree. These cells also carry water from the roots to the uppermost parts of the tree. Various salts obtained from the soil and dissolved in the water are carried by the ascending current from the most minute rootlet to the topmost branches and leaves. Food for the plant is also stored in the wood cells, to be used when needed.

A young tree is composed entirely of sapwood. The heartwood is formed in the central portion as the tree grows older. As the cells mature and become inactive, the heartwood usually turns darker in color. The thickness of the sapwood varies in different kinds of trees, and depends to some extent upon the age of the tree. The conditions under which growth takes place may also affect the thickness of the sapwood.

All heartwood was once sapwood. During the transition period of growth, the changes which take place have no effect upon the mechanical properties of the wood. Hence, so far as strength is concerned, there is no difference between sapwood and heartwood. However, when in contact with the soil and under conditions conducive to decay, heartwood is more durable than sapwood. Therefore, it is better to use heartwood if the material is not to be treated with preservatives and conditions are conducive to decay. But it is better to use sapwood if preservatives are to be used, because heartwood does not absorb preservatives readily.

Rings of Annual Growth. There is a marked difference in the manner of growth in different kinds of trees. The trees with which this study is especially concerned show annual growth rings and include both the broad-leaved trees and the evergreens. These are known as *exogens* because they grow from without. However, there are certain exogenous trees which show no distinct annual growth rings, for example some species of evergreen tropical trees. The palms and bamboos do not show annual growth rings. These are known as *endogens* because they grow from within.

In cool temperate climates, examination of the cross section of a freshly cut tree shows a number of concentric rings starting at the center of the pith and continuing outward to the bark. Each of these rings represents the growth the tree makes during one year; that is, from the time active growth begins in the spring to the time the tree becomes dormant in the fall. Therefore, the approximate age of the tree can be determined by counting the rings of annual growth on a cross section cut as closely as possible to the ground, because the oldest part of a tree trunk is its base. The annual rings of a cross section taken fifteen feet above the ground would perhaps show fewer rings because that section would be of a more recent growth than the lower section. These annual rings vary in width according to conditions under which growth takes place. Narrow rings being formed during years when there is a short dry season and wider rings during years when conditions are more favorable for growth. The annual growth rings appear in the cross section of lumber as concentric circles or portions of circles.

Springwood and Summerwood. In many woods each ring of annual growth is made up of two parts: (a) an inner light-colored portion known as *springwood*, and (b) an outer darker portion of later growth known as *summerwood*, also sometimes called *autumnwood*.

Springwood is made up of relatively large, thin-walled cells formed during the early part of each growing season. Summerwood is formed later in the year and is made up of cells having thicker walls and smaller openings. Therefore, summerwood or autumnwood contains more solid wood substances and appears to be darker in color than springwood. In both softwoods and hardwoods growing in regions having climatic seasons this phenomenon appears although it is less noticeable in hardwoods.

The proportion of springwood and summerwood present in pieces of softwood lumber has an important effect upon its strength properties and physical characteristics. In some species there is a gradual change from springwood to summerwood. In other softwoods the change from springwood to summerwood is more or less abrupt, thus resulting in well-marked bands of darker, more solid wood substance, and usually in a large proportion of summerwood and correspondingly stronger material.

Rate of Growth and Density. The rate at which trees grow and form wood substance has an important effect upon their strength properties. It has been shown by experiments that, in the softwoods commonly used for structural purposes, an accurate measure of this strength is provided by the relative width and the character of wood in each annual growth ring. In these woods, pieces having medium to narrow growth rings have been found to have generally higher strength properties than those having wide growth rings.

In addition, in certain woods, pieces with a considerable proportion of each annual ring made up of the dense, darker summerwood have still higher strength properties. Therefore, in grading structural material for use under known loads, a part of the specification is consideration of the number of rings per inch radially and the density, or proportion of summerwood.

Material having a specific minimum number of annual rings per inch is termed *close grained* and that having in addition 33 per cent or

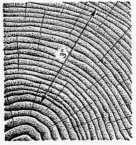 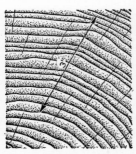 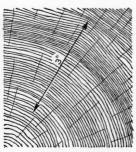

Fig. 3. Section of Structural Timber Showing Wood Which Is Both Close Grained and Dense

Fig. 4. Section of End of Structural Joist Which Is neither Close Grained nor Dense

Fig. 5. Section of End of Structural Joist Which Is Close Grained but Not Dense

more summerwood is termed *dense*. Examples are given in the illustrations, Figs. 3, 4, and 5. In Fig. 3, the section of structural timber shown has 7 annual growth rings per inch and 35 per cent summerwood, therefore, it is close grained and dense. In Fig. 4, the section of the structural joist shown has 5 annual growth rings per inch and 25 per cent summerwood, hence is considered neither close grained nor dense. In Fig. 5, the section of structural joist illustrated has 15 annual growth rings per inch and 30 per cent summerwood, therefore, it is considered close grained but *not* dense.

Grain and Texture. The terms *grain* and *texture* are used in various ways to describe certain characteristics of wood. The wood from slow-growing trees in which the annual growth rings are narrow is sometimes described as *close grained;* that from rapidly growing trees with wide rings as *coarse grained.* This is another way of describing the number of rings per inch and is important in strength grading.

Wood in which the direction of the fibers (*not* the annual rings) are parallel to the sides of the piece is called *straight grain;* while *cross grain* is used to describe wood in which the fibers are at an angle with the sides of the piece. *Cross grain* also includes *spiral grain* in which the fibers wind around the trunk of the tree. The expression *slope of grain* is employed in the grading of structural material to describe the extent of coarse grain permitted, since slope of grain has an important influence on strength.

However, *grain* and *texture* usually refer to the physical properties of appearance rather than properties of strength. For example, *fine grain* is used to describe woods in which the cells are small and thick walled, making a compact wood with smooth surface, as in maple, birch, and pine. The *coarse-grain* woods, such as oak, walnut, and chestnut, are those in which the cells are large and open, producing a slightly roughened surface due to the large cells being cut where they intersect the surface.

When sawed in such a manner that the annual rings (grain) form an angle of 45 degrees or more with the wide faces, lumber is described as *edge grain, vertical grain,* or *rift-sawed* in softwoods, and *quartersawed* or *comb-grained* in hardwoods. The term *flat-grain* or *flat-sawed* in softwoods and *plain-sawed* in hardwoods describes lumber in which the annual growth rings are at an angle of 45 degrees or less with the wide faces of the piece. Flat-grain is also known as *tangential section.* *Bastard-sawed* in hardwoods is material midway between true *quartersawed* and true *plain-sawed,* Fig. 6. The appearance of edge grain in

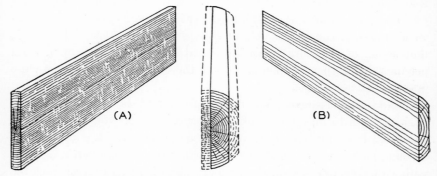

Fig. 6. *(A)* Edge Grain in Softwoods and Quartersawed in Hardwoods; *(B)* Flat-Sawed in Softwoods and Plain-Sawed in Hardwoods
Courtesy of United States Forest Products Laboratory

softwoods and quartersawed in hardwoods is shown at (*A*), Fig. 6. The illustration at (*B*), Fig. 6, shows a piece of lumber described as *flat-grain* or *flat-sawed* in softwoods and *plain-sawed* in hardwoods.

Moisture in Wood. Wood in standing trees contains moisture in two forms: as free water held in the cell cavities; and as imbibed hydroscopic moisture held in the cell walls. When green wood begins to lose its moisture, the cell walls remain saturated until all free water has been evaporated. The point at which all the free water has been evaporated and the walls of the fibers or cells begin to lose their moisture is called the *fiber saturation point*. Although varying somewhat between species, the fiber saturation point is about 25 per cent of most woods.

The moisture in wood is expressed as a percentage of the oven-dried weight. This percentage is determined as follows: a representative sample of wood is weighed; then the same piece of wood is dried in an oven, at a temperature of slightly more than 212 degrees, until no further loss of weight takes place. The wood is weighed again and the difference between the original weight and final weight is found. This difference divided by the final (oven-dry) weight gives the percentage of the oven-dried weight.

Except for seasonal variations, wood in use over a period of time arrives at a moisture content corresponding to the humidity of the atmosphere surrounding it. Thus when exposed to similar atmospheric conditions, different woods will have the same moisture content regardless of their density.

The moisture-content requirements are more exacting for lumber or wood products to be used for the interior finish of buildings than for lumber or wood products that are to be used out of doors. Requirements of moisture content in wood intended for outdoor purposes do not need to be so exacting as for interior-finish lumber because, under ordinary atmospheric conditions, lumber used outdoors does not reach so low a moisture content. Then, too, a higher character of service is required of the interior-finish lumber. In most cases, lumber for both exterior and interior use should be dried to approximately the value of moisture content to which it will come when in service. The moisture-content values for various wood items and for various regions in the United States are shown in Table I. The values given here are the recommendations of the United States Department of Agriculture for moisture content for various wood items at the time of installation.

TABLE I. MOISTURE-CONTENT VALUES FOR VARIOUS WOOD ITEMS

USE OF LUMBER	MOISTURE CONTENT (PERCENTAGE OF WEIGHT OF OVEN-DRY WOOD) FOR—					
	Dry Southwestern States		Damp Southern Coastal States		Remainder of the United States	
	Average	Individual pieces	Average	Individual pieces	Average	Individual pieces
	Per Cent	Per Cent	Per Cent	Per Cent	Per Cent	Per Cent
Interior finish woodwork and softwood flooring..	6	4–9	11	8–13	8	5–10
Hardwood flooring......	6	5–8	10	9–12	7	6–9
Siding, exterior trim, sheathing, and framing	9	7–12	12	9–14	12	9–14

When the moisture content of wood falls below the fiber saturation point, the wood changes in size. However, in seasoning, the surface of green wood dries more rapidly than the interior and reaches the fiber saturation point first. In such a case shrinkage may start while the average moisture content is considerably above the fiber saturation point. Wood shrinks most in the direction of the annual growth rings (tangentially), about one-half to two-thirds as much across these rings (radially), and very little, as a rule, along the grain (longitudinally).

The fact that wood changes in size with change in moisture content is an important consideration to be remembered when constructing the frame for a building. For example, a stud in a wall will not shrink appreciably in length, whereas it will shrink somewhat in both the 2-inch and the 4-inch dimensions. Therefore, it is well to avoid as much as possible the use of cross-section material in wall construction. If a joist is green when put in place it will shrink in depth as it seasons in the building. The combined effects of radial and tangential shrinkage on the shape of various sections in drying from the green condition are illustrated in Fig. 7. In this diagram are shown the characteristic shrinkage and distortion of flats, squares, and rounds as affected by the direction of the annual rings. Tangential shrinkage is about twice as much as radial shrinkage.

When wood is drying, shrinkage is proportional to the moisture lost below the fiber saturation point. Approximately one-half of the total shrinkage possible has occurred in wood seasoned to an air-dry condition (12 to 15 per cent moisture content) and about three-fourths in lumber kiln-dried to a moisture content of about 7 per cent. Hence, if wood is properly seasoned, manufactured, and installed at a moisture content in accordance with its service conditions there will be excellent possibilities of satisfactory service without any serious changes in size or distortion of the cross section.

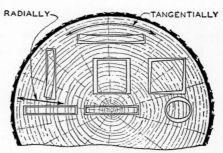

Fig. 7. Cross Section of Tree Trunk Showing Characteristic Shrinkage and Distortion of Flats, Squares, and Rounds as Affected by the Direction of the Annual Rings

DEFECTS AND BLEMISHES IN WOOD

Timber is not a manufactured material like iron or cement but is a natural product developed through many years of growth in the open air and exposed continually to varying conditions of wind and weather. Since wood is a natural product it is peculiarly liable to contain defects of different kinds. Most of these defects cannot be corrected. Therefore, they render much of the wood unsuitable for use in construction work. Moreover, it cannot be assumed safely that several different pieces of timber, even though cut from the same log, will have similar characteristics or will give exactly the same service under the same conditions. In addition to injuries incurred during growth there are other injuries due to improper handling or to preparatory processes, such as sawing. In view of these injuries, regardless of the cause, each piece of timber must be judged separately and subjected to careful inspection to insure satisfactory results when the piece is used in an important position. Oftentimes, such careful inspection will reveal some hidden weakness, defect, or blemish which will warrant the rejection of this particular timber as inferior and not suitable for the service for which it was intended.

As the term is used in the trade, a *defect* is an irregularity occurring in or on wood that will tend to impair its strength, durability, or utility value. Though not classified as a defect, a *blemish* is any imperfection which mars the appearance of wood. Some of the commonly recognized defects and blemishes in yard lumber are discussed in the following paragraphs.

Bark Pockets. A patch of bark nearly, or wholly, enclosed in the wood is known as a *bark pocket.*

Checks. A lengthwise separation of wood tissues is known as a *check.* Checks usually occur across the rings of annual growth and are due to shrinkage. In any log of wood there is always the possibility of shrinkage in two directions—along the radial lines following the direction of the medullary rays, and around the circumference of the log following the direction of the annual rings. If the wood shrinks in both directions at the same rate, the result will be only a decrease in the volume of the log, but if it shrinks more rapidly around the circumference of the log than along the radial lines, the log will develop cracks, or checks, along the outside, as shown in Fig. 8.

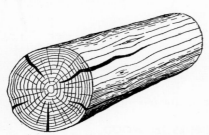

Fig. 8. Checks Caused by Wood Shrinking More Rapidly Around the Circumference of a Log Than Along the Radial Lines

Cross Grain. When the cells, or fibers, of wood do not run parallel with the axis or sides of a piece of timber, the result is a twisting and interweaving of the wood fibers known as *cross grain.*

Decay. A disintegration of the wood substance due to the action of wood-destroying fungi is called *decay.* Incipient decay is the early stage of deterioration in which the disintegration has not proceeded far enough to soften or to otherwise perceptibly impair the hardness of the wood. In typical or advanced decay the disintegration is readily recognized because the wood has become punky, soft, spongy, stringy, pitted, or crumbly.

Holes. A piece of wood may be defective because of *holes* extending partially or entirely through the piece. Such holes may be due to many different causes, such as injury through improper handling, or from wood-boring insects or worms. Whatever the cause, holes in wood make it unfit for use in construction work.

Imperfections Occurring at the Mills. Many defects or blemishes occur during the process of milling lumber. These include such imperfections as: chipped, loosened, raised, or torn grain; skips in dressing; variations in sawing; miscut lumber; machine burns; gouges; mismatching; and insufficient depth in tongue and groove.

Knots. At the juncture of the branches with the main trunk of a tree, some fibers of the wood turn aside to follow along the limb. When a branch is broken off near the trunk leaving a small piece attached to the tree, the tree continues to grow, but the broken piece of limb dies. As the tree increases in size the piece of dead limb becomes embedded in the trunk. In the course of time the dead wood is buried and entirely covered over by living woody tissue. These bits of wood, known as *knots*, have no connection with the living wood but occupy a place within the body of the tree with sound wood all about them. When a section of a tree, containing knots, is sawed into lumber and the knots are cut through, they will loosen eventually and fall out, leaving round or irregular *knot holes* in the boards. Knots are more or less common in all lumber. So long as they remain in place, the presence of a limited number of knots will not harm a piece of lumber which is subjected to a compressive stress. However, knots tend to weaken greatly a piece of timber subjected to a tension stress or when used as a beam. Knots also spoil the appearance of polished woodwork.

Knots are differentiated according to size, form, quality, and occurrence. A *pin knot* is $\frac{1}{2}$ inch in diameter or less; a *small knot* is over $\frac{1}{2}$ inch but not more than $\frac{3}{4}$ inch in diameter; a *medium knot* is over $\frac{3}{4}$ inch but not more than $1\frac{1}{2}$ inches in diameter; a *large knot* is one more than $1\frac{1}{2}$ inches in diameter. A *spike knot* occurs where a limb is sawed in a lengthwise direction.

Pitch Pockets. Sometimes between rings of annual growth well-defined openings or cracks occur. These are known as *pitch pockets*, and usually contain or have contained more or less pitch, in either solid or liquid form.

Pith. In the structural center of a log occurs the *pith* which is made up of soft spongy cellular tissue. When cut from a portion of the log containing pith, a board is not suitable for first-class structural work.

Shake. A lengthwise split, commonly called a *shake,* in a piece of timber usually causes a separation of the wood between the rings of annual growth. Shakes usually are parallel to the growth rings. Such defects always decrease the value of timber.

Heart Shake. When a defect in the central portion of the trunk shows itself at the heart of a tree and in a cross section the shake appears running in a radial direction, the defect is known as a *heart shake,* Fig. 9. First a small cavity caused by decay occurs at the center of the trunk, then later flaws or cracks develop and extend from this cavity outward toward the bark.

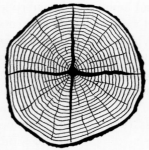

Fig. 9. Heart Shake Caused by Decay Beginning at the Center of a Tree Trunk and Extending Outward

Fig. 10. Wind Shake Caused by Racking and Wrenching of a Tree by Wind

In a cross section of the trunk of a tree, when a heart shake assumes the form of a single split across the center, the defect is known as a *simple heart shake.* If such a split is crossed at right angles by another similar split this defect is known as a *double heart shake.* Sometimes a number of splits may radiate from the center of the trunk and produce what is known as a *star shake* which is associated with discoloration and decay.

Wind Shakes. A growing tree is subjected to much racking and wrenching by high winds. Defects believed to be caused by the action of high winds are called *wind shakes,* Fig. 10. However, some people believe these defects are produced by the expansion of the sapwood which causes a separation of the annual rings from each other, thus leaving a hollow space in the body of the trunk. This belief and the cup-shaped appearance of the defect on a cross section of the tree has suggested the term *cup shakes,* also commonly used.

Split. A lengthwise separation of wood due to the tearing apart of the wood cells is called a *split.* Usually a split occurs across the rings of annual growth, extending from one surface through the piece of timber to the opposite surface, or to an adjoining surface.

Blue Stain. Due to the growth of certain moldlike fungi, a bluish or grayish discoloration, known as *blue stain,* sometimes appears on

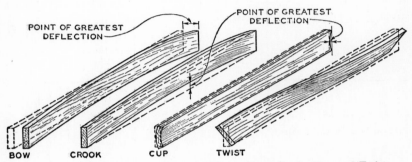

POINT OF GREATEST DEFLECTION

POINT OF GREATEST DEFLECTION

BOW   CROOK   CUP   TWIST

Fig. 11. Various Kinds of Warp in Wood—Bow, Crook, Cup, and Twist

the surface and in the interior of a piece of unseasoned lumber. Although the appearance of blue stain is objectionable, it does not have any particular effect on the strength of the timber, which can be used in structural work where appearance is not important.

Wane. A defect on the edge or corner of a piece of timber or plank due to a lack of wood or bark, regardless of the cause, is known as a *wane.*

Warping. Any variation from a true or plane surface is called *warping,* Fig. 11. When a piece of timber is permanently distorted or twisted out of shape as by moisture or heat, it is said to be *warped.* Warping is the result of the evaporation or drying out of the water which is held in the cell walls of the wood in its natural state, and the shrinkage which follows. If wood were perfectly regular in structure, so that the shrinkage could be the same in every part, there would be no warping; but wood is made up of a large number of fibers, the walls of which are of different thicknesses in different parts of the tree or log, so that when drying, one part shrinks much more than another part. Since the wood

TABLE II. AMERICAN STANDARD SOFTWOOD YARD LUMBER SIZES*

Product	Rough Green or Nominal Sizes (Board Measure)		Dressed Dimensions	
	Thickness	Width	Thickness, Standard Yard	Width (Face When Worked)
	Inches	Inches	Inches	Inches
Finish......................	—	3	$5/16$	$2 5/8$
	—	4	$7/16$	$3 1/2$[a]
	—	5	$9/16$	$4 1/2$[a]
	—	6	$11/16$	$5 1/2$[a]
	1	7	$25/32$	$6 1/2$[a]
	$1 1/4$	8	$1 1/16$	$7 1/4$[a]
	$1 1/2$	9	$1 5/16$	$8 1/4$[a]
	$1 3/4$	10	$1 7/16$	$9 1/4$[a]
	2	11	$1 5/8$	$10 1/4$[a]
	$2 1/2$	12	$2 1/8$	$11 1/4$[a]
	3	—	$2 5/8$	—
Common boards and strips..	1	3	$25/32$	$2 5/8$
	$1 1/4$	4	$1 1/16$	$3 5/8$
	$1 1/2$	5	$1 5/16$	$4 5/8$
	—	6	—	$5 5/8$
	—	7	—	$6 5/8$
	—	8	—	$7 1/2$
	—	9	—	$8 1/2$
	—	10	—	$9 1/2$
	—	11	—	$10 1/2$
	—	12	—	$11 1/2$
Dimension and heavy joist..	2	2	$1 5/8$	$1 5/8$
	$2 1/2$	4	$2 1/8$	$3 5/8$
	3	6	$2 5/8$	$5 5/8$
	4	8	$3 5/8$	$7 1/2$
	—	10	—	$9 1/2$
	—	12	—	$11 1/2$
Bevel siding...............	—	4	$7/16$ by $3/16$	$3 1/2$
	—	5	$10/16$ by $3/16$	$4 1/2$
	—	6	—	$5 1/2$
Wide bevel siding..........	—	8	$7/16$ by $3/16$	$7 1/4$
	—	10	$9/16$ by $3/16$	$9 1/4$
	—	12	$11/16$ by $3/16$	$11 1/4$
Rustic and drop siding (ship-lapped).................	—	4	$9/16$	$3 1/8$
	—	5	$3/4$	$4 1/8$
	—	6	—	$5 1/16$
	—	8	—	$6 7/8$
Rustic and drop siding (dressed and matched)....	—	4	$9/16$	$3 1/4$
	—	5	$3/4$	$4 1/4$
	—	6	—	$5 3/16$
	—	8	—	7

*Recommended by the United States Department of Agriculture.
ᵃBased on kiln-dried lumber.

TABLE II. AMERICAN STANDARD SOFTWOOD YARD LUMBER SIZES*—*Continued*

PRODUCT	ROUGH GREEN OR NOMINAL SIZES (BOARD MEASURE)		DRESSED DIMENSIONS	
	Thickness	Width	Thickness — Standard Yard	Width (Face When Worked)
	Inches	Inches	Inches	Inches
Flooring...................	—	2	$5/16$	$1\frac{1}{2}$
	—	3	$7/16$	$2\frac{3}{8}$
	—	4	$9/16$	$3\frac{1}{4}$
	1	5	$25/32$	$4\frac{1}{4}$
	$1\frac{1}{4}$	6	$1\frac{1}{16}$	$5\frac{3}{16}$
Ceiling...................	—	3	$5/16$	$2\frac{3}{8}$
	—	4	$7/16$	$3\frac{1}{4}$
	—	5	$9/16$	$4\frac{1}{4}$
	—	6	$1\frac{1}{16}$	$5\frac{3}{16}$
Partition..................	—	4	$3/4$	$3\frac{1}{4}$
	—	5	—	$4\frac{1}{4}$
	—	6	—	$5\frac{3}{16}$
Shiplap..................	—	6	$25/32$	$5\frac{1}{8}$
	—	8	—	$7\frac{1}{8}$
	—	10	—	$9\frac{1}{8}$
	—	12	—	$11\frac{1}{8}$
Dressed and matched.......	1	4	$25/32$	$3\frac{1}{4}$
	$1\frac{1}{4}$	6	$1\frac{1}{16}$	$5\frac{1}{4}$
	$1\frac{1}{2}$	8	$1\frac{5}{16}$	$7\frac{1}{4}$
	—	10	—	$9\frac{1}{4}$
	—	12	—	$11\frac{1}{4}$

*Recommended by the United States Department of Agriculture.

fibers are in close contact with each other and are interlaced making the piece of wood rigid, one part cannot shrink or swell without changing the shape of the whole piece, because the piece as a whole must adjust itself to the new conditions; consequently the timber warps. The distortion due to warping may take different forms, such as a twist, a crook, cupped, or bow-shaped; or any combination of these.

GRADING OF LUMBER

The various defects and blemishes found in lumber necessitate the establishment of certain classification and grading rules. The American Lumber Standards for grading lumber were formulated by the National Bureau of Standards of the United States Department of Commerce. The purpose of setting up such standards was to insure uniform grading throughout the country. Lumber is classified according to its principal uses, as: *yard lumber, factory* or *shop lumber,* and *structural timber.*

Yard Lumber. The lumber known as *yard lumber* is less than 5 inches in thickness and is intended for general building purposes. See Table II. Grading rules are given in Table III.

Strips. The yard lumber known to the trade as *strips* is less than 2 inches in thickness and less than 8 inches in width.

Boards. Yard lumber, commonly called *boards,* is less than 2 inches thick and 8 inches or more in width.

Dimension Lumber. When cut to specified sizes yard lumber, of any width and at least 2 inches but not more than 5 inches thick, is called *dimension lumber.*

TABLE III. AMERICAN STANDARD SOFTWOOD YARD LUMBER GRADES*

	YARD LUMBER		GRADES
Total products of a typical log arranged in series according to quality as determined by appearance	Select lumber	Suitable for natural finishes	Grade A (practically free from defects) Grade B (allows a few small defects or blemishes)
	Finish items (lumber of good appearance and finishing)	Suitable for paint finishes	Grade C (allows a limited number of small defects or blemishes that can be covered with paint) Grade D (allows any number of defects or blemishes which do not detract from the appearance of the finish, especially when painted)
	Common lumber (lumber containing defects or blemishes which detract from the appearance of the finish but suitable for general-utility and construction purposes)	Lumber suitable for use without waste	No. 1 (sound and tight-knotted stock; size of defects and blemishes limited; may be considered watertight lumber) No. 2 (allows large and coarse defects; may be considered grain-tight lumber)
		Lumber permitting waste	No. 3 (allows larger and coarser defects than No. 2 and occasional knot holes) No. 4 (low-quality lumber admitting the coarsest defects, such as decay and holes) No. 5 (must hold together under ordinary handling)

*Recommended by the United States Department of Agriculture, *Wood Handbook.*

Besides the square-edge lumber, lumberyards also carry a variety of stock-lumber patterns. The exact dimensions of some of the most common patterns are illustrated at (A) and (B), Fig. 12. Lumberyard stock includes moldings, Fig. 13. Moldings and other trim members can be obtained in different shapes and sizes, also in a variety of stock designs. When building specifications call for designs not carried in the stock-lumber patterns, a special job of millwork is required to handle this order. Any specification which makes additional work necessary increases the cost of construction.

Factory or Shop Lumber. Lumber intended for additional cutting in the process of further manufacturing is known to the trade as *factory lumber* or *shop lumber*. Such lumber is used principally in window sashes, doors and door frames, in different types of millwork, and in furniture factories. This lumber is graded on the basis of the percentage of area which will produce a limited number of cuttings of a given minimum, or specified, size and quality. Grading is shown in Table IV.

Structural Timber. Lumber, commonly termed *structural timber*, is 5 inches or more in both thickness and width. It is graded according to its strength and to the use which is to be made of an entire piece. Such lumber is used principally for bridge or trestle timbers, for car and ship timbers, for ship decking, and for framing of buildings.

Shingles. Western red cedar, white cedar, redwood, and cypress are woods commonly used for making shingles. The grading varies with the kind of wood used. The western cedar is graded as: No. 1, No. 2, and No. 3. In cypress the grades include: No. 1, *bests, prime, economies,* and *clippers*. In white cedar the grades are: *extra star A star, standard star A star,* and *sound butts*. Redwood comes in two grades: No. 1 and No. 2. Shingles of the highest quality are all clear, all heartwood, and all edge grain.

Shingles come in three lengths—16, 18, and 24 inches—and in *random* widths; or *dimension* widths all cut to the same width. The thickness of shingles is indicated as $\frac{4}{2}$, $\frac{5}{2}$ and $\frac{5}{2}\frac{1}{2}$; that is, 4 shingles to 2 inches of butt thickness; 5 shingles to 2 inches of butt thickness; and 5 shingles to $2\frac{1}{2}$ inches of butt thickness.

Lumber Measurements. Lumber is sold by the *board foot, surface* or *square foot,* and *lineal foot* measurement.

Board Foot. Strip lumber, boards, dimension lumber, structural

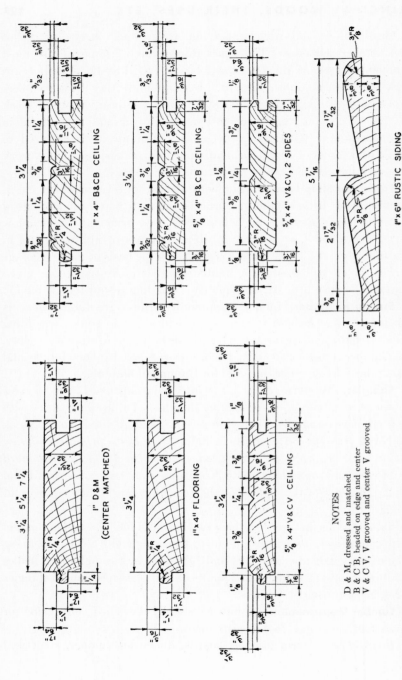

NOTES

D & M, dressed and matched
B & C B, beaded on edge and center
V & C V, V grooved and center V grooved

Fig. 12. *(A)* Typical Stock-Lumber Patterns of Dressed and Matched Flooring, Ceiling, and Siding (Softwood)

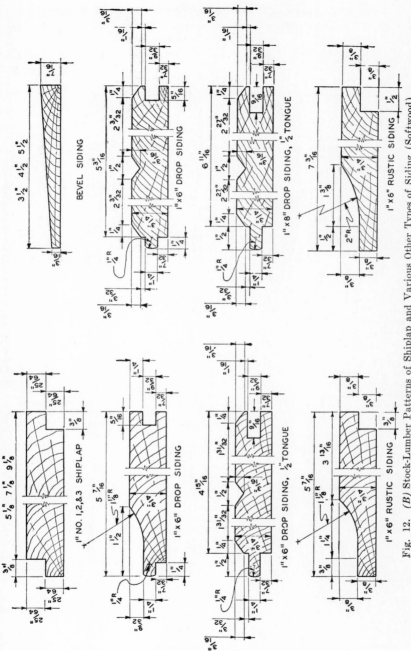

Fig. 12. *(B)* Stock-Lumber Patterns of Shiplap and Various Other Types of Siding (Softwood)

Courtesy of West Coast Lumbermen's Association, Seattle, Wash.

TABLE IV. AMERICAN STANDARD HARDWOOD SHOP LUMBER GRADES*

GRADE AND LENGTHS ALLOWED (FEET)	WIDTHS ALLOWED	SURFACE MEASURE OF PIECES (SQUARE FEET)	PERCENTAGE OF EACH PIECE THAT MUST WORK INTO CLEAR-FACE CUTTINGS	MAXIMUM CUTTING ALLOWED	MINIMUM SIZE OF CUTTINGS REQUIRED
	Inches		Per Cent	Number	
Firsts: 8 to 16 (will admit 25 per cent of 8- to 11-foot, half of which may be 8- and 9-foot)	6+	4 to 9 10 to 14 15+	91⅔ 91⅔ 91⅔	1 2 3	4 inches by 5 feet, or 3 inches by 7 feet
Seconds: 8 to 16 (will admit 25 per cent of 8- to 11-foot, half of which may be 8- and 9-foot)	6+	4 and 5 6 and 7 6 and 7 8 to 11 8 to 11 12 to 15 12 to 15 16+	83⅓ 83⅓ 91⅔ 83⅓ 91⅔ 83⅓ 91⅔ 83⅓	1 1 2 2 3 3 4 4	Ditto
Selects: 6 to 16 (will admit 30 per cent of 6- to 11-foot, one-sixth of which may be 6- and 7-foot)	4+	2 and 3 4+	91⅔	1	Ditto
No. 1 Common: 4 to 16 (will admit 10 per cent of 4- to 7-foot, half of which may be 4- and 5-foot)	3+	1 2 3 and 4 3 and 4 5 to 7 5 to 7 8 to 10 11 to 13 14+	100 75 66⅔ 75 66⅔ 75 66⅔ 66⅔ 66⅔	0 1 1 2 2 3 3 4 5	4 inches by 2 feet or 4 inches by 3 feet
No. 2 Common: 4 to 16 (will admit 30 per cent of 4- to 7-foot, one third of which may be 4- and 5-foot)	3+	1 2 and 3 2 and 3 4 and 5 4 and 5 6 and 7 6 and 7 8 and 9 10 and 11 12 and 13 14+	66⅔ 50 66⅔ 50 66⅔ 50 66⅔ 50 50 50 50	1 1 2 2 3 3 4 4 5 6 7	3 inches by 2 feet
Sound Wormy: 4 to 16 (will admit 10 per cent of 4- to 7-foot, half of which may be 4- and 5-foot)	3+	—	—	—	—

*Recommended by the United States Department of Agriculture, *Wood Handbook*.

TABLE IV. AMERICAN STANDARD HARDWOOD SHOP LUMBER GRADES*—*Continued*

GRADE AND LENGTHS ALLOWED (FEET)	WIDTHS ALLOWED	SURFACE MEASURE OF PIECES (SQUARE FEET)	PERCENTAGE OF EACH PIECE THAT MUST WORK INTO CLEAR-FACE CUTTINGS	MAXIMUM CUTTING ALLOWED	MINIMUM SIZE OF CUTTINGS REQUIRED
	Inches		Per Cent	Number	
No. 3A Common: 4 to 16 (will admit 50 per cent of 4- to 7-foot, half of which may be 4- and 5-foot)	3+	1+	33⅓	—	3 inches by 2 feet
No. 3B Common: 4 to 16 (will admit 50 per cent of 4- to 7-foot, half of which may be 4- and 5-foot)	3+	1+	25	—	1½ inches wide and contain · ing at least 36 square inches

*Recommended by the United States Department of Agriculture, *Wood Handbook*.

timbers, and shop lumber are sold by the *board foot*. A board foot is 1 inch thick, 12 inches wide, and 1 foot long.

$$\frac{\text{Thickness in inches} \times \text{width in inches} \times \text{length in feet}}{12} = \text{board feet}$$

To find the board feet in a piece $1'' \times 6'' \times 12'0''$

$$\frac{1 \times 6 \times 12}{12} = 6, \text{ or 6 board feet}$$

To find the board feet in a piece of dimension $2'' \times 10'' \times 16'0''$

$$\frac{2 \times 10 \times 16}{12} = \frac{80}{3}, \text{ or } 26\frac{2}{3} \text{ board feet}$$

When the size is entirely in inches—$1'' \times 6'' \times 8''$

$$\frac{1 \times 6 \times 8}{144} = \frac{6}{18}, \text{ or } \frac{1}{3} \text{ board feet}$$

Surface or *Square Feet*. Thin lumber material ½- or ¼-inch thick, such as veneer, siding, and plywood is sold by the *square foot*—12 inches wide by 1 foot long—and is priced accordingly. A piece of ½-inch plywood 4'x8' would contain 32 square feet ($4 \times 8 = 32$).

Lineal Foot. Materials sold by the *lineal* or *running foot*, regardless

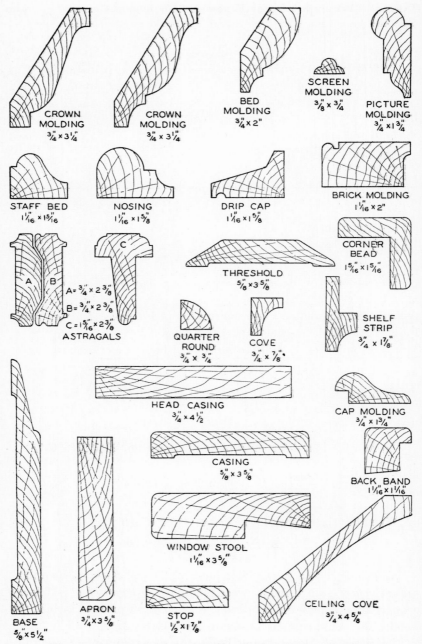

CROWN
MOLDING
3/4" × 3 1/4"

CROWN
MOLDING
3/4" × 3 1/4"

BED
MOLDING
3/4" × 2"

SCREEN
MOLDING
3/8" × 3/4"

PICTURE
MOLDING
3/4" × 1 3/4"

STAFF BED
1 1/16" × 1 5/16"

NOSING
1 1/16" × 1 5/8"

DRIP CAP
1 1/16" × 1 5/8"

BRICK MOLDING
1 1/16" × 2"

A
B
C
A = 3/4" × 2 3/8"
B = 3/4" × 2 3/8"
C = 1 5/16" × 2 3/8"
ASTRAGALS

THRESHOLD
5/8" × 3 5/8"

CORNER
BEAD
1 5/16" × 1 5/16"

QUARTER
ROUND
3/4" × 3/4"

COVE
3/4" × 7/8"

SHELF
STRIP
3/4" × 1 7/8"

HEAD CASING
3/4" × 4 1/2"

CAP MOLDING
3/4" × 1 3/4"

CASING
5/8" × 3 5/8"

BACK BAND
1 1/16" × 1 1/16"

WINDOW STOOL
1 1/16" × 3 5/8"

CEILING COVE
3/4" × 4 5/8"

BASE
5/8" × 5 1/2"

APRON
3/4" × 3 5/8"

STOP
1/2" × 1 7/8"

Fig. 13. Common Softwood Moldings Stocked by Lumber Yards

of width or thickness, include moldings, interior trim, furring strips, and grounds.

Lumber Prices. Lumber is priced per thousand (M) square feet or board feet. Material priced at $50.00 per M would cost 5 cents per board foot, or square foot. Prices on lineal measurements are based on 100 (C) lineal feet. A molding priced at $8.00 per C would cost 8 cents per foot.

Commercial Lumber. The commercial forest lands of the United States in 1941 included about 462 million acres from which approximately 31,500,000,000 board feet of timber was cut, Fig. 14. Of the many different species of trees found in the United States only about 180 of them may be ranked as commercially important.

Local lumber dealers usually carry in their stock, for general building purposes, those species most easily obtainable and in greatest demand in that particular locality. Hence, as a rule, we will find in the local lumberyards of the Pacific Northwest: Douglas fir, spruce, ponderosa pine, western hemlock, and western cedar. In Illinois, lumber dealers usually carry in stock: eastern hemlock, western pine, ponderosa pine, southern yellow pine, spruce, and Douglas fir. An eastern lumber dealer might carry in stock: eastern spruce and hemlock, northern white pine, cypress, ponderosa pine, southern yellow pine, and Douglas fir.

However, if given adequate time to secure the stock, most lumber dealers are able to obtain any kind of commercial lumber, either hard or soft, which an individual might desire. As a guide in selecting woods for special purposes, we have given in this text a brief description of the characteristics and localities of growth of some of the woods most commonly used in building construction. The primary uses made of each particular kind of wood is also given. The weights are based upon air-dry 12 per cent moisture content.[1]

SOFTWOODS

Of the great variety of lumber used in construction work the greatest bulk comes from the softwoods obtained from the conifers or needle-

---

[1] For more detailed information on commercial woods see the *Wood Handbook*, United States Department of Agriculture, Washington, D.C.

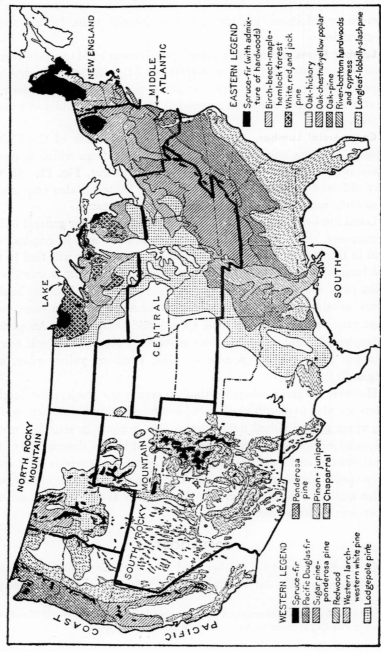

Fig. 14. Forest Regions of the United States and Predominating Type of Trees Native to Each Region

EASTERN LEGEND

Spruce-fir (with admixture of hardwoods)
Birch-beech-maple-hemlock forest
White, red, and jack pine
Oak-hickory
Oak-chestnut-yellow poplar
Oak-pine
River-bottom hardwoods and cypress
Longleaf-loblolly-slash pine

WESTERN LEGEND

Spruce-fir
Pacific Douglas fir
Sugar pine-ponderosa pine
Redwood
Western larch-western white pine
Lodgepole pine
Ponderosa pine
Piñon-juniper
Chaparral

NEW ENGLAND
MIDDLE ATLANTIC
SOUTH
CENTRAL
LAKE
NORTH ROCKY MOUNTAIN
SOUTH ROCKY MOUNTAIN
PACIFIC COAST

leaved trees. Therefore, in this discussion the softwoods are considered first.

Cedars. The term *cedar* is a general name for all fragrantly scented softwoods, Fig. 15. Cedar is a wood which seasons rapidly, yet shrinks and checks but little. It also has the advantage of being durable and also decay resisting. The wood is light, soft, and stiff but not strong. The sapwood is distinct and easily distinguishable from the heartwood, since the former is light in color and the latter is a dull, grayish brown or red.

Alaska Cedar (*Chamaecyparis nootkatensis*). This wood is sometimes called *yellow cypress, Alaska yellow,* or *yellow cedar.* It grows in the region of the Pacific Coast of North America from Alaska to Oregon.

Physical Characteristics. The weight of Alaska cedar is 31 pounds per cubic foot. It is rather light, hard, firmly strong, and brittle. The grain is fine, even, and straight. The wood is compact in structure, and the annual rings are narrow and distinct. It is easily worked, is

Fig. 15. Eastern Red Cedar, Near Clinton, Maryland

The tree at left in picture is about sixty-six feet in height

United States Forest Service Photo

satiny, and takes a good polish. It holds paint well, requiring little paint protection for weathering.

Uses. This cedar is used for cabinet work, doors, blinds, furniture, interior finish, ship and boat building, and novelties.

Port Orford Cedar (*Chamaecyparis lawsoniana*). This tree grows naturally only in a narrow belt bordering the coast of southern Oregon and Northern California.

Physical Characteristics. The weight of this wood is 29 pounds per cubic foot. The heartwood, which is highly resistant to decay, is light yellow to pale brown in color, and the unusually thin sapwood is of a similar appearance. This wood is of moderate strength and hardness with an unusually uniform texture and spicy odor.

Uses. The better grades of Port Orford cedar are used for shingles, siding, chests, lawn furniture, battery separators, boats, and interior finish. The lower grades are useful for general construction purposes.

Western Red Cedar (*Thuja plicata*). The largest of the cedars is the western red cedar. It grows in the humid regions along the North Pacific Coast, extending inland from Washington to Montana.

Physical Characteristics. The weight of western red cedar is 23 pounds per cubic foot. The heartwood, which is reddish brown in color, is highly resistant to decay. The narrow sapwood is white. The wood is easily worked, rather soft and weak. It has good nail-holding qualities and little shrinkage. It finishes well. Shingles made from western red cedar take and hold the stain of the finest tint without discoloration. They also hold paint well and require little protection for weathering.

Uses. This wood is valuable for shingles, siding, porch columns, greenhouse construction, ship and boat building, and wooden novelties.

Northern White Cedar (*Thuja occidentalis*). The northern white cedar grows in the region of the Great Lakes and in the northeastern part of the United States.

Physical Characteristics. The weight of the northern white cedar is 22 pounds per cubic foot. The wood is soft, brittle, and weak in structure. It has a low shrinkage and splits easily. The heartwood is light yellow brown in color with a reddish tinge which darkens upon exposure to the weather. It is highly resistant to decay. The sapwood is thin and nearly white in color.

Uses. The northern white cedar is used extensively for shingles, tanks, silos, caskets, professional and scientific instruments, planing-mill products, and ship and boat building. This wood makes good fence posts, railway ties, telegraph and telephone poles, and because of its decay-resistant qualities is in demand for use where contact with the ground is required.

Cypress. Coastal cypress is known as *tidewater* or *red cypress* and inland cypress is known as *yellow* or *white cypress.*

Southern Cypress (*Taxodium distichum*). The southern cypress is a large deciduous tree, Fig. 16. It is one of the few conifers which sheds its leaves. It occupies much of the swamps and overflow land along the coast and rivers of the Southern States extending as far north as Missouri.

Physical Characteristics. The weight of the southern cypress is 32 pounds per cubic foot. The wood is moderately strong. The heartwood is the most decay-resistant lumber manufactured in the United States. The heartwood of the tidewater cypress varies from slightly reddish in

Fig. 16. Southern Cypress Along Wadboo Creek, Francis Marion
National Forest, South Carolina
In the foreground are shown the cypress knees through which the tree breathes
United States Forest Service Photo

color to a deeper red and much of it is almost black. The sapwood is white to cream in color. The grain is uniformly close and generally straight. However, some is also figured. The wood is resinous and peculiarly greasy like paraffin. It is easy to work.

Uses. Because of its decay resistance southern cypress is used extensively for outside work, gutters, shingles, siding, casings, water tanks, vats, tubes, and wooden buckets. Cypress is also desirable for interior trim as well as for wall covering.

Firs. The name *fir* is applied frequently to various wood and trees which are not firs. Although fir is easily distinguishable because of its lack of resin ducts, yet the term *fir* is commonly applied to such resinous woods as pine, spruce, and larch. There are eight species of fir. The most common are: balsam fir, two species of white fir, and two of red fir. Of these, the white fir has the greatest commercial value.

White Fir (*Abies concolor*). The white fir grows in the mountainous regions of California.

Physical Characteristics. White fir weighs 27 pounds per cubic foot. This fir is moderately low in strength and moderately soft. It is

Fig. 17. Douglas Fir with Section of Wood Shown at Left

straight-grained with a medium and fairly uniform texture, and is easily worked. Its resistance to decay is extremely low. In color the heartwood is white with a reddish tinge. The sapwood is not distinguishable from the heartwood. Of all the commercial softwoods white fir has the least color.

Uses. The white-fir wood is used chiefly as dimension lumber and common boards for construction work. It is used also for sashes, doors, blinds, boxes, crates, and general millwork.

Douglas Fir (*Pseudotsuga taxifolia*). Douglas fir is distinctively a North American tree, no other species of its genus occurs in commercial quantities in any other section of the world, Fig. 17. For a long time after its discovery this tree remained without a specific name. It was not classified botanically until 1826, when the Royal Horticultural Society sent David Douglas, a Scotch botanist, to the Oregon country. Although called *Douglas fir*, this giant of the forest is distinctly not of the *fir* family. Regardless of the fact that the first water-borne cargoes of this species were labeled *Oregon Pine* it is likewise not a *pine;* neither is it a *spruce*, although for some time it was called *Douglas spruce*. It is a species in itself, known popularly as *Douglas fir*.

Physical Characteristics. The weight of Douglas fir is 34 pounds per cubic foot. These trees sometimes measure as much as six feet in diameter and reach a height of 200 feet. The largest Douglas fir which has been located measures fifteen feet in diameter and is 300 feet in height. The quality of wood and its color vary in the same tree. Some is pale reddish yellow in color, fine grained, fairly uniform in texture, moderately soft, and is easily worked. Other parts are deep red in color, coarse grained, uneven in texture, and splinters easily. In general, the wood of the Douglas fir has a tendency to check and split. It does not hold paint well unless it is given a special priming coat of paint, such as exterior aluminum. In proportion to its weight, Douglas fir is one of the strongest woods ever tested.

Uses. Because of its great strength this wood is used chiefly for structural purposes. A section of Douglas-fir wood is shown at left in Fig. 17. Wood from the outer portion of a Douglas-fir log is suitable for the finest grades of interior finish woodwork, exterior siding, window sashes and frames, doors, long ladder rails, and many other similar uses. Large quantities of the wood are cut into veneer for plywood and other purposes.

Hemlock. In North America the name *hemlock* is given commonly to trees of the pine family of the genus *Tsuga*. These trees are tall, pyramidal evergreen, conifers. The bark is of a cinnamon-red color. The branches are slender and grow horizontally or slightly drooping. The cones are pendulous with rounded, slightly woody scales. Four species of the hemlock are native to the temperate regions of North America.

Eastern Hemlock (*Tsuga canadensis*). This tree is found principally in the region of the Great Lakes and in the mountain regions of the eastern part of the United States. The eastern hemlock is a handsome tree, usually growing to a height of about 60 to 80 feet. It is one of the most beautiful of the evergreens and numerous varieties are cultivated because of their ornamental value.

Physical Characteristics.   The weight of eastern hemlock is 28 pounds per cubic foot.   The heartwood is pale buff in color with a red-

Courtesy—West Coast Lumbermen's Association, Seattle, Wash.   *Courtesy of United States Forest Service, Photo by Bureau of Aeronautics, U.S. Navy*

Fig. 18. Mountain Hemlock, Mount Baker National Forest, Washington

dish tinge.   The wood is moderately low in strength and has a tendency to splinter; it is subject to *ring shake*, is not decay resistant, and does not hold paint well.   However, the lumber holds nails well, and the knots are comparatively small.

Uses.   The bark of the eastern hemlock is valuable for tanning purposes.   The soft, coarse-grained, splintery wood, although much inferior to pine or spruce, is used extensively for building purposes.

Western Hemlock (*Tsuga heterophylla*).   Western hemlock grows along the Pacific Coast from Alaska to Northern California.   This is a valuable lumber-producing tree, Fig. 18.   It often reaches a height of 200 feet, with a trunk measuring from six to ten feet in diameter.   A section of wood is shown at the left in Fig. 18.

Physical Characteristics. Western hemlock weighs 29 pounds per cubic foot. The heartwood is light, sometimes pink or red brown in color. The sapwood is thick and white to cream in color. It has a uniform fine-textured wood, comparatively free from *ring shakes.* Its resistance to decay is low.

Uses. The wood of this tree is used chiefly for framing, sheathing, and subfloors. Western hemlock is used also for sashes, doors, blinds, and general millwork.

Pine. In building construction, pine is the timber most extensively used. Commercial pines include about fifteen different varieties. These different varieties are recognized in different parts of the country under various names. However, broadly speaking, they can be placed in two general classes—*southern yellow* or *pitch pine* and *white* or *soft pine.* The white or soft pine is found principally in the northern and western parts of the United States. The most important species of this pine are: northern white, ponderosa, sugar, and western white pine.

Southern Yellow Pine. The name *southern yellow pine* is applied to a number of closely related species which grow as far south as Texas and as far north as New Jersey and Pennsylvania. These species include chiefly: the *longleaf (Pinus palustris), shortleaf (Pinus echinata), loblolly (Pinus taeda), slash (Pinus caribaea),* and *pond pine (Pinus rigida serotina).* These various species of southern pine all have similar qualities, such as are found in pine wood ranging from extremely dense to wood of a low density or lightweight. The southern pines are classified commercially into two groups: *longleaf* and *shortleaf.* All pines having a heavy, dense, and close-ringed wood with not less than six annual growth rings per inch, is known commercially as *longleaf,* regardless of the species to which it belongs. The southern pines having wood that is less dense and lighter in weight is known as *shortleaf,* regardless of the species.

Physical Characteristics. The heartwood, which is yellowish to orange brown in color, is resistant to decay. The sapwood, forming the greater portion of the timber, is usually white, although sometimes it is yellow or even orange in color. Since the sapwood absorbs preservatives readily this wood is highly adaptable for treatment.

Uses. The qualities of southern yellow pine make it especially valuable for construction work.

Longleaf Pine. Sometimes called *Georgia pitch pine*, this is one of the most valuable pine timbers in the United States. The tree often grows to a height of more than 100 feet and the tall columnar trunk makes it especially suitable for heavy construction work.

Fig. 19. White Pine, Rogue River, Oregon

United States Forest Service Photo

Physical Characteristics. This dense southern pine weighs 41 pounds per cubic foot. The wood which is straight-grained is highly resinous. It checks and does not hold paint well. Although the spring wood is soft, the summer growth is especially hard and flint-like, splitting easily when nailed.

Uses. Because of its great strength and rigidity, this wood is valued highly for structural purposes, such as for heavy timbers in factory construction, bridges, trestles, docks, and wharves. It is used also in lighter structural work for floor joists and sheathing.

Shortleaf Pine. Growing in the southern part of the United States, the shortleaf pine belongs to a group of pitch pines with leaves usually arranged in two-leaved clusters. The leaves are short and flexible. The bark is cinnamon colored and the wood yellow. Although lighter in weight, less dense, and with less strength than the longleaf pine, the shortleaf pine is more desirable for many purposes.

Physical Characteristics. This particular species of southern pine weighs 36 pounds per cubic foot. It is softer and more easily worked than the dense pine. It is straight-grained and moderately resinous.

Uses. The yellow wood is valuable for general utility purposes. It is used extensively for interior trim, flooring, sashes, doors, and planing-mill products.

White Pine or Soft Pine. The white pines are found principally in the northern and western parts of the United States, Fig. 19. The wood is soft and easily worked. It keeps its shape fairly well. Most of the wood of this class is manufactured into millwork products; such as, sashes, doors, interior trim, and cabinets. This wood also is used extensively for exterior trim. Of the several species, the four commonly used for lumber are: soft white pine, sugar pine, western white pine, and ponderosa pine.

White Pine (*Pinus strobus*). This species is also commonly known under several different names; such as, *northern pine, Minnesota pine, Wisconsin pine, cork pine, pumpkin pine,* and *soft white pine.* The virgin growth is considered the finest of soft pine but this is becoming scarce. This particular species is found from Maine westward as far as Minnesota and in the Appalachian Mountains as far south as northern Georgia.

Physical Characteristics. The weight of white pine is 25 pounds per cubic foot. The heartwood is cream to light reddish brown in color. When in contact with the soil, the heartwood is decay resistant. The sapwood is white to pale ivory in color. The wood dries rapidly but with little shrinkage or swelling. The wood is close-grained and has a fine texture. The small resin ducts are much less conspicuous than in the western white pine. There is little if any color distinction between the spring and summer growth.

Uses. White pine is an ideal pattern wood. It is also desirable for the making of products for which softwoods can be used but which must retain their shape and not be affected by moisture changes. White pine is used extensively for sashes, doors, blinds, and matches.

Sugar Pine (*Pinus lambertiana*). The sugar pine, also called *big pine,* is the largest of the white pines. It has many of the same properties as the northern white pine and is considered one of the most valuable of timber trees. It is a native of California and southern Oregon.

Physical Characteristics. Sugar pine weighs 25 pounds per cubic foot. The heartwood is cream in color darkening slightly with exposure to the weather. The sapwood is yellowish white, with a satiny luster when polished. Because of the unusual size of the sugar pine, lumber can be obtained from the tree in large sizes free from defects. It is straight-grained, easily worked, decay resistant to some extent, and keeps its shape well.

Uses. Much of the sugar pine is used in planing-mill products, sashes, doors, and for interior trim. It is also used for pattern wood.

Western White Pine (*Pinus monticola*). The western white pine is known commercially as *Idaho white pine*. It grows principally in northern Idaho, eastern Washington, and western Montana.

Physical Characteristics. The weight of western white pine is 27 pounds per cubic foot. Its heartwood and sapwood closely resemble the northern white pine, previously described under *white pine*. However, western white pine is a little more difficult to work and swells and shrinks more with moisture changes.

Fig. 20.   Redwood, Humboldt County, California

Courtesy of the American Forestry Association

Uses. The western, or Idaho white pine, is used chiefly for sashes, doors, blinds, and matches.

Ponderosa Pine (*Pinus ponderosa*). The ponderosa pine grows in the northwestern part of the United States from Washington eastward as far as the Black Hills of South Dakota, and southward in the Rocky Mountains and the Pacific Coast regions. Because of its growth over such extensive areas, it has been given various names by the trade; the names depending upon the locality; such as, *Arizona white pine* and *California white pine*. That coming from Oregon is known as *pondosa pine* or *Oregon pine*.

Physical Characteristics. Ponderosa pine weighs 28 pounds per cubic foot. The heartwood is variable in color from nearly white to yellow cream and even reddish brown. The sapwood is white to cream, sometimes yellow. The grain is fine; it approaches white pine in softness and is easily worked.

Uses. The ponderosa pine is valuable for many purposes. It is used for millwork of all kinds, as well as for sashes and doors. It is also used extensively for both exterior and interior trim. The low-density cell structure makes it an excellent material for insulation purposes.

Redwood. The redwood is a gigantic tree of the northwestern part of North America. It is a coniferous tree sometimes reaching a height of 340 feet, with a diameter measuring as much as 20 feet or more, Fig. 20.

Redwood (*Sequoia sempervirens*). The redwood grows commercially in a narrow belt, 10 to 30 miles wide, on the western slope of the mountains of the Pacific Coast Range of California and southern Oregon. These trees grow extremely large and commonly have diameters of as much as five to ten feet, while some have grown to a diameter of 18 feet or more. However, the redwood should not be confused with the California *Big Trees* (*Sequoia gigantea*) which are no longer used for lumber, Fig. 21.

Physical Characteristics. Redwood weighs 28 pounds per cubic foot. The heartwood varies in color from light cherry red to a dark mahogany, while the narrow band of sapwood is almost white. The heartwood is decay resistant, not resinous, has a low shrinkage, and stays in place well. It also holds paint well, is easy to work, and has the advantage of being highly resistant to termites. Like Douglas fir, its hardness ranks between Southern pine and white pine.

Fig. 21. Sequoia, Yosemite National Park, California

The Grizzly Giant is one of the oldest trees in existence. Its age has been estimated at 3800 years

Courtesy of American Forestry Association

Uses. The redwood is especially desirable for use in places where wood is apt to decay easily; such as, crossties, fence posts, water tanks, pipes, gutters, flumes, greenhouses, and structural timbers for bridges. It is used extensively for exterior trim, shingles, and siding, as well as, for sashes, doors, and other millwork products.

Spruce. There are seven species of spruce native to North America. Of these only four of the most important commercially are discussed here. Three of these are found chiefly in the region of the Great Lakes,

New England, and the Appalachian Mountains, and are known as *eastern spruce*. The other species most important commercially is the *sitka spruce* found in a narrow strip extending along the Pacific Coast from Northern California to Alaska. The blue spruce is one of the most distinctive American species, Fig. 22.

Fig. 22. Blue Spruce, Powell National Forest, Utah

Photo by United States Forest Service

Eastern Spruce. Included in this group are: *white spruce* (*Picea glauca*), *black spruce* (*Picea mariana*), and *red spruce* (*Picea rubra*). White spruce found in the New England states and the Great Lakes region grows over an area extending from Maine to Minnesota. It sometimes reaches a height of 150 feet, with a trunk diameter of four feet. The cylindrical cones are about two inches in length. This species is used extensively for lumber and is especially valuable for pulp wood. The black spruce, sometimes called *bog spruce*, is native to swampy regions. It is found in the Great Lakes region and in swampy areas extending from Minnesota southward as far as Virginia. It commonly grows to a height of from 20 to 30 feet but sometimes reaches a height of 90 feet. It is used for pulp wood and is the source of spruce gum, an ingredient of chewing gum. Red spruce grows in the New England states southward as far as the Tennessee mountains. In the Adirondack region this spruce reaches a height of from 60 to 100 feet, with small brownish-red, egg-shaped cones about 1½ inches in length. Red spruce is used extensively for pulp wood and lumber. No distinction is made commercially between these three species as they closely resemble each other in general structure.

Physical Characteristics. The weight of all eastern spruce is 28 pounds per cubic foot. The heartwood and sapwood are both reddish to pale pink or even white in color. The grain is generally straight and close. The texture is soft and satiny with a pearly luster. It is exceptionally strong for its weight, easy to work, but not decay resistant.

Uses. The lower grades are used for framing or general construction of boxes and crates. The better grades are used as sounding boards for musical instruments.

Sitka Spruce (*Picea sitchensis*). The sitka spruce, also known as *tidewater spruce*, is found along the Pacific Coast, growing from Kodiak Island, Alaska, southward as far as Northern California, and extending inland about 50 miles. This is the tallest of the spruces, sometimes attaining massive proportions, reaching a height of 190 feet with a basal trunk diameter of 20 feet. However, it commonly grows to a height of about 100 feet with a trunk diameter of approximately three feet. Sitka spruce is a highly valued timber tree and is used extensively for lumber.

Physical Characteristics. The sitka spruce weighs 28 pounds per cubic foot. The heartwood varies from straw-colored to pinkish, with a thin light-colored sapwood. This particular spruce has a moderate degree of hardness and stiffness. It is strong for its weight and is straight-grained. It undergoes only moderate shrinkage and is easily worked.

Uses. In aircraft construction the sitka spruce is used extensively because of its straight, uniform texture, strength, lightness, and shock-resisting qualities. It is used also for both exterior and interior finish, and for millwork products.

HARDWOOD

Hardwoods or broad-leaved trees are seldom used for structural work. However, the hardwoods do play an important part in the building industry where they may be used for interior trim, floors, cabinets, and furniture, and occasionally hardwood is used for exterior trim.

Hardwoods have large cells which conduct the sap from the roots to the leaves. Such cells are not found in the softwoods. When the cells in hardwood are split in the process of lumber manufacturing they show as pores in the wood; as a result the hardwoods are also known as *porous woods*. Because of this peculiar cell structure, greater care must be exercised in seasoning and drying of hardwoods to prevent warping, twisting, and general distortion of the lumber.

Beech (*Fagus grandifolia*). The beech tree is characterized by its smooth light-gray bark, deep-green foliage, and small triangular-shaped

nuts enclosed in burs. The tree grows over a wide range in the eastern
part of the United States and over large areas in the region of the Great
Lakes extending from Minnesota as far south as Florida and Texas.
The American species includes many varieties, Fig. 23. It is an important forest plant and is one of the largest of our forest trees, often growing
to a height of 100 feet. Owing to its handsome foliage, spreading or

Fig. 23. Beech, Pisgah National Forest, North Carolina
Photo by United States Forest Service

drooping branches, and its conspicuous smooth gray bark, the beech
tree is unsurpassed as an ornamental tree. The American species includes many horticultural forms that are propagated and grown especially for ornamental purposes. It is commonly called *red beech* or
white beech. Beechwood makes excellent fuel and charcoal.

Because of its inferior quality for construction work, beech did not
play an important part in our domestic lumber trade until recent years.
Though not especially suitable for building purposes beechwood is now
used extensively in the manufacture of furniture and for many other
millwork products. The hard, close-grained wood is suitable also for
making handles for tools.

Physical Characteristics. Beechwood weighs 45 pounds per cubic foot. The heartwood is red to brown in color. There is little distinction between the heartwood and sapwood. The wood is hard, strong, and close-grained. It is also fine in texture. Its decay resistance is low.

Uses. It is used extensively for flooring, furniture, and laundry appliances. When treated it is used also for railroad ties. It is desirable for making butchers' blocks, woodenware, and similar products, as it does not impart a taste or odor to food and resists abrasion.

Birch. There are between fifteen and twenty species of birch growing in the United States. The yellow, sweet birch produces most of the important commercial lumber used. The terms *select* and *unselect birch* refer to color and not to grade. When uniform delicate color stains are desired, select birch will give the best results. Unselect birch is cheaper but is satisfactory for use with dark stains or paint. The sapwood of both species is known as *white birch* and the heartwood as *red birch*.

Yellow Birch (*Betula lutea*). The species of birch which is most abundant and has the greatest commercial value in the United States grows in the northeastern part of the country. It is cut for lumber chiefly in the region of the Great Lakes growing south as far as central Iowa, and in the state of New York. In the eastern states it is found as far south as North Carolina. It is abundant in the Appalachian Mountain region. It is one of the largest of the deciduous trees growing in this section of the country. The trunk of the birch often measures from three to four feet in diameter and occasionally the trees grow to a height of 100 feet. Little trade distinction is made between the yellow and the sweet birch.

Physical Characteristics. Birch is a heavy, hard, close-grained wood weighing 44 pounds per cubic foot. The heartwood is brown, red, and yellow in the same board. The sapwood is thick and white in color. The sapwood is easily affected by fungi. The close-grained wood is generally straight and is slightly more fibrous in appearance than maple wood. The wood is hard, stiff, strong, and shock resisting.

Uses. Birchwood is used extensively for interior finishing and trim. It is also used for various millwork products, including cabinets, furniture, fixtures, and wood turning. Much of the imitation mahogany is made from birch.

Sweet Birch (*Betula lenta*). The sweet, or black, birch grows principally in the eastern part of the United States. Pennsylvania and West Virginia usually yield our largest cut of sweet-birch lumber, often called *cherry birch* in the trade. The sweet birch also is found as far west as Iowa and as far south as Florida. It attains its greatest height in the Appalachian Mountains where it sometimes reaches 80 feet with a trunk diameter measuring from two to five feet. It has a smooth, red-brown, cherrylike aromatic bark from which an oil similar to wintergreen oil is extracted. The strong, hard, yellowish-brown wood, as heavy as that of white oak, is highly valued for making furniture, agricultural implements, and woodenware.

Physical Characteristics. Sweet birch is heavy, weighing 44 pounds per cubic foot. The heartwood is dark brown in color, tinged with red. The sapwood is light brown. Sweet birch is slightly harder and stronger than yellow birch, otherwise its properties are similar to those of the yellow birch.

Uses. Because of its hardness sweet birch is better for flooring than yellow birch. Otherwise the uses made of these two species are similar.

Butternut (*Juglans cinerea*). This is also sometimes called *white walnut* as it is similar structurally to the black walnut. The butternut is native to the eastern part of the United States and is found from Maine to North Dakota and Kansas. It grows southward as far as Georgia and Alabama.

Physical Characteristics. The butternut weighs 27 pounds per cubic foot. It is one of the softer hardwoods and is not strong. The grain is fine and straight. The texture is soft, satiny, and brittle. The heartwood is brown to gray in color. The sapwood is pale cream to white and extremely thin.

Uses. Butternut makes a good wood for interior trim. It is used also for cabinet work and for furniture to replace black walnut which it closely resembles.

Red Gum and Sap Gum (*Liquidambar styraciflua*). The hard reddish-brown lumber sawed from the heartwood of the sweet-gum tree is known to the lumber trade as *red gum* or *satin-walnut*. This tree belongs to the witch-hazel family. The earliest record of red gum appears in a work published in 1651, where it is described as a large tree producing a fragrant gum-resin resembling liquid amber, whence the name *liquidamber* or *liquidambar*. It is a tall handsome tree sometimes attaining a height of 140 feet with a straight trunk measuring five feet in diameter. It has a rough bark, corky-winged branches, large deeply lobed leaves, and drooping, spiny, globose fruiting heads containing winged seeds. The sapwood is nearly white in color. The trade term *sap gum* is applied to lumber cut from the sapwood of any tree of the genus *Nyssa*. Red gum is native in the United States. It is found from Connecticut westward to Missouri and southward to Florida. Red gum comprises a large part of the hardwoods that grow in the lower Mississippi River Basin and the Gulf States, in lowlands which are dry the greater part of the year. Careful research has made it possible to control warping and distortion during seasoning and handling. As a result red gum is today one of our commercial woods. The annual cut during a recent year was more than 600,000,000 board feet. Lumber sawed from the sapwood is sold as *sap gum*.

Physical Characteristics. Red gum weighs 34 pounds per cubic foot. The heartwood varies in color from a light to a deep reddish brown. The sapwood is nearly white. The wood is strong and of a fine uniform texture. The grain is cross, spiral, and interlocking. Some red-gum trees produce a figured gum highly prized for panel work.

Uses. Red-gum wood is used extensively for interior finish and trim. It is used also for millwork products, such as doors and furniture. Much of it is used for veneer stock. It takes a good finish and can be stained readily to imitate mahogany and walnut.

Maple. The name *maple* is applied to trees of the genus *Acer*. There are fifteen species of maple native in the United States. Of these, nine are found east of the Great Plains, two grow along the Pacific Coast, and two occur in the Rocky Mountain region. The eastern maples include: *sugar maples, soft maples, mountain maples,* and the *box-elder*.

The varieties of soft maple which are important commercially are the silver, red, and Oregon maples. The silver maple (*Acer saccharinum*) has leaves which are white on the under side, giving it decorative value. The red maple (*Acer rubrum*) has dull red flowers in the spring and flame-red foliage in autumn. The silver and red maples are both common trees, similar in size to the sugar maple and with nearly the same geographical range of growth. The soft maples furnish softwood lumber and are widely planted because of their ornamental value. The bigleaf Oregon maple grows along the Pacific Coast from Southern

California to Alaska.   The Oregon maple is a valuable timber tree, sometimes reaching a height of 100 feet.   It is also called the *broad-leaved
maple* because of its wide leaves which often measure from four to ten
inches in width.   The two species most important commercially are the

*Courtesy of Appalachian Hardwood Manufacturers,   United States Forest Service Photo
Inc., Cincinnati, Ohio*

Fig. 24. Sugar Maple, Pisgah National Forest, North Carolina

sugar maple and the black maple.   Both of these are known to the trade
as *hard maples*.

Sugar Maple (*Acer saccharum*).   The sugar maple, also known as
hard or *rock maple*, is valued highly as a timber and shade tree, Fig. 24.
It is also the chief source of our maple sugar.   It grows in the eastern part
of the country extending westward as far as South Dakota and southward
to South Carolina and Texas.   It sometimes reaches a height of 120 feet
with a trunk diameter of four feet.   The heavy, hard, strong wood is
utilized extensively for commercial purposes.   The varieties known as
bird's-eye, curly, and *wavy-maple* are prized highly for cabinet work and
finishings.   A section of hard-maple wood is shown at left in Fig. 24.

Black Maple (*Acer nigrum*).   The black maple is similar to the
sugar maple in physical characteristics and uses.   It grows in a more
restricted region and is valued highly for its lumber.

Physical Characteristics. Of the hard maples, the sugar maple weighs 44 pounds per cubic foot, and the black maple weighs 40 pounds per cubic foot. They both grow over a wide range, principally in the region of the Great Lakes, the Appalachian Mountain region, and in the northeastern part of the United States. The heartwood of both these maples is light reddish brown. The sapwood is white with a slight reddish-brown tinge. The wood has a fine, crisp texture. It is generally straight-grained, extremely hard, tough, and strong. It does not swell or shrink to any appreciable degree, and takes a good finish.

Uses. These maples are two of the most important hardwoods and are used extensively for flooring and stair treads, fine furniture, pianos, ship keels, shoe lasts, and bowling pins.

Oak. There are more than sixty species of oak native to the United States. Approximately fifteen of these are used commercially. These are found principally in the Mississippi Valley and the Southern States. The lumber industry divides the oaks into three groups: white oak, red oak, and live oak. The latter, which is becoming scarce, was used extensively in ship building.

White Oak (*Quercus alba*). The white oak is one of the finest of North American trees, Fig. 25. It sometimes reaches a height of 100 feet with a trunk diameter of four feet. It is the most desirable of all the oaks for making furniture. It is found chiefly in Indiana and Kentucky.

Physical Characteristics. White oak weighs 47 pounds per cubic foot. The heartwood is grayish brown, occasionally reddish brown. For the most part the pores are plugged with a growth called *tyloses* (*A*, Fig. 1) which makes the wood of the white oak less subject to the penetration of liquids than red oak. The quartersawing of oak exposes the medullary rays which appear as *flakes* enhancing the appearance of the wood. White-oak wood is extremely hard, stiff, and strong. It is porous and decay resistant. A section of white-oak wood is shown at left in Fig. 25.

Uses. White oak is used in heavy timber construction where strength is demanded. It is also used in cooperage, flooring, interior trim, fine furniture, and cabinet work.

Red Oak (*Quercus rubra*). The red oak grows in the same regions where the white oak is found, and has many of the same properties as the white oak. It is an important timber tree sometimes reaching a height of 150 feet.

Physical Characteristics. Red oak weighs 44 pounds per cubic foot. The heartwood is generally red or red-brown in color. The sapwood is thick, white, or nearly white. The wood is coarse-grained and porous. In appearance red oak is inferior to the white oak and is less decay resistant. In other properties, red oak is similar to white oak.

Courtesy of Appalachian Hardwood Manufacturers,   *United States Forest Service Photo*
Inc., Cincinnati, Ohio

Fig. 25. White Oak, Mount Vernon Estate, Virginia

Uses. Red oak is used extensively for flooring, but white oak is more desirable for fine furniture and cabinet work.

Black Walnut (*Juglans nigra*). For making cabinets the black walnut is the finest wood native to the United States, Fig. 26. It grows commercially in the North Central States, east of the Mississippi River. It is highly valuable as a timber tree sometimes reaching a height of 150 feet with a trunk diameter of approximately seven feet. It is found over an extensive area from New England to Texas.

Physical Characteristics. Black walnut weighs 38 pounds per cubic foot. The heartwood is light brown to dark brown in color. The sapwood is nearly white. The wood has good shock-resisting qualities, and shrinks moderately in seasoning. Walnut is a hard, strong, stiff, and straight-grained wood. Some of the finest figured wood obtainable is cut from walnut stumps and crotches in the form of veneer. It takes an exceptionally good finish, and is comparable to the finest mahogany in this respect. It is easily worked and holds its shape well.

Uses. The wood of black walnut is used for making fine furniture

Courtesy American Walnut Manufacturers Association, Chicago, Ill.   *United States Forest Service*

Fig. 26. Walnut, West Virginia, with Section of Veneer at Left

and for cabinet work. It is highly prized for interior trim and for gun stocks. Great quantities of black-walnut wood are cut into veneer stock. A section of plain walnut veneer is shown at left in Fig. 26.

IMPORTED WOOD

Mahogany. Since it is a tropical wood, many people assume that all mahogany used in the United States is imported. However, it may be of interest to our readers to know that mahogany trees can be grown in some of our southern states. During the ten-year period ending 1945, Florida yielded 1,000,000 feet of beautiful mahogany. Much of this home-grown mahogany is equal in quality to that grown in the West Indies, Fig. 27.

Although used chiefly for the making of fine furniture, mahogany plays an important part in building construction for interior finish work. It is used extensively in many of our best buildings for doors and cabinets, as well as for window and door trim. Because of its inherent

Fig. 27. Mahogany Tree with Section of Veneer Shown at Left
Courtesy of Mahogany Association, Inc., Chicago, Ill.

ability to hold its shape under variable moisture conditions, it is an excellent wood for boat construction and an ideal pattern wood. Much of the mahogany wood used in this country is cut into veneer which gives it wider usage and accentuates the beauty of the wood, producing the stripe, crotch, swirl, scuttle, and fiddleback figures.

Kinds and Uses of Genuine Mahogany. The three widely known regions which produce genuine mahogany for commercial purposes are: the West Indies, tropical America, and Africa.

The variety known as *Swietenia mahagoni* is grown in the West Indies region, including: Cuba, Santo Domingo, Bermuda, and southern Florida.

Physical Characteristics. This wood is close grained with a silky, fine to medium texture. It is heavier and harder than other species of mahogany. The color is yellowish white when freshly cut changing to golden brown and later to a deep red-brown upon exposure to sunlight, but retains the rich, deep-orange undertone peculiar to the species. The sapwood is thin, white to brown-cream in color. The spring and summer woods are usually distinct. Genuine mahogany can be distinguished from substitutes by the prominent annual growth rings. A distinguishing feature of this particular species is the white mineral deposits in the pores which are hard and solid and in no way to be confused with the transparent tyloses of other species. This condition can best be seen in the freshly planed board before it is sanded.

Uses. This species of mahogany is the standard cabinet wood of the world, and is the one by which all other cabinet woods are judged. It is highly prized for making the finest furniture, whether solid or veneered. Because of its unusual wearing qualities, it is used extensively not only for cabinet making but also in the manufacture of Pullman cars, sleeping cars, and railroad-dining cars.

Confined to the region of Mexico and Central America, the species known as *Swietenia macrophylla* (King) is a light, soft-textured wood often used by pattern makers in place of white pine. This tree grows in tropical America, ranging from southern Mexico through Guatemala, Honduras, British Honduras, Nicaragua, Colombia, Venezuela, and the upper Amazon Valley in Brazil and Peru. At the left in Fig. 27 is shown a section of mottled broken-stripe veneer of Honduras mahogany.

Physical Characteristics. The chief characteristic of this mahogany is the straight grain and more mellow texture which distinguishes it from the West Indies mahogany. The larger trees and straighter grain produce longer and wider cuttings. This species is yellowish white to pink in color when freshly cut, changing to rich golden brown when exposed to the sunlight.

Uses. This species is used for high quality furniture and woodwork. It is especially suitable for aircraft construction, also for making of speed boats.

The species *Khaya senegalensis* known to the trade as *African mahogany* is a distant member of the mahogany family. It comes from the Gold, Ivory, and Nigerian coasts of Africa, where the tree grows to great proportions.

Physical Characteristics. The large stately tree with its umbrella-like top often grows to a height of 100 feet or more. It is heavily buttressed, the trunk averaging from 4 to 6 feet in diameter for a distance of from 40 to 60 feet up from the base at the ground. Its texture is milder and the pores slightly larger than the American mahogany. Its lavish figures range from the simple stripe to rich and complex mottles, crotches, and swirls of unusual beauty rarely surpassed by other woods. When freshly cut it is salmon pink in color changing to a pale golden brown when exposed to sunlight.

Uses. Because of the large size of the logs of African mahogany and the exceptionally fine-figured stock it is used extensively for veneer. During the preparation of the veneer there is little waste and the smooth faces of consecutive sheets match each other perfectly producing a highly satisfactory result. These veneers are especially desirable for decorative purposes. During normal peacetime conditions, three-fourths of all mahogany veneer comes from African trees.

CHECKING ON YOUR KNOWLEDGE

If you have read this chapter carefully you should be able to answer the following questions. If you have any difficulty, you should read the chapter again so that you will have the information well in mind before you go on with your reading.

DO YOU KNOW

1. In what important respect wood differs from other building materials, such as brick and cement blocks?
2. Of what substance wood is composed?
3. How trees grow? How the fibers in wood are held together?
4. The size and shape of wood fibers or cells?
5. How the cells in hardwoods differ from the cells in softwoods?
6. The meaning of the terms *hardwoods* and *softwoods* as used in the lumber trade? Are hardwoods always *hard* and softwoods always *soft?*
7. A softwood that is *hard?* A hardwood that is *soft?*
8. The names of ten important commercial softwoods used in the United States and ten or more hardwoods?
9. The difference between *springwood* and *summerwood?* How they compare in strength?
10. How heartwood is formed? Where the sapwood is located in the tree?
11. The difference between *coarse-grained, straight-grained,* and *close-grained* woods?

12. In what two forms moisture is contained in standing trees?

13. How knots and pitch pockets are formed in wood?

14. The difference between *heart shake, wind shake,* and *starshake?*

15. What causes warping of lumber?

16. How lumber is graded and priced by lumber dealers?

17. How to find the number of board feet in a piece of structural timber?

18. How to determine the moisture content of any particular kind of wood?

19. The physical characteristics and common uses of the commercially important softwoods and hardwoods?

20. Which is more important for construction purposes, hardwood or softwood?

21. Why southern cypress is used extensively for water tanks, water buckets, and gutters?

22. The difference between *Sequoia sempervirens* and *Sequoia washingtoniana?* Which of these is no longer used for lumber?

23. The meaning of the terms *exogens* and *endogens?*

24. To which group palms and bamboos belong?

25. The name of an imported lumber which is important commercially for making cabinets and fine furniture?

WITH PICTURE WINDOWS THE OUTDOORS BECOMES AN INTEGRAL PART OF INDOOR LIVING

Photo by Suter, Hedrich-Blessing Studio

Insulation

QUESTIONS THIS CHAPTER WILL ANSWER

1. *What is meant by the term* Thermal Building Insulation? 2. *What materials did our forefathers use to insulate their homes?* 3. *Was the type of insulation in use in early Colonial days in America effective?* 4. *Of what material is* Zostera Marina *made?* 5. *Can you name four types of building insulation commonly used by the building trade today?*

INTRODUCTION TO CHAPTER VI

In the North Atlantic coastal region of America during early Colonial days, home builders often filled the air spaces in the walls of their houses with sea grasses, or sawdust and shavings. One of the oldest houses in America was built in 1635, in Dorchester, Massachusetts. This house, known as the *Old Pierce House,* was insulated with Zostera Marina stuffed between the studdings. Sometimes the early Colonial builders used back plaster between the studdings, thus creating a double air space in the outside walls of their homes.

A blanket type of insulation, *Cabot's Quilt,* came into use in the United States about fifty years ago (1891). This product which takes its name from the manufacturer, Samuel Cabot, Inc. (Boston, Mass.), is still used extensively for insulating purposes. About 1901, an industrial plant in Alexandria, Indiana, began the manufacture of an unrefined form of rock-wool material for building insulation. The manufacture of *Gimco Rock Wool,* under its present trade name, began about 1912; and production of *Gimco* has been practically uninterrupted since that time.

The production of corkboard began in Germany at least a decade before its manufacture was undertaken in the United States. About the year 1900, the Armstrong Cork Company acquired patent rights to produce this material at Beaver Falls, Pennsylvania. Structural insulating board had its beginning in Minnesota where climatic conditions tended to encourage the development of effective insulating materials. The manufacture of *Universal Insulite,* now known merely as *Insulite,* was begun at International Falls, Minnesota, in 1914.

Other types of insulation also have interesting histories. Among these is the reflective insulating material. Although the first patent rights for the use of bright metallic surfaces for thermal insulation were obtained in 1804, reflective insulating material was not developed commercially until comparatively recent years. Today there are various types on the market. Trade names of reflective insulating material commonly known to the building industry include: *Alfol, Metallation,* and *Gold Bond Aluminum Foil Insulating Board.*

The development of the different types of thermal building insulation and the effective methods used in their application are examples of scientific and engineering skills of a high order. The history of the progress made in manufacturing processes, for building insulation, provides interesting reading for the student of building construction. The various loose fills, blankets, pads, bats, slabs, and reflective types of insulation, now used, are remarkable achievements when compared with the insulating methods of our forefathers who stuffed sea grasses between the studdings in the walls of their homes.

This chapter contains much worthwhile information which will be of value to a student who is preparing to enter the carpentry trade. Because of the constantly changing materials and methods used in constructing homes, insulation has become an extremely important factor in the building industry. A carpenter, today, must not only be familiar with the various types of insulating material on the market, but he must also know the best methods of application of the different types of thermal building insulations. In connection with the instructions concerning application of insulating material, the student should study the information given in the tables.

THERMAL BUILDING INSULATION

Constructing buildings so they will have a higher degree of heat resistance is a problem to which various authorities have given much attention in recent years. The house should be built so that it will be comfortably warm in winter and relatively cool in summer; that is, a building should be constructed so as to retain the heat which is generated by the heating plant in the winter and keep out the heat developed by the hot rays of the sun during the summer. If the walls and roof can be constructed in such a way that the passage of heat through them becomes relatively difficult, fuel will be saved during the cold months and increased comfort will be provided during the hot weather. The use of thermal building insulation produces these desirable results. By *thermal insulation* we mean the use of materials which possess concentrated heat resistance; that is, materials which have a high degree of heat resistance per unit of thickness.

Our forefathers filled the wall spaces of buildings with sea grasses or sawdust and shavings, or back plastered[1] them. However, today we have available many different types of insulation in forms which are easy to handle. If properly installed these insulation materials are effective.

---

[1] *Back plaster* consisted of lath and plaster in the stud space midway between the outside sheathing and the inside lath and plaster. This provided a double air space in outside walls, the back plaster acting as a separate wall inside the outer wall of the building.

Thermal Insulation. Manufacturers have utilized many different kinds of materials in the process of developing thermal insulation. Now on the market in various forms these materials may be classified as: *flexible blankets, fills, bats, pads, rigid* (structural insulating board), *slabs,* and *reflective.* There is some overlapping of these classifications. For example, since wall-thick pads fill the entire space, they are sometimes referred to as *fills,* especially if used between 2x4-inch studs.

FLEXIBLE INSULATION

Flexible Insulation Material. Known as *blankets* or *quilts* flexible insulations are made from processed wood fiber, animal hair, mineral wool, *Zostera Marina,* and other fibers which in many cases are highly resistant to fire, moisture, and vermin, or have been treated to render them resistant to these hazards. The matted or felted fibers are encased generally with sheets of craft paper and stitched or cemented together, then the paper is asphalt-saturated or coated, Fig. 1. The thickness of this insulation varies from ½ inch to 2 inches and in some cases is full wall thickness (3⅝ inches).

The trade names of some of these flexible insulations are: *Balsam Wool,* a wood fiber; *Cabot's Quilt,* made of

Fig. 1. Application of Red Top Blanket
Courtesy of United States Gypsum Co., Chicago, Ill.

Zostera Marina (eelgrass), a marine plant; *Ozite All-Hair Building Blanket,* made of 100 per cent cattle hair; *Kimsul,* creped layers of wood fiber; and *Rock Wool,* made from clean fibers of molten rock, clayey (argillaceous) limestone or chalky (calcareous) shale. Rock wool is sold under various trade names, such as: *Celotex Rock Wool, Rocktex,*

Flintkote, Gold Bond, Gimco, Eagle Insulation Products, Johns-Manville Rock Wool, and other names. *Mineral Wool,* fiber glass, made from dolomite and silica is found under different names, such as: *Century Mineral Wool Insulation, Red Top Insulation Wool,* and *Fiberglas.*

Installing Flexible Insulation. The fibers in this type of insulation are held in place between two layers of paper. Flexible insulation is made wide enough to fit in the usual stud and rafter spacings of 16, 20, or 24 inches. In case of thinner blankets, that is, ½ inch or ¾ inch in thickness, the material is bent and nailed against the framing members.

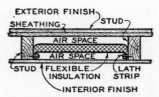

Fig. 2. Application of Flexible Insulation to Frame Construction by Means of Lath Strips Nailed through Insulation into Sides of Framing Members
The flanges must be strong enough to hold nails securely

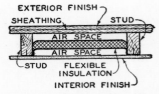

Fig. 3. Application of Flexible Insulation with Nailing Flange to Frame Construction; if Insulation Has Spacer Flange, Two Air Spaces Will Be Provided as Shown When the Interior Finish Is Installed

However, in the case of 2-inch blankets, or thicker, the edges of the paper are cemented and turned up to make a ¾-inch flange on each side. These flanges are rather stiff and are strong enough for nails to be driven through them to hold the insulation in place. In either case, it is advisable to use wood, or lath, strips to insure a tight seal all around the edges, Fig. 2. Some manufacturers create a double ¾-inch fold along the edges, one to nail to the edge of the framing member, the other to act as a spacer, Fig. 3. This form needs to be nailed only lightly as the interior-wall finish will cover the joints. The insulation will be held securely in place also and the joints sealed by the interior-wall covering.

Another way of installing the thinner insulation is to apply it horizontally across the studs, Fig. 4. In this case, wider blankets can be used but it will be necessary to have crosspieces between the framing members to seal the joints.

When flexible insulation is applied to masonry walls it is necessary to use furring strips. In order to create an air space between the insulation and the wall, it is advisable to use 2x2-inch furring strips. The furring strips also keep the paper away from the damp masonry. The insulation can be applied either vertically between the furring strips or horizontally across the strips, as in Fig. 5. If applied horizontally, a second set of 1x2-inch furring strips can be nailed over the insulation to which is fastened the plaster base, Fig. 5. This creates a second air space.

Much of the value of flexible insulation is lost by poor installation. Frequently careless workmen will push the material tightly against the

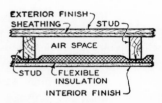

Fig. 4. Application of Flexible Insulation to Face of Studs with Interior Finish Applied Directly over Insulation

This method permits the use of wider blankets but requires cross-pieces to seal the joints

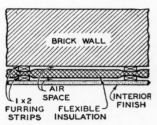

Fig. 5. Alternate Method of Applying Flexible Insulation to Masonry Walls, Using Second Layer of Furring Strips over Insulation to Provide Air Space between Insulation and Interior Finish

sheathing in the stud spaces. Consequently, the insulating value of extra air space on the outside of the insulation material is lost. The insulation material must be sealed tightly in each stud space, not only on the sides but also across the top and at the bottom where the insulation material meets the floor. The purpose of sealing the insulation is to prevent the circulation of air around the material.

FILL INSULATION

Fill Materials. Loose fill insulations are made generally from mineral substances and are supplied in granulated, powdered, cellular, and fibrous wool forms. As the name implies, fill-type insulation is installed so as either to completely or partially fill the spaces between the framing members. The granulated and powder types of fill insulations are necessarily poured into place between the structural members, whereas the fibrous type of loose mineral wool may be hand-packed between the framing members or installed pneumatically. In the case of old buildings, the methods commonly used are the hand-packed or the pneumatic type of installation.

A granulated fill, *mica pellets*, is made from a mineral ore known as *expanded vermiculite* (aluminum magnesium silicated). This type of fill is found on the market under different trade names, such as, *Homart Mineral Fill, Zonolite, Unifil, Porosil,* and *Masterfil.* Another type of fill is *granulated cork.* However, granulated cork is used chiefly in refrigeration.

Powdered-fill and cellular-fill insulations are made chiefly of finely ground gypsum and sold under various trade names, such as, *Thermofill* and *Gold Bond Dry Fill Insulation.*

Rock wool and mineral wool are used as fill, in granulated and nodulated forms, and sold under the same trade names as the flexible-rock and mineral-wool insulation.

Installation of Fills. Fill insulation usually comes in bags and is poured into the stud spaces of the wall as the work of applying the lath or plaster base progresses. For ceilings or attic floors fill can be poured after the plaster base is applied.

Vapor Barrier. A vapor barrier, consisting of a vapor-proof asphalt paper, is advisable for any form of insulation. This vapor barrier should be applied on the inside surface of outside walls. The purpose of a vapor barrier is to prevent the vapor within the building getting into the wall space and insulation where it might condense and form ice. Most flexible insulations now come with such barriers on one side, but for the fill type of insulation the barrier must be provided. This can be done by tacking a piece of vapor-proof asphalt paper to the inside of the stud frame horizontally before applying the lath or plaster base. The barrier should be installed as work progresses on nailing the plaster base in place. Beginning at the bottom of the wall the vapor barrier is applied, then the lath, plaster base, or interior finish, is placed over the paper and nailed. The fill should then be poured from the bags into the stud spaces up to the height of the top edge of the paper barrier. Another piece of asphalt paper is then applied and the plaster base or interior finish nailed in position. Insulation fill is again poured into the stud space until it is filled to the height of the top of the second piece of vapor barrier. This procedure should be repeated until the top of the wall is reached. In the case of ceilings, joists, and rafters the entire area can be covered first with the vapor barrier and then with

Fig. 6. Mica Pellets (Vermiculite) Poured from Bags between the Ceiling Joists; Note the Use of a Template to Gauge the Depth or Thickness of the Insulation

Fig. 7. Fiberglas Granulated Wool Being Applied Pneumatically

Courtesy of Owens-Corning Fiberglas Corp., Toledo, Ohio

the plaster base. Then the fill is applied from above until the joist spaces are filled to whatever depth is desired, Fig. 6.

This type of insulation can be applied also by the pneumatic method, blowing the material into place, Fig. 7. This method is commonly used when insulating old buildings. Boards are removed near the top of the wall and holes bored through the sheathing between the studs in order to get the fill into the wall spaces of old buildings, Fig. 8. The insulation is blown into the wall as shown in the illustration.

Fig. 8. Pneumatic Method of Insulating Existing Walls
with Mineral Wool
Courtesy of Johns-Manville, New York, N.Y.

PADS AND BATS INSULATION

Pads and Bats Materials. Mineral-wool and rock-wool products are made also in small units called *bats* or *pads*. These units are made to fit the standard stud spacing, usually 15 or 23 inches wide by 18, 23, 36, and 48 inches long. The thickness of bats and pads usually varies from $3\frac{5}{8}$ inches to 2 inches. Most bats are backed with vapor-proof paper to provide protection against moisture. They are sold under the same trade names as other mineral-wool or rock-wool insulation products.

Installation of Pads and Bats. Plain bats without paper backing are installed simply by inserting them between framing members. The bats are held in place in walls by fitting them tightly against the sheathing and between the studs. To avoid leaving heat-leaking crevices, adjoining bats should be butted snugly together. Odd-shaped spaces

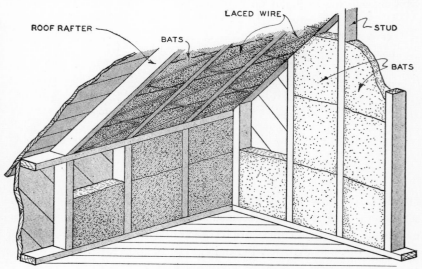

Fig. 9. Mineral-Wool Bats Held in Place under Roof, with Wire Lacing

are filled by breaking the bats to the proper size to fit into such spaces. When plain bats are installed between roof rafters and no interior finish is planned, nails should be driven into the sides of the rafters and staggered on 8-inch centers. Then a soft annealed, galvanized wire should be laced back and forth between the nails to support the bats when they are put in place, Fig. 9. When the bats are installed between ceiling joists from above, the finished ceiling, if previously installed, supports the bats. If ceiling joists are inaccessible from above, the bats may be installed from the under side and a vapor barrier nailed immediately to the under side of the joists to hold the bats in place until the interior finish is installed. A vapor barrier is recommended where plain bats are used. The barrier should be installed on the warm side of the wall or other construction as soon as the bats are in place. A vapor barrier should be used similarly when bats are installed between roof rafters, but it is advisable to hold the bats in place by means of a lacing of wire as previously described rather than to depend upon the vapor barrier to hold the bats, unless an interior finish is to be applied over the vapor barrier.

Most manufacturers now furnish bats with a vapor-proof paper backing which serves not only as a vapor barrier but is used also for

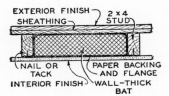

Fig. 10. Application of Wall-Thick Flanged Bats between 4-Inch Studding, with Backing Wider Than Bat to Serve as Flange for Nailing

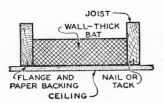

Fig. 11. Application of Wall-Thick Flanged Bats between Ceiling Joists; Bats Are Installed before Ceiling Is Applied

installing the bats. This backing usually is wider than the bat and serves as a flange by which the insulation may be nailed to the framing members. Bats with flanges are installed like blanket insulation except, of course, the bats are in smaller units, Figs. 10 and 11.

RIGID INSULATION BOARD

Rigid Insulation Material, also known as *Structural Insulation Board,* is made out of wood and vegetable fibers, Fig. 12. Many uses have been found for this material. It may be used as wall and roof sheathing to replace wood sheathing; as a plaster base to replace wood, metal, and gypsum lath; and as interior-finish wall covering in place of plaster or wood covering. In addition to these uses rigid insulation board also serves as a thermal insulation whenever applied to outside walls or roof of a building. Table I shows the many sizes, thicknesses, and uses of this building material.

Some of the trade names under which it is sold are: *Weatherwood, Flintkote Insulation Board, Celotex, Fir-Tex, Insulite, J-M Insulating Board, Masonite, Canec,* and many others. The manufacturer of each

TABLE I. SIZES, THICKNESSES AND USES OF INSULATING BOARD PRODUCTS

Product	Sizes	Thicknesses	Type of Edge	Major Uses
Building Board*	4 x 6 ft., 4 x 7 ft. 4 x 8 ft., 4 x 9 ft. 4 x 10 ft., 4 x 12 ft.	½", ¾", 1"	Square	General purpose structural insulating board; interior finish, base for plastic paints, wall coverings and other interior decorative finishes.
Sheathing	4 x 8 ft., 4 x 8½ ft. 4 x 9 ft., 4 x 9½ ft. 4 x 10 ft., 4 x 12 ft.	½", 25/32"	Square	Wall sheathing under siding, brick veneer, shingles or stucco, also as roof sheathing on pitched roofs under various types of roofing. Also to insulate floors of basementless houses.
	2 x 8 ft.	25/32"	Long edges fabricated†, short edges square	
Lath	16" x 48" 18" x 48" 24" x 48"	½", 1"	Long edges fabricated†	Insulating plaster base for walls, partitions and ceilings.
Roof Insulation	23" x 47" Note ‡	½", 1", 1½", 2"	Square edges on ½" thickness. Square edges and/or offset on 1", 1½" and 2" thickness	For roof insulation under built-up roofing on flat roofs and under certain types of roofing on pitched roofs. Floor insulation for masonry floors.
Tileboard (Panels)	8" x 8" 12" x 12" 12" x 24" 16" x 16" 16" x 32"	½", ¾", 1"	Fabricated edges†	Decorative, insulating wall and ceiling panels. Frequently used in conjunction with building board and plank.
Plank	Widths: 8", 10", 12" and 16" Lengths: 6', 8', 10', 12'	½"	Fabricated long edges†	Decorative, insulating wall and ceiling finish. Frequently used in conjunction with building board and tileboard (panels).

*Standard colors and finishes of Building Board are (1) natural finish on both surfaces and (2) one surface natural and the other with light colored finish such as white, ivory, cream or buff.
†Fabricated edges means any type of edge treatment other than square edges without reinforcement.
‡Also available in a 22" x 47" and other sizes.

of these products makes the boards in different sizes and thicknesses with a variety of colors and textures to suit the individual's need.

Application of Rigid Insulation Board. The board is used as thermal insulation in a variety of ways previously mentioned and should be applied according to manufacturers' instructions. The different

Fig. 12. Structural Insulation Board Exterior and Interior Use
Courtesy of Flintkote Company, New York, N.Y.

kinds and lengths of nails recommended for use with different kinds of insulating board are given in Tables II and III.

Wall Sheathing Installation. Today, for insulation on buildings, the boards commonly used are 2x8-foot sheathing $\frac{25}{32}$-inch thick coated with asphalt. These boards have the long edges matched; that is, tongued and grooved or lapped, while the short edges are square. They should first be nailed to the intermediate framing members, spacing the nails six inches on center, and then spacing the nails along the edges four inches on center and $\frac{3}{8}$ inches in from the edges. Drive the nails so the heads are flush with the surface of the insulating board. The

TABLE II. NAILS RECOMMENDED FOR VARIOUS STRUCTURAL INSULATING
BOARD PRODUCTS

Product	Thickness In.	Nails Recommended (See Table 2)
Sheathing..	$\frac{25}{32}$	N
Sheathing..	$\frac{1}{2}$	M
Lath...	$\frac{1}{2}$	K
Lath...	1	L
Building board (nails exposed)....................	$\frac{1}{2}$	A, C or E
Building board (nails exposed)....................	$\frac{3}{4}$ or 1	B, D or F
Building board (nails covered)....................	$\frac{1}{2}$	G, I, M or O
Building board (nails covered)....................	$\frac{3}{4}$ or 1	H, J, N or P
Tileboard (panels) (nails exposed)................	$\frac{1}{2}$	A, C or E
Tileboard (panels) (nails exposed)................	$\frac{3}{4}$ or 1	B, D or F
Plank (nails exposed)............................	$\frac{1}{2}$	A, C or E
Roof insulation.................................	$\frac{1}{2}$	M
Roof insulation.................................	1	N

TABLE III. DESCRIPTION OF NAILS USED FOR STRUCTURAL INSULATING
BOARD PRODUCTS

No.	Name	Length In.	Size	Gage	Head	No. per Pound
A	Brad*................	$1\frac{1}{4}$	3d	14	11 ga.	568
B	Brad*................	$1\frac{3}{4}$	5d	$12\frac{1}{2}$	$9\frac{1}{2}$ ga.	271
C	Finishing.............	$1\frac{1}{4}$	3d	$15\frac{1}{2}$	$12\frac{1}{2}$ ga.	807
D	Finishing.............	$1\frac{3}{4}$	5d	15	12 ga.	500
E	Cadmium-plated "Insulation Board" nail diamond point....	$1\frac{1}{4}$	..	17	$\frac{5}{32}''$	1139
F	Cadmium-plated "Insulation Board" nail diamond point....	$1\frac{3}{4}$	..	17	$\frac{5}{32}''$	831
G	Box..................	$1\frac{1}{2}$	4d	14	$\frac{7}{32}''$	473
H	Box..................	2	6d	$12\frac{1}{2}$	$\frac{17}{64}''$	236
I	Common..............	$1\frac{1}{2}$	4d	$12\frac{1}{2}$	$\frac{1}{4}''$	316
J	Common..............	2	6d	$11\frac{1}{2}$	$\frac{17}{64}''$	181
K	Blued plasterboard......	$1\frac{1}{4}$	..	13	$\frac{5}{16}''$	387
L	Blued plasterboard......	$1\frac{3}{4}$	..	13	$\frac{5}{16}''$	291
M	Galvanized roofing......	$1\frac{1}{2}$	..	11	$\frac{7}{16}''$	163
N	Galvanized roofing......	2	..	11	$\frac{7}{16}''$	128
O	Galvanized shingle......	$1\frac{1}{2}$	4d	12	$\frac{9}{32}''$	274
P	Galvanized shingle......	2	6d	12	$\frac{9}{32}''$	204

*Galvanized Brads should be used where available as the heads are less conspicuous.

boards should be fitted tightly around all openings and all cracks should be sealed and flashed. Boards which are uncoated should be moistened lightly in dry weather, as directed by the manufacturer's instructions.

The builder will find it more economical to use 4x8-foot sheathing, 4x9-foot sheathing, or even larger sheets if the building is low enough so these sheets can be used vertically with each sheet covering the full

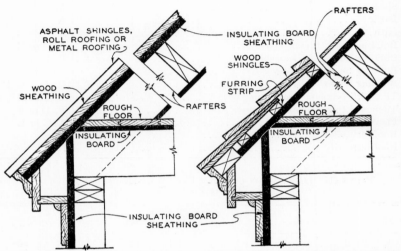

Fig. 13. Two Sections through Eaves of Roofs Showing Wood Sheathing over Insulating Board to Receive Asphalt Shingles and Other Types of Roofing, and Shingle Lath over Insulating Board to Receive Shingles or Slate

height. Nail these sheets to the intermediate studs first, spacing the nails six inches on center, then spacing the nails along the edges three inches on center, and $\frac{3}{8}$ inch in from the outer edge.

Insulation boards should never be forced into place. Between adjoining boards and at the ends of the boards $\frac{1}{8}$-inch spaces should be left. Most insulating boards are cut scant in width and length to allow for this spacing.

Pitched Roof Installation. Where structural insulating board is to be applied directly to roof rafters of pitched roofs, either the four-foot wide wall sheathing or building board may be used. The boards should be applied lengthwise and directly to all framing members with ample bearing for nailing along all edges. Nail to intermediate framing members first, spacing the nails six inches on center; then along all edges spacing nails three inches on center, ⅜ inch from outer edges of wall sheathing. When wood shingles or slate are to cover the roof, 1x3-inch nailing strips must be applied over the insulation board. Asphalt shingles, roll or metal roofing, or tiles require the installation of solid wood sheathing over which these types of roofing material are laid, Fig. 13.

Flat Roof or Deck Installation. The structural-insulating board is designed especially as an insulation under built-up roofing. The most common size is 23x47 inches and the thicknesses are ½, 1, 1½, and 2

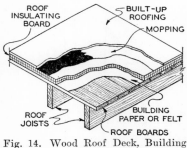

Fig. 14. Wood Roof Deck, Building Paper or Felt, Roof Insulation Board and Built-Up Roofing

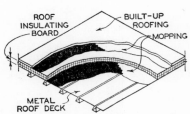

Fig. 15. Metal Roof Deck, Roof Insulation Board, and Built-Up Roofing

inches. Frequently the regular structural board 2x8-foot sheathing is used. This board is used as insulation over wood, monolithic concrete, precast concrete, gypsum structural board, and steel decks.

It is advisable to use a vapor barrier over the deck and under the insulation. Where the insulation is to be applied in one layer, the entire roof area should be covered with two plies (lapped half) of heavy vapor-proof asphalt paper. The roof deck should be mopped with either hot asphalt or coal tar. However, coal-tar pitch and asphalt should not be used together on the same job. Each piece of insulation board should be embedded firmly in the hot bituminous mopping, Figs. 14 and 15. Over the top of this mopping the built-up roofing is laid according to whatever specifications are desired.

When used as lath for a plaster base for walls, rigid insulating board should be applied with long edges at right angles to the framing or furring strips. Manufacturers' instructions should be followed where lath with special joints are used.

Structural insulating-board products used as interior finish include: building board, plank, and tileboard, the latter being known as *panels*. The proper application of insulating board for interior-finish purposes is important. To obtain the best results, the specific instructions of the manufacturer, of each particular product used, should be followed.

Fig. 16. Commercial Sizes of Corkboard
Courtesy of Armstrong Cork Co., Lancaster, Pa.

SLAB INSULATION

Slab Insulation Materials. These slabs are small rigid units usually one to four inches or even more in thickness and ranging from 12x32 inches to 20x96 inches in size. These slabs are fire and moisture resistant, termite proof, and sealed against attack by fungus growth. This type of insulation is used principally for refrigeration and cold storage construction work. There are several types of this product available. (1) *Corkboard*, made from the bark of the cork oak by grinding the bark and compressing it while at the same time subjecting it to high heat. The heat liquefies the gum or rosin which binds the granules together and also seals them, producing a solid slab of pure corkboard, Fig. 16. It is sold under the various manufacturers' names, such as, *Armstrong's Corkboard; Corkduc* (Cork Import Co.) ; *Jointite* (Mundet

Cork Corp.) ; and others. (2) *Wood Fiber and Cement,* made by combining shredded wood or wood fibers with fire-resisting Portland cement.
Thermax and *Porex* are examples of this type of slab insulation.
(3) *Rockwool Slab,* made from rock wool, wood pulp, and asphaltic
binder. One such product is called *rock cork* and is manufactured by
the Johns-Manville Company. (4) *Rigid Insulation Slab* is made of
the same materials as the structural-insulation board, but differs in the
thickness and size of the sheets, and is of low density. It is manufactured by the makers of the structural-insulation board.

Installation of Slab Insulation. Slabs are designed for special purposes and are not in general use in building. As a special type of insulation, each manufacturer always recommends his own particular method
for its application. These detailed instructions, of course, should be followed carefully. In many cases these instructions for installing the
slabs require the use of special clips or other fastening provided by the
manufacturer. Oftentimes nailing is impractical because of the rigid
form and thickness of most slab-insulation materials. However, slabs
usually are held firmly in place by the use of cement.

REFLECTIVE INSULATION

Reflective Insulation Materials. The reflective materials are distinguished from other types by the fact that, to be effective, they must
always be installed in conjunction with air spaces so that the reflective
surface is exposed to an air space of comparatively large size. The principle of this insulation is that of reflecting the radiated heat. An absolutely black body or surface absorbs all the radiation which strikes it
and reflects or transmits none. Bright metallic reflective surfaces, such
as aluminum foil, have low absorption and are more efficient than the
nonmetallic reflective surfaces such as wood. Reflective insulations
now on the market are of four general types, namely:

1) Aluminum foil found under the trade names of *Alfol,* a crimped
blanket of one or two layers of reflective insulation; *Metallation,* a
Reynolds Metals Insulation, consisting of heavy flat foil mounted on
one or both sides of heavy kraft paper with asphalt; *Ecod Metal Lath,*
a plaster base consisting of steel reinforcing wire, backed with metalated
(aluminum foil) kraft paper; *Reflect-O,* an aluminum-colored paper
similar to reflective insulation.

2) *Aluminum Foil-Surfaced Plaster Board,* a gypsum wallboard

with aluminum-foil surface. It is available in large-sized sheets up to 48 inches wide and 12 feet long, also in small plaster-base or lath sizes 16x32 or 16x48 inches. In addition to the gypsum board is the structural insulation-sheathing board with an aluminum foil on one side.

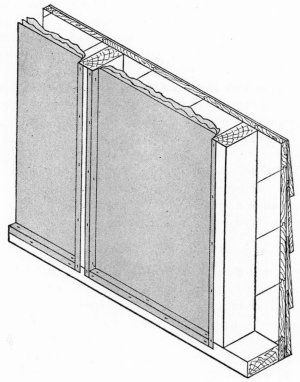

Fig. 17. Application of Two Layers of Alfol Insulation and One Layer of Vapor Barrier
Courtesy of Alfol Insulation Co., Inc., New York, N.Y.

3) *Ferro-Therm,* a dull sheet-metal type of reflective insulation made of sheet steel coated with an alloy of lead and tin for protection against corrosion.

4) *Blanket or Flexible Reflective Insulation* is the same as blanket and flexible insulation, except that the surface of the paper is covered with an aluminum reflective material.

Installing of Reflective Insulation. Reflective insulations are usually installed in much the same manner as flexible insulations; that is, either between and fastened to the sides of framing members or fastened to the edges of framing members. It should be remembered that proper installation is particularly important with this type of insulation because, to be of value, the reflective surfaces must always be exposed to an air space of appreciable size. To be of maximum value, the air space should be an inch or more in width because the value of reflective insulation diminishes as the width of the air space decreases below one inch. As the width of the air space to which the reflective surface is exposed diminishes toward zero, the insulating value of the reflective material likewise diminishes toward zero; that is, no value. Reflective insulation should be installed in such a manner as to divide the air

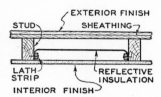

Fig. 18. Application of Reflective Insulation between Framing Members Using Lath Strips

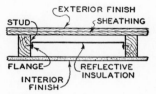

Fig. 19. Application of Reflective Insulations with Flanges between Framing Members

space into two air spaces, and, when thus installed, the value will be greater if both sides of the material are reflective instead of only one.

The method of application of Type II *Alfol*, with two *Alfol* layers and a vapor barrier, is shown in Fig. 17. Note the vapor barrier is on the inside with the reflective surface exposed to the air space. The method of installing a single curtain reflective insulation, using lath strips and nailing through the strips to the sides of the studs, is shown in Fig. 18. A method of application suitable for *Ferro-Therm* or *Reynolds Metal Insulation* is shown in Fig. 19. In this case the reflective insulation has flanges for nailing or stapling the material to the sides of the studs. The foregoing methods usually are suitable also for application of these materials to furring strips of masonry walls, to ceiling joists, or to roof rafters. Insulating lath of the reflective type are installed in the same manner as insulating board lath, with the reflective surface exposed to the air space and with plaster applied to the other surface. The blanket, or flexible, reflective type is installed in the same manner as the blanket and flexible type except that in the reflective type the surface of the paper is covered with aluminum foil.

MISCELLANEOUS INSULATIONS

Sprayo-Flake. A specially constructed air gun is used to apply *Sprayo-Flake* to any surface, such as wood, masonry, or metal, Fig. 20. These fibrous flakes are forcibly projected with the air gun simultaneously with an atomized adhesive. When the confetti-like flakes leave

Fig. 20. Sprayo-Flake Application
Courtesy of Sprayo-Flake Co., Chicago, Ill.

the nozzle of the air gun, they are coated with the atomized adhesive and when blown against the surface to be insulated a cellular blanket can be built up to any thickness desired.

Precast Masonry Units. There are a number of lightweight masonry units which have insulation value due to their cellular construction or the lightweight properties of the aggregates of which they are made, Fig. 21. The lightweight aggregates available include: *Haydite*, a lightweight burned clay aggregate; *Celocrete* is an aggregate made by converting molten blast-furnace slag into hard, cellular clinkers which are crushed and screened to commercial sizes; *Waylite,* a light-weight aggregate produced by passing molten blast-furnace slag through a processing machine in which it is centrifuged and beaten in an atmosphere of steam. When mixed with Portland cement and cast into building units, these lightweight aggregates have the required strength for wall construction as well as thermal heat insulation qualities.

Another form of masonry unit is the glass block known in the trade as *Insulux,* Fig. 22. Another kind is known as *Architectural Glass.*

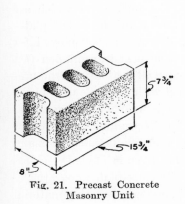

Fig. 21. Precast Concrete
Masonry Unit

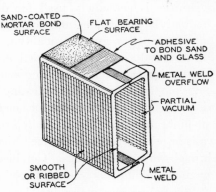

SAND-COATED
MORTAR BOND
SURFACE

FLAT BEARING
SURFACE

ADHESIVE
TO BOND SAND
AND GLASS

METAL WELD
OVERFLOW

PARTIAL
VACUUM

SMOOTH
OR RIBBED
SURFACE

METAL
WELD

Fig. 22. Insulux Glass Block
Courtesy of Owens-Illinois Glass Co., Chicago, Ill.

These glass units, molded into two half blocks and hermetically sealed into a single unit at the time of manufacture, are finished on the mortar-bearing surface with a gritty mortar bond. The glass block is used in wall construction to produce attractive, light-transmitting panels. Because of the partial vacuum in the blocks, they have thermal insulation value in addition to being resistant to sound transmission. Glass blocks generally are translucent, but transparent blocks are obtainable.

COMPARATIVE VALUES OF INSULATION

The more or less exact method of comparing insulations enters into a field of engineering which is beyond the scope of this book and probably beyond the interest of the average builder. However, considerable information is available[1] to the public. This information is the result of experiments by reliable laboratories of the United States Govern-

---

[1] *Building Insulation,* by Paul D. Close, American Technical Society, 1946.

ment, state universities, and private industries. It is advisable to make sure that the proper type of insulation is selected and that it is properly installed. This will avoid trouble with condensation that might arise in cold climates if walls are too heavily insulated.

Methods of Testing. The apparatus most commonly used for testing building materials, insulations, and compound structures is of three types: (1) the guarded hot-plate apparatus; (2) the guarded hot-box apparatus; and (3) the Nicholls heat meter. The guarded *hot-plate apparatus* is commonly used for determining the surface-to-surface conductivity or conductance of materials, the surfaces of which are smooth enough to give reasonably good contact between the test plates and the material. The guarded *hot-box apparatus* is employed for determining the over-all *air to air* coefficient of heat transmission (U) and is particularly adapted to testing built-up wall sections or structures whose surfaces are too rough for good contact with the plate used in the hot-plate method. The *Nicholls heat meter* is used for testing actual walls or other structures in place; that is, for determining the heat flow through walls of buildings. Conductivities and conductances of many common building materials and insulations are given in Table IV. Most of these values were determined by means of the hot-plate apparatus.

Coefficient of Conductivity. Every building and insulating material has a certain heat transmission value which depends on the nature or character of the substance of which it is composed, the condition of subdivision and density of the material, the moisture content, mean temperature, and other factors. This heat transmission value is represented numerically in each case by a coefficient, known as the *coefficient of thermal conductivity;* for brevity this is usually referred to as *conductivity* of material. A coefficient of any material is simply a numerical quantity expressed in terms of certain units, such as a unit of time, unit of length, unit of area, or unit of thickness. Thus the coefficient of thermal conductivity of a material is the number of heat units (B.t.u.) that will pass through *one square foot* of the material, *one inch thick,* in *one hour* for a *one degree Fahrenheit temperature* difference between the two surfaces. The coefficient of conductivity is designated by the letter k.

The coefficient of transmission of any type of construction can be determined by actual test in either the hot-box apparatus or by means

TABLE IV CONDUCTIVITIES (k) OF INSULATING MATERIALS

These constants are expressed in Btu per hour per square foot per degree Fahrenheit temperature difference.

Material	Description	Density (Lbs. per Cu. Ft.)	Mean Temperature Deg. Fahrenheit	Conductivity (k)	Resistance (R)	Authority*
Balsam Wool..	Chemically treated wood fibers between layers of strong paper..............	3.6	70	0.25	4.00	(3)
Cabot's Quilt.	Zostera Marina (eel grass) between kraft paper.......	4.60	90	0.26	3.85	(1)
Cabot's Quilt.	Zostera Marina (eel grass) between kraft paper.......	3.40	90	0.25	4.00	(1)
Celotex.......	Insulating board made from sugar cane fiber...........	13.5	70	0.33	3.03	(3)
Cotton Seed..	Loose Hulls.................	4.43	86	0.31	3.22	(1)
Corkboard....	No added binder............	10.6	90	0.30	3.33	(1)
Corkboard....	No added binder............	7.0	90	0.27	3.70	(1)
Corkboard....	No added binder............	5.4	90	0.25	4.00	(1)
Dry Zero.....	Flexible insulation of kapok.	1.00	90	0.24	4.17	(1)
Dry Zero.....	Flexible insulation of kapok.	1.90	75	0.23	4.35	(3)
Dry Zero.....	Flexible insulation of kapok.	1.60	75	0.24	4.17	(3)
Hairinsul.....	100% Cattle hair............	13.0	90	0.26	3.84	(1)
Hairinsul.....	75% Cattle hair, 25% jute....	6.30	90	0.27	3.70	(1)
Hairinsul.....	50% Cattle hair, 50% jute....	6.10	90	0.26	3.85	(1)
Homasote....	Insulating board of wood and other vegetable fibers.....	25.0	75	0.375	2.66	(3)
Housfil.......	Expanded vermiculite.......	5.62	75	0.38	2.63	(3)
Insulating Boards.....	½ in. insulating boards without special finish*f* (eleven samples).................	16.5 to 21.8	90	0.33 to 0.40	3.03 to 2.50	(1)
	1 in. insulating board*a*.......	13.2	..	0.34	2.94	(4)
Insulite......	Insulating board made from wood fiber...............	16.0	70	0.33	3.03	(4)
Kimsul.......	Flexible insulation consisting of creped layers stitched together..................	1.5	70	0.27	3.70	(3)
Lockaire (Maftex)........	Insulating board made from licorice root.............	16.1	81	0.34	2.94	(3)
Maizewood...	Insulating board made from cornstalks...............	15.0	71	0.33	3.03	(3)
Masonite.....	Insulating board made from exploded wood fibers......	15.0	75	0.33	3.03	(3)
Mineral Wool.	3 in. mineral wool bats, barrier lapped on warm side; horizontal position*b*.......	3.67	..	0.30	3.33	(4)
	3 in. mineral wool bats, barrier laid on warm side; horizontal position*b*.......	2.24	..	0.26	3.84	(4)
	3 in. mineral wool bats, barrier laid on warm side; vertical position*b*...........	2.24	..	0.25	4.00	(4)

TABLE IV. CONDUCTIVITIES (k) OF INSULATING MATERIALS—*Continued*

These constants are expressed in Btu per hour per square foot per degree Fahrenheit temperature difference.

Material	Description	Density (Lbs. per Cu. Ft.)	Mean Temperature Deg. Fahrenheit	Conductivity (k)	Resistance (R)	Authority*
Mineral Wool .	4 in. mineral wool bats, barrier lapped on warm side; horizontal position[b]	3.0	..	0.31	3.22	(4)
	4 in. mineral wool bats, barrier lapped on warm side; vertical position[b]	3.0	..	0.33	3.03	(4)
	4 in. mineral wool bats, no barriers; horizontal[b]	1.77	..	0.30	3.33	(4)
	Hand applied granular mineral wool 2 in. to 6 in. thick; horizontal position[b]. No covering.	6.05 to 7.13	.. ..	0.30 to 0.33	3.33 to 3.03	(4)
	4 in. machine blown granular mineral wool, horizontal position[b]. No covering. . . .	5.74	..	0.30	3.33	(4)
	Rock wool.	10.0	90	0.27	3.70	(1)
Natur-temp. .	Cotton insulating batt.	0.875	72	0.24	4.17	(3)
Natur zone ..	Treated hog hair covered with film of asphalt.	10.0	75	0.28	3.57	(3)
Nu-Wood.	Insulating board, wood fiber.	15.0	72	0.33	3.03	(3)
Palco Wool. . .	Fill insulation made from shredded redwood bark. . . .	3.00	90	0.31	3.22	(1)
	Fill insulation made from shredded redwood bark . . .	5.00	75	0.26	3.84	(3)
Red Top Wool	Glass wool 0.0003 in. to 0.0006 in. in diameter.	1.5	75	0.27	3.70	(3)
Regranulated Cork.	About 3/16″ particles.	8.10	90	0.31	3.22	(1)
Rock Cork. . . .	Rock wool with a binding agent.	14.5	77	0.33	3.03	(1)
Sprayo-Flake.	Paper and asbestos fibers with emulsified asphalt binder. .	4.2	94	0.28	3.57	(1)
Temlok.	Insulating board made from wood fiber.	15.0	70	0.33	3.03	(3)
Thermax.	Slab insulation made from shredded wood and cement.	24.2	72	0.46	2.17	(3)
Thermofill. . . .	Powdered gypsum fill.	34.0	90	0.60	1.67	(1)
Thermofill. . . .	Powdered gypsum fill.	26.0	90	0.52	0.92	(1)
Thermofill. . . .	Powdered gypsum fill.	24.0	75	0.48	2.08	(3)
Thermofill. . . .	Powdered gypsum fill.	19.8	90	0.35	2.86	(1)
Thermofill. . . .	Powdered gypsum fill.	18.0	75	0.34	2.94	(3)
Vermiculite. . .	Expanded vermiculite.	. . . .	..	0.48	2.08	(1)
	Expanded vermiculite, particle size −3 +14.	6.2	..	0.32	3.12	(4)
Weatherwood.	Insulating board, wood fiber.	15.2	70	0.33	3.03	(3)

of the Nicholls heat meter. However, with hundreds of different materials and their varying thicknesses entering into construction, it is impossible to make individual tests of all conceivable types of wall structure, since to test every type of construction material would be an endless task. Therefore, it is necessary to determine the best transmission coefficients of different types of construction by calculation, using an approved method of checking results.

Comparison of Conductivities. It is common practice to compare the conductivities of various insulating materials. While it is true that a lower conductivity means greater heat resistance, conductivities alone do not necessarily afford a reliable basis of comparison. In making comparisons other factors to be taken into consideration include: the thickness of materials installed, the manner of installation, materials replaced, if any, and increase or decrease in the number of air spaces in the construction due to the installation of the insulation.

Heat transmission tests to be reliable must be made by an experienced and accredited laboratory; otherwise the results obtained may not be acceptable to an experienced builder. Certain insulating materials are listed in Table IV. All of these materials have been tested in accredited laboratories indicated as (*1*), (*2*), (*3*), (*4*), and (*5*) under the head *Authority*. The names of the authorities are given under the head *Notes for Table IV*.

Heat transmission coefficients (*U*) of a few common types of construction are given in Table V. However, this table gives only one

NOTES FOR TABLE IV

* AUTHORITIES:
    (1) U. S. Bureau of Standards, tests based on samples submitted by manufacturers.
    (2) A. C. Willard, L. C. Lichty and L. A. Harding, tests conducted at the University of Illinois.
    (3) J. C. Peebles, tests conducted at Armour Institute of Technology, based on samples submitted by manufacturers.
    (4) F. B. Rowley, et al, tests conducted at the University of Minnesota.
    (5) A.S.H.V.E. Research Laboratory.
    a See Thermal Conductivity of Building Materials, by F. B. Rowley and A. B. Algren (University of Minnesota *Engineering Experimental Station Bulletin* No. 12).
    b Heat Transmission Through Insulation as Affected by Orientation of Walls, by F. B. Rowley and C. E. Lund (A.S.H.V.E. JOURNAL SECTION OF *Heating, Piping & Air Conditioning*, July, 1943).
    c The Effect of Convection in Ceiling Insulation, by G. B. Wilkes and L. R. Vianey (A.S.H.V.E. JOURNAL SECTION OF *Heating, Piping & Air Conditioning*, February, 1943).
    d See A.S.H.V.E. RESEARCH REPORT No. 915—Conductivity of Concrete, by F. C. Houghten and Carl Gutberlet (A.S.H.V.E. TRANSACTIONS, Vol. 38, 1932, p. 47).
    e Recommended value. (See Heating, Ventilating and Air Conditioning, by Harding and Willard, revised edition, 1932).
    f See BMS13, U.S. Department of Commerce, National Bureau of Standards, Washington, D.C.
    g Roofing, 0.15 in. thick (1.34 lb. per square foot), covered with gravel (0.83 lb. per square foot), combined thickness assumed 0.25.
    h Conductance values for horizontal air spaces depend on whether the heat flow is upward or downward, but in most cases it is sufficiently accurate to use the same values for horizontal as for vertical air spaces.

Table V. Coefficients of Transmission (*U*) of Frame Walls

Coefficients are expressed in Btu per hour per square foot per degree Fahrenheit difference in temperature between the air on the two sides, and are based on a wind velocity of 15 mph.

No Insulation between Studs[a] (See Table VI)

Exterior Finish	Interior Finish	TYPE OF SHEATHING: Gypsum (½ In. Thick) A	Ply-wood (5/16 In. Thick) B	Wood[f] (25/32 In. Thick) Bldg. Paper C	Insu-lating Board (25/32 In. Thick) D	Wall Number
WOOD SIDING (Clapboard)	Metal Lath and Plaster[b]	0.33	0.32	0.26	0.20	**1**
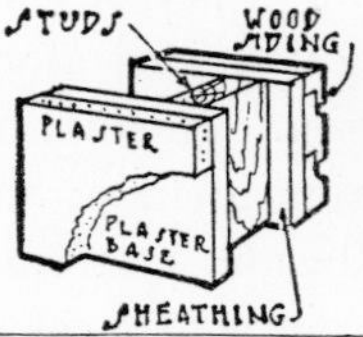	Gypsum Board (⅜ in.) Decorated	0.32	0.32	0.25	0.20	**2**
	Wood Lath and Plaster	0.31	0.31	0.25	0.19	**3**
	Gypsum Lath (⅜ in.) Plastered[c]	0.31	0.31	0.25	0.19	**4**
	Plywood (⅜ in.) Plain or Decorated	0.30	0.30	0.24	0.19	**5**
	Insulating Board (½ in.) Plain or Decorated	0.23	0.23	0.19	0.16	**6**
	Insulating Board Lath (½ in.) Plastered[c]	0.22	0.22	0.19	0.15	**7**
	Insulating Board Lath (1 in.) Plastered[c]	0.17	0.17	0.15	0.12	**8**
WOOD[d] SHINGLES	Metal Lath and Plaster[b]	0.25	0.25	0.26	0.17	**9**
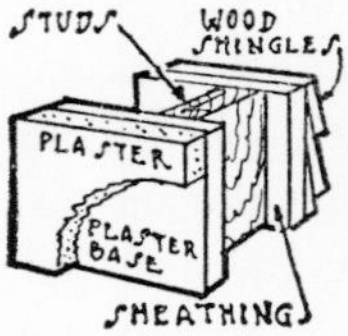	Gypsum Board (⅜ in.) Decorated	0.25	0.25	0.25	0.17	**10**
	Wood Lath and Plaster	0.24	0.24	0.25	0.16	**11**
	Gypsum Lath (⅜ in.) Plastered[c]	0.24	0.24	0.25	0.16	**12**
	Plywood (⅜ in.) Plain or Decorated	0.24	0.24	0.24	0.16	**13**
	Insulating Board (½ in.) Plain or Decorated	0.19	0.19	0.19	0.14	**14**
	Insulating Board Lath (½ in.) Plastered[c]	0.19	0.18	0.19	0.13	**15**
	Insulating Board Lath (1 in.) Plastered[c]	0.14	0.14	0.15	0.11	**16**
STUCCO	Metal Lath and Plaster[b]	0.43	0.42	0.32	0.23	**17**
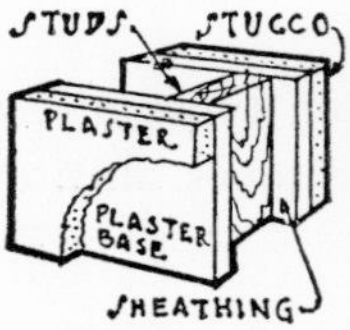	Gypsum Board (⅜ in.) Decorated	0.42	0.41	0.31	0.23	**18**
	Wood Lath and Plaster	0.40	0.39	0.30	0.22	**19**
	Gypsum Lath (⅜ in.) Plastered[c]	0.39	0.39	0.30	0.22	**20**
	Plywood (⅜ in.) Plain or Decorated	0.39	0.38	0.29	0.22	**21**
	Insulating Board (½ in.) Plain or Decorated	0.27	0.27	0.22	0.18	**22**
	Insulating Board Lath (½ in.) Plastered[c]	0.26	0.26	0.22	0.17	**23**
	Insulating Board Lath (1 in.) Plastered[c]	0.19	0.19	0.16	0.14	**24**
BRICK VENEER[e]	Metal Lath and Plaster[b]	0.37	0.36	0.28	0.21	**25**
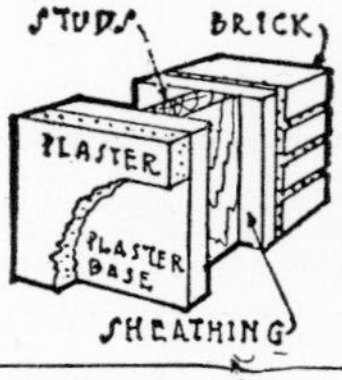	Gypsum Board (⅜ in.) Decorated	0.36	0.36	0.28	0.21	**26**
	Wood Lath and Plaster	0.35	0.34	0.27	0.20	**27**
	Gypsum Lath (⅜ in.) Plastered[c]	0.34	0.34	0.27	0.20	**28**
	Plywood (⅜ in.) Plain or Decorated	0.34	0.33	0.27	0.20	**29**
	Insulating Board (½ in.) Plain or Decorated	0.25	0.25	0.21	0.17	**30**
	Insulating Board Lath (½ in.) Plastered[c]	0.24	0.24	0.20	0.16	**31**
	Insulating Board Lath (1 in.) Plastered[c]	0.18	0.18	0.15	0.13	**32**

[a]Coefficients not weighted; effect of studding neglected.
[b]Plaster assumed ¾ in. thick.
[c]Plaster assumed ½ in. thick.
[d]Furring strips between wood shingles and all sheathings except wood.
[e]Small air space and mortar between building paper and brick veneer neglected.
[f]Nominal thickness, 1 in.

TABLE VI. COEFFICIENTS OF TRANSMISSION (U) OF FRAME WALLS WITH INSULATION BETWEEN FRAMING[a, b]

Coefficients are expressed in Btu per hour per square foot per degree Fahrenheit difference in temperature between the air on the two sides, and are based on a wind velocity of 15 mph.

COEFFICIENT WITH *NO* INSULATION BETWEEN FRAMING	COEFFICIENT WITH INSULATION BETWEEN FRAMING				Number
	BLANKET OR BAT INSULATION BETWEEN FRAMING [c] (Thickness below)			3⅝ IN. LOOSE MINERAL WOOL BETWEEN FRAMING	
	1 In.	2 In.	3 In.		
	A	B	C	D	
0.11	0.078	0.064	0.055	0.051	33
0.12	0.083	0.067	0.057	0.054	34
0.13	0.088	0.070	0.059	0.056	35
0.14	0.092	0.073	0.061	0.058	36
0.15	0.097	0.075	0.062	0.059	37
0.16	0.10	0.077	0.065	0.060	38
0.17	0.10	0.080	0.066	0.062	39
0.18	0.11	0.082	0.068	0.063	40
0.19	0.11	0.084	0.069	0.064	41
0.20	0.12	0.087	0.070	0.066	42
0.21	0.12	0.088	0.072	0.067	43
0.22	0.12	0.090	0.073	0.069	44
0.23	0.12	0.093	0.074	0.069	45
0.24	0.12	0.094	0.076	0.070	46
0.25	0.13	0.095	0.076	0.072	47
0.26	0.13	0.096	0.077	0.072	48
0.27	0.14	0.097	0.078	0.073	49
0.28	0.14	0.098	0.078	0.073	50
0.29	0.14	0.10	0.080	0.075	51
0.30	0.14	0.10	0.080	0.075	52
0.31	0.14	0.10	0.082	0.076	53
0.32	0.15	0.10	0.082	0.076	54
0.33	0.15	0.11	0.083	0.077	55
0.34	0.15	0.11	0.083	0.078	56
0.35	0.15	0.11	0.085	0.078	57
0.36	0.16	0.11	0.085	0.079	58
0.37	0.16	0.11	0.087	0.080	59
0.38	0.16	0.11	0.087	0.080	60
0.39	0.16	0.11	0.087	0.081	61
0.40	0.16	0.11	0.088	0.082	62
0.41	0.16	0.11	0.088	0.082	63
0.42	0.16	0.11	0.088	0.082	64
0.43	0.17	0.11	0.090	0.083	65
0.44	0.17	0.12	0.090	0.083	66

[a]This table may be used for determining the coefficients of transmission of frame constructions with the types and thicknesses of insulation indicated in Columns A to D inclusive between framing. Columns A, B and C may be used for walls, ceilings or roofs with only one air space between framing but are not applicable to ceilings with *no* flooring above. Column D is applicable to walls only. *Example:* Find the coefficient of transmission of a frame wall consisting of wood siding, $^{25}\!/_{42}$ in. insulating board sheathing, studs, gypsum lath and plaster, with 2 in. blanket insulation between studs. According to Table V, a wall of this construction with *no insulation* between studs has a coefficient of 0.19 (Wall No. 4D). Referring to Column B above, it will be found that a wall of this value with 2 in. blanket insulation between the studs has a coefficient of 0.084.

[b]Coefficients corrected for 2x4 framing, 16 in. o. c.

[c]Based on one air space between framing.

Copyright, American Society of Heating and Ventilating Engineers—From Chapter 4, Heating Ventilating, and Air Conditioning Guide, 1944 measure of comparison of insulation materials and should not be relied on entirely. Heat transmission coefficients (*U*) for the same types of construction (Table V) with insulation between framing members are given in Table VI. A careful study of the example given in the footnote, Table VI, will help the student to understand how to apply the information given in Tables V and VI.[1]

CHECKING ON YOUR KNOWLEDGE

The following questions give you the opportunity to check up on yourself. If you have read the chapter carefully, you should be able to answer the questions. If you have any difficulty, read the chapter over once more so that you have the information well in mind before you go on with your reading.

DO YOU KNOW

1. The trade names of three or more types of reflective insulation?
2. Some of the requirements for installing reflective insulation in order to insure satisfactory results?
3. The most common use of rigid insulation?
4. The method commonly used when applying mineral wool insulation to old buildings?
5. The names and classification of six popular types of insulating material?
6. The purpose of vapor barriers? What types of vapor barriers are most effective?
7. To what classification *Cabot's Quilt* belongs? When and where Cabot's Quilt was first manufactured? From what it takes its name?
8. What type of insulation is used principally for refrigeration and cold-storage construction work?
9. The names of three types of precast-masonry units which have insulation value?
10. How building materials are tested for heat conductivity?
11. Why it is important that flexible insulating material should be applied carefully?
12. Of what materials loose fill insulations are usually made?
13. How plain bats are installed between roof rafters?
14. Where corkboard was first manufactured in the United States?
15. What basic materials are used in the manufacture of the following insulations: *Cabot's Quilt, Celotex, Insulite, Lockaire, Maizewood, Naturtemp, Naturzone, Palco Wool, Sprayo-Flake,* and *Thermax*.

---

[1] All tables used in this chapter were taken from *Building Insulation,* by Paul D. Close, American Technical Society, 1946.

Wood Fastenings

QUESTIONS THIS CHAPTER WILL ANSWER

1. *What did the carpenter use for wood fastenings before nails came into use?*
2. *What devices are used as wood fastenings by the modern carpenter?* 3. *When nailing wood how can splitting be prevented?* 4. *How long is a two-penny nail?* 5. *What is a* Skotch fastener? *What devices are commonly known as* builders' hardware?

INTRODUCTION TO CHAPTER VII

Among the many interesting facts you will study in this chapter is the report of an experiment conducted at the United States Forest Products Laboratory.[1] This report is important not only because of the information gained from the experiment but also because it demonstrates the fact that improvements are taking place continually and new developments are being made steadily in the field of carpentry. This is a fact well worth remembering.

Since carpentry is such an old trade, some people may think its practices are all established and firmly set, and that important improvements are no longer being made. Such a belief is far from the truth. Because the work of the carpenter is practical, it is necessary for him to make every effort possible to improve the efficiency of his methods of construction. Competition in his field requires him to keep up to date.

When you consider that the nail industry still employs the ancient *penny system* to indicate the length of the most commonly used nails, in contrast you must be impressed particularly with the progressive attitude of those engaged in the carpentry industry. On every hand there is evidence of the fact that carpentry is one of the oldest of all trades, and yet it continues to develop new and better tools and methods of construction.

Modern science, such as chemistry, has contributed in many ways to improvements advantageous to the carpentry trade. In this chapter you will learn how different coatings and other treatment applied to nails increase their holding power, reduce corrosion, add sanitary protection, and also improve their appearance. Since World War I chemistry tests have greatly improved the various glues used by the carpenter and cabinetmaker. For example, *casein glue*, which has come prominently into use in recent years, is valued highly by the carpentry trade because of its water resistance; the better grades are highly waterproof, making this glue desirable for use in construction work.

Study this chapter carefully. It contains information which will be of great value to you as a carpenter.

---

[1] United States Forest Products Laboratory, Madison, Wis.

MODERN FASTENING DEVICES

In the process of any construction, whether it is a house, an item of furniture, or any other object, the materials must be fastened together in a more or less permanent manner. Although the carpenter works chiefly with wood, he must sometimes fasten wood to metal, or to concrete, brick or other materials.

In early years the carpenter employed interlocking wood joints which were carefully made and held in place by their own peculiar construction, or wood dowels, or with glue; later, iron nails and bolts came into use. Today we have not only nails, but metal fastening devices of many descriptions, each designed for a special application, yet some serving several uses with satisfactory results.

Fastenings used in carpentry work may be classified as follows:

1. Nails	2. Screws	3. Bolts
4. Anchors	5. Metal wood connectors	6. Builders' hardware
7. Glue	8. Dowels	9. Wood joints

NAILS

The most common method of fastening one wooden member to another is with nails; it is also usually the simplest method, and therefore the quickest, although it may not result in the strongest of joints. It is therefore expedient for the carpenter to be fully familiar with all the characteristic details of nails of various types, for without this knowledge, he will never achieve the status of a master craftsman.

Nails are divided into two general types: wire and cut nails. Hereafter when we refer to a *type* of nail we will be referring to this general category. There are many *kinds* of nails, whose uses will be explained, but nevertheless, all kinds of nails still fall into the two type classifications. *They are either wire nails, or cut nails.*

The three main characteristics of nails that you should know are:

1. The proper name of the nail
2. The appearance of the nail
3. The proper uses of the nail

This knowledge will make your work easier and your construction better. The master carpenter constructs with the *minimum amount of time and material;* it is this which distinguishes him from the poorly trained carpenter.

Nails are made in many different sizes and various shapes of heads, points, and shanks, each type designed for a particular purpose depending upon the nature of the work, the kind of wood into which they are to be driven, and the holding power required.

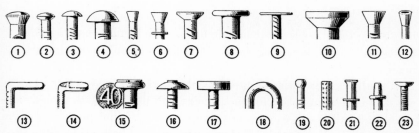

Fig. 1. Nail Heads, Different Types Available: (*1*), (*2*) Oval Countersunk; (*3*) Oval; (*4*) Round; (*5*) Flooring Brad; (*6*) Double-Head Countersunk; (*7*), (*10*), (*11*) Flat Countersunk; (*8*), (*9*) Flat; (*12*) Cupped; (*13*) Metal Lath; (*14*) Hoop Fastener; (*15*) Tree and Pole Dating; (*16*) Umbrella; (*17*) Lead Head; (*18*) Staple; (*19*) Brad; (*20*) Headless; (*21*) Scaffold Anchor; (*22*) Shade Roller Pin; (*23*) Curved

After Continental Steel Corp.

Nail Heads. Examples of a number of different shaped nail heads are shown in Fig. 1. The *flat-headed nail* is the one most commonly used. The *large flat* heads are used for soft materials such as roofing paper, fiber boards, and similar materials. The *brad* and the *deep countersunk head* are used for finish work when nails must be set below the surface. For decorative purposes the *oval-shaped head* is desirable. The *double-* or *duplex-headed nail* is used for temporary work which must be taken apart, including scaffolds and blocking; the extra head, which extends above the surface of the board, is easily hooked by a claw hammer or wrecking bar.

Nail Points. Carpenters and other woodworkers use nails with various types of points as shown in Fig. 2. The *diamond point* is the one most commonly used. The *long diamond point* is found on nails used with parquet flooring, plaster board, hinges, and some roofing materials. Such a point increases the holding power of the nail and also makes the nail easier to drive. Small brads are made with the so-called *needle point.* Boat spikes and large spikes used for various types of woodwork have *chisel points.* Cut nails have *blunt points* as

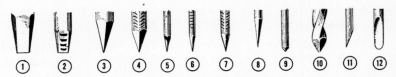

Fig. 2.   Nail Points, Different Types Available: (*1*), (*2*) Chisel; (*3*), (*4*), (*5*), (*6*) Diamond; (*7*) Barbed, Beer-Case; (*8*) Needle; (*9*) Blunt, Shooker; (*10*) Screw; (*11*) Side; (*12*) Duck Bill

After Continental Steel Corp.

do also certain flooring and shingle nails. Clinch nails have the *duck-bill point* which allows clinching of the nail without danger of breaking it.

Usually a nail with a long or needle point will hold better in softwood than a common or diamond-point nail, providing the wood into which the nail is driven does not split easily. A blunt point will cut a path through the wood instead of pushing the fibers aside, thus preventing splitting; however, a blunt point reduces the holding power of a nail.

Shank of Nails.   Since the holding power of a nail depends to a great extent upon the area of the surface of the nail in contact with the wood, various kinds of shanks have been designed to increase this surface, Fig. 3. Among these types of shanks the most common are the *square,* the *longitudinally grooved,* and the *spiral.* Holding power also is increased by *barbing* the shank, or by coating or etching the surface.

There is also the helical shank, which means that it is in the form of a spiral, or that it is screw shaped; and the annular shank which describes it as having a ring, or several protruding rings around the nail shank. Laboratory findings by the Virginia Polytechnic Institute have proven the superior holding power of these nails.

Splitting Prevented.   Many types of wood split easily when nailed. These include practically all of the denser hardwoods and a few of the softwoods, such as white cedar, Douglas fir, and eastern hemlock. However, danger from splitting can be reduced or entirely eliminated by boring a pilot hole, by using lighter gauge or blunt nails, or by dipping the nails in oil or wax. When heavy gauge nails are replaced by lighter gauge nails, in order to insure the same holding power, the lighter gauge nails should be coated or etched.

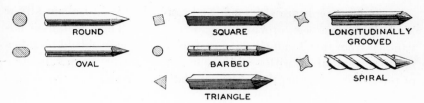

Fig. 3. Nail Shanks, Different Types Available

Experiments made with nails at the United States Forest Products Laboratory show that a good quality of cement coating will increase a nail's resistance to withdrawal immediately after driving it into softwoods from 85 to 100 per cent, as compared to the plain nails. Little holding power is gained by using coated nails in hardwood. This increased resistance partially disappears with passing of time so that after a month or so only about one-half of the increased resistance remains. The chemically etched nail developed at the Forest Products Laboratory has from 180 to 200 per cent higher holding power than a plain nail, in softwoods, and from 90 to 175 per cent more holding power in the denser hardwoods.

Metals, Coatings, and Finishes of Nails. Nails are made of various kinds of metals including steel, brass, copper, and stainless steel. The three last-named will resist different types of corrosion, such as that caused by exposure to salt brine, acids, alkaline solutions, or fumes.

Different coatings and treatments are applied to steel nails to increase their holding power, reduce corrosion, add sanitary protection, and improve appearance. Coatings and finishes now in use are as follows:

Cement-coated	Cadmium-plated
Resinous coatings	Nickel-plated
Acid etching	Chromium-plated
Galvanized	Blued
Copperplated	Painted
Tin-coated	Parkerized
Brass-plated	Japanned

Besides the various finishes, some nails are also hardened so they can be driven into concrete or masonry while others are annealed to soften them so they can be riveted.

Aluminum nails are also made and can be had in just about all the kinds that have been previously made of steel. There is a great advantage from the standpoint of non-rusting, but care should be taken not to use aluminum with certain other metals, such as copper, because of the risk electrolysis; that is to say, that the metal would tend to decompose.

Sizes and Weights of Nails. The nail industry still adheres to the ancient *penny system* to indicate the length of the most commonly used nails, ranging in length from one inch to six inches. This penny system originated in England. Two explanations are offered as to how this curious designation came about. One is that the six penny, four penny, ten penny, and so forth, nails derived their names from the fact that one hundred nails cost sixpence, fourpence, and so on. The other explanation, which is more probable, is that one thousand tenpenny nails,

TABLE I. COMMONLY USED NAILS, THEIR SIZE, GAUGE, AND NUMBER PER POUND

PENNY SIZE	LENGTH IN INCHES FOR COMMON, BOX AND FINISH*	COMMON NAILS			 BOX AND CASING NAILS 		
		Gauge	Thickness in Thousandths	Number per Pound	Gauge	Thickness in Thousandths	Number per Pound
2d	1	15	.072	876	15½	.069	1010
3d	1¼	14	.083	568	14½	.078	635
4d	1½	12½	.102	316	14	.083	473
5d	1¾	12½	.102	271	14	.083	406
6d	2	11½	.115	181	12½	.102	236
7d	2¼	11½	.115	161	12½	.102	210
8d	2½	10¼	.131	106	11½	.115	145
9d	2¾	10¼	.131	96	11½	.115	132
10d	3	9	.148	69	10½	.127	94
12d	3¼	9	.148	63	10½	.127	88
16d	3½	8	.165	49	10	.134	71
20d	4	6	.203	31	9	.148	52
30d	4½	5	.220	24	9	.148	46
40d	5	4	.238	18	8	.165	35
50d	5½	3	.259	14	—	—	—
60d	6	2	.284	11	—	—	—

*Coated nails are ⅛ inch shorter.
Note: Flooring nails are similar in appearance to the casing nail but are about 1½ gauge thicker for each size. They are made in sizes from 6d to 20d. Wire nails are gauged by the old standard Birmingham wire gauge.

TABLE I. COMMONLY USED NAILS, THEIR SIZE, GAUGE, AND NUMBER PER POUND—*Continued*

PENNY SIZE	LENGTH IN INCHES FOR COMMON, BOX, AND FINISH*	COATED NAILS 6d Coated			FINISH NAILS 6d Finish		
		Gauge	Thickness in Thousandths	Number per Pound	Gauge	Thickness in Thousandths	Number per Pound
2d	1	16	.065	1084	16½	.062	1351
3d	1¼	15½	.069	848	15½	.069	807
4d	1½	14	.083	488	15	.072	584
5d	1¾	13½	.088	364	15	.072	500
6d	2	13	.095	275	13	.095	309
7d	2¼	12½	.102	212	13	.095	238
8d	2½	11½	.115	142	12½	.102	189
9d	2¾	11½	.115	130	12½	.102	172
10d	3	11	.120	104	11½	.115	121
12d	3¼	10	.134	77	11½	.115	113
16d	3½	9	.148	61	11	.120	90
20d	4	7	.180	37	10	.134	62
30d	4½	6	.203	29	—	—	—
40d	5	5	.220	21	—	—	—
50d	5½	4	.238	16	—	—	—
60d	6	3	.259	13	—	—	—

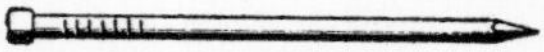

*Coated Nails ⅛ inch shorter.

Note: Flooring nails are similar in appearance to the casing nail but are about 1½ gauge thicker for each size. They are made in sizes from 6d to 20d. Wire nails are gauged by the old standard Birmingham wire gauge.

for instance, weighed ten pounds. The ancient, as well as the modern, abbreviation for penny is *d*, which is the first letter of the Roman word *denarius* (a coin), in English monetary reckoning, *a penny*.

Nails shorter than 2d (two penny) or one inch, or those longer than 60d (sixty penny), or six inches, as well as many of the special nails, are listed by inches or fractions of an inch. The five types of nails most commonly used by the trade are given in Table I, which shows the length, gauge, thickness in thousands of an inch, and the number of nails per pound.

Kinds of Nails. *Common nails,* (Fig. 4) are available from 2d to 60d in length. As their name implies, they are the most commonly used kind of nail, and will usually be supplied if no other specification is made. They are used when the appearance of the work is not important; for example in the framing-in of houses, and building of concrete forms.

Box nails, (Fig. 4) are similar in appearance to common nails, however they are not quite as thick and are only obtainable from 2d to 40d in size. Their applications are similar to common nails except that they are used on refractory materials; that is, wood that splits easily. The box nail has a cooler type head, whereas the common nail is available with both cooler and sinker (countersunk) type head.

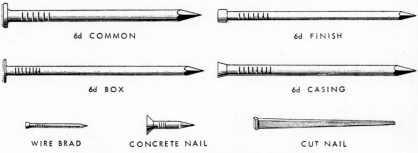

Fig. 4. Some Commonly Used Types of Nails

Finish nails, (Fig. 4) are available in lengths from 2d to 20d. The head is barrel shaped and has a slight recess in the top. As the name implies, these nails are used for finished work where the final appearance is of importance, such as trimming in buildings, cupboards, and cabinets, as are any nails with small heads. The small head is intended to be sunk into the wood with a nail set.

Casing nails, (Fig. 4) are similar to finish nails with these exceptions; the head is conical, it is a thicker nail than the finish nail and it is available in lengths from 2d to 40d. It is used in finish work where the wood in which it is used is heavy enough to take a thicker nail than a finish nail. The use of this nail is governed by the knowledge and judgment of the carpenter.

Brad nail lengths (Fig. 4) are specified in inches, from $\frac{3}{16}$ inch to 3 inches. They can be obtained in a lighter gage than finish nails, from 20 to 10 gage. Brad nails are used for refractory finish work, and should not be confused with the common or flooring brad.

Concrete nails (Fig. 4) are not specified by the penny system. They are available in lengths from $\frac{1}{2}$ inch to 3 inches, with a sinker head, and are usually hardened. Concrete nails are comparatively thick, from 10 gage to 5 gage and are used to fasten wood or metal to concrete, or masonry.

Cut nails (Fig. 4) are available from 2d to 20d in length; they are made by a shearing process from flat nail plate. For most applications, wire nails are now used instead of cut nails, but since cut nails cut the wood fibres and drive with the wood grain, they are less likely to split the wood, and are also used for fastening wood to harder materials like concrete. Cut nails are used for fastening wood to concrete and masonry. They can be obtained case-hardened.

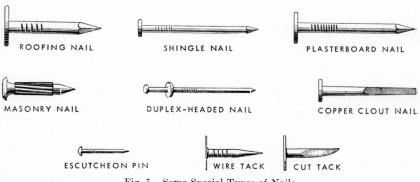

ROOFING NAIL   SHINGLE NAIL   PLASTERBOARD NAIL

MASONRY NAIL   DUPLEX-HEADED NAIL   COPPER CLOUT NAIL

ESCUTCHEON PIN   WIRE TACK   CUT TACK

Fig. 5. Some Special Types of Nails

Roofing nails (Fig. 5) are not specified by the penny system, they are available in lengths from ¾ inch to 2 inches, and have large cooler heads. Roofing nails are used to apply asphalt shingles, short ones on new roofs and long ones for re-roofing. They are also used to apply composition sheathing (Celotex, Firtex) to the studs. Most roofing nails are galvanized.

Shingle nails (Fig. 5) are sized from 3d to 6d. They are used for cedar shingles and have thin shanks with small heads. Two nails are used for each shingle.

Plaster board nails (Fig. 5) are specified by their actual length; 1 inch to 1¾ inches. They are blue in color and are sterilized, for the carpenter usually holds them in his mouth while working. They are used for applying both rock lath and plaster board. Rock lath is a base for plastering. Plaster-board or dry-wall is a finished product.

Masonry nails (Fig. 5) are hardened electrogalvanized and coated, their lengths range from 1¾ inches to 2½ inches. They are used to apply galvanized area-way wall to the foundation wall of a building.

Tacks (Fig. 5) are sold by weight, and are available as both wire tacks and cut tacks, as shown in Fig. 5. The larger the number of the tack, the longer it is. For example, a #8 tack is %6 of an inch in length. Some tacks are sterilized so that the carpenter can hold them in his mouth; they are also available with a galvanized or copper finish.

Double head nails (Fig. 5) are specified by the penny system, and are used in temporary construction such as form work and scaffolds. The advantage of using this nail is that it is easy to remove because it eliminates the need to strike pieces of lumber to get them apart, which preserves the timber and extends its useful life.

Clout nails (Fig. 5) vary in length from ¾ of an inch to 1½ inches. Unlike most other nails the clout nail is intended to go through the second piece of material and then be clinched (bent over) for greater holding power. A *boat* nail is used in a similar manner.

Escutcheon pins (Fig. 5) range from %6 inch to 2 inches long. This nail is considered a finish nail, because it matches the hardware with which it is used. Escutcheon pins are used for fastening metal trim on store fixtures, and house numbers, where the nail heads will show.

Staples are used to fasten metal, in the form of fence wire or metal screens to wood. They are also used for installing insulation or acoustical tile. Special tools in the form of tackers and staple hammers are often used to drive staples. Fig. 6 shows a selection of staples and on the left a new kind of staple which has great holding power due to its annular shank.

Dowel pins (Fig. 6) have no head. They are available from ¾ inch to 2½ inches in length, and have a barbed shank for greater holding power. They are used in mortise and tenon joints, and must be set.

Lead capped nails (Fig. 6) have a lead head which seals the nail hole. They are used for exterior work such as roof flashing and metal siding. Lead capped nails are sold by weight.

Roofing nails with neoprene washers (Fig. 6) range in size from 1¾ inches to 2½ inches and are not specified by the penny system. They are obtainable with both plain and helical shanks, and are used for aluminum and fiberglass roof and siding installations. The helical

FENCE STAPLE   FENCE STAPLE   LEAD-CAPPED NAIL

DOWEL PIN   ROOFING NAIL (SCREW SHANK)   ROOFING NAIL (PLAIN SHANK)

Fig. 6. Some Further Types of Special Nails and Staples
Special Fence Staple and Roofing Nails, after Independent Nail & Packing Co.

shank provides greater holding power, while the neoprene washer makes a weather-proof seal.

SCREWS

In addition to nails, screws are another means of fastening one member to another. Three types of screws will be considered in this chapter; wood, metal and machine screws.

WOOD SCREWS

Wood screws are used extensively for all types of work in the building trades where various materials must be fastened to wood. The most important use of wood screws probably is for fastening building hardware. Wood screws are used also for fastening in place various trim members, as well as in cabinet construction. Because of their greater holding power, screws are superior to nails. Screws also present a neater appearance and have more decorative possibilities. They have the advantage of being more easily removed with less danger of injury to materials. However, the use of screws often is discouraged because the screws cost more than nails and besides it requires less time to drive a nail into place than it does to drive a screw.

Sizes and Shapes. Wood screws are made in about 200 different stock lengths and thicknesses, ranging from ¼ inch to 5 inches. The diameter, or screw gage, is indicated by a number. The sizes range from 0 to 24. The higher the number the greater the diameter of the screw. This is the reverse of the wire gage used to indicate the nail diameter where the smaller the gage number the thicker the nail.

There are three different kinds of standard wood screws commonly used by the trade. These are named from the shape of the head and are known as *flat, round,* and *oval,* Fig. 7(*A*). Slots in the heads of

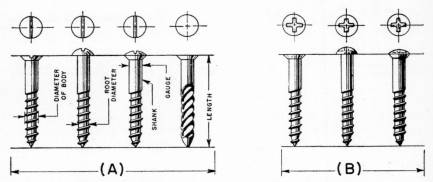

Fig. 7. Wood Screws, Styles of Standard Types, *from Left to Right;* (*A*) Flat Head, Round Head, Oval Head, Drive Screw, (*B*) Phillips Flat Head, Phillips Round Head, Phillips Oval Head

screws were standardized many years ago. However, recently a new type of screw head has been developed, known as the *Phillips Recessed Head,* Fig. 7(*B*). Although this type of screw head requires a special type of screw driver, the screw has the advantage of giving a neater appearance to the finished job. This screw also has a greater drawing power with less damage to the head when being driven into place. In addition to these screws there are many specially designed screws ranging from the *headless* to the *ball head.*

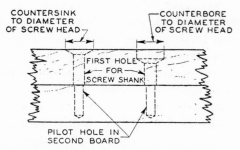

Fig. 8.   Details for Shank, Pilot, and Counterbore Holes for Flat Head Screws

When applying screws it is necessary to bore pilot holes to receive them, especially in hardwoods, Fig. 8. This practice of boring pilot holes insures drawing of the materials together tightly. The pilot holes also make driving of the screws much easier and prevent damage to the screw as well as to the materials. The bit sizes which should be used when boring pilot holes and shank clearance holes for different sizes of screw gages are shown in Table II.

Finishes. Screws are made principally of steel although some screws are made of brass, copper, and bronze. The brass, copper, and bronze screws are used where corrosive action from moisture, chemical solution, or fumes require this type of screw. To meet the demand for decorative as well as utility values, screws are also made in the following finishes:

Nickel	Galvanized	Spartan
Cadmium	Hot tinned	Statuary bronze

TABLE II. BIT SIZES FOR BORING PILOT HOLES AND SHANK CLEARANCE HOLES FOR WOOD SCREWS

	BIT OR DRILL SIZES										NUMBER OF AUGER BIT
	For Shank Clearance Holes		For Pilot Holes								
			Hardwoods				Softwoods				
NUMBER OF SCREW	Twist Bit (Nearest size in fractions of an inch) Slotted or Phillips	Drill Gauge No. or Letter (To be used for maximum holding power) Slotted or Phillips	Twist Bit (Nearest size in fractions of an inch) Slotted	Phillips	Drill Gauge No. (To be used for maximum holding power) Slotted	Phillips	Twist Bit (Nearest size in fractions of an inch) Slotted	Phillips	Drill Gauge No. (To be used for maximum holding power) Slotted	Phillips	(To counterbore for sinking head by 16ths) Slotted or Phillips
0	1/16	52	1/32	—	70	—	1/64	—	75	—	—
1	5/64	47	1/32	—	66	—	1/32	—	71	—	—
2	3/32	42	3/64	1/32	56	70	1/32	1/64	65	75	3
3	7/64	37	1/16	1/32	54	66	3/64	1/32	58	71	4
4	7/64	32	1/16	3/64	52	56	3/64	1/32	55	65	4
5	1/8	30	5/64	1/16	49	54	1/16	3/64	53	58	4
6	9/64	27	5/64	1/16	47	52	1/16	3/64	52	55	5
7	5/32	22	3/32	5/64	44	49	1/16	3/64	51	53	5
8	11/64	18	3/32	5/64	40	47	5/64	1/16	48	52	6
9	3/16	14	7/64	3/32	37	44	5/64	1/16	45	51	6
10	3/16	10	7/64	3/32	33	40	3/32	5/64	43	48	6
11	13/64	4	1/8	7/64	31	37	3/32	5/64	40	45	7
12	7/32	2	1/8	7/64	30	33	7/64	3/32	38	43	7
14	1/4	D	9/64	1/8	25	31	7/64	3/32	32	40	8
16	17/64	I	5/32	1/8	18	30	9/64	7/64	29	38	9
18	19/64	N	3/16	9/64	13	25	9/64	7/64	26	32	10
20	21/64	P	13/64	5/32	4	18	11/64	9/64	19	29	11
24	3/8	V	7/32	3/16	1	13	3/16	9/64	15	26	12

Chromium   Japanned   Antique copper
Silver plate   Parkerized   Sand brass
Gold plate   Lacquer   Steel blued

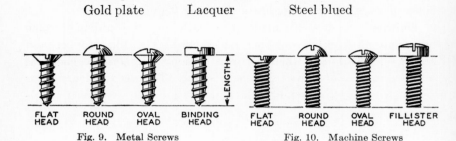

FLAT HEAD | ROUND HEAD | OVAL HEAD | BINDING HEAD   FLAT HEAD | ROUND HEAD | OVAL HEAD | FILLISTER HEAD

Fig. 9.   Metal Screws   Fig. 10.   Machine Screws

METAL SCREWS

Metal trim is rapidly replacing wood trim in fireproof construction. Since carpenters also apply metal trim they should become familiar with some of the fastenings used with metal.

Sheet-Metal Screws.   Self-tapping screws are used in sheet-metal work, shown in Fig. 9.   The larger sizes are driven into clean-punched or drilled holes, but in lighter metal only pierced holes are necessary for starting the screws.   These screws come in lengths ranging from $\frac{1}{8}$ of an inch to 2 inches with diameters ranging from a No. 2 to No. 14 screw gauge.   This type of screw is used to fasten two pieces of metal together without riveting or soldering.   Metal screws are used in light steel framing.   Houses and all other buildings now being built by carpenters of steel plates and studs, along with joists and other parts of the structure, are being assembled by means of sheet metal screws. An example of such practice is the quonset hut.

Machine Screws.   For the assembling of metal parts, *machine screws* are used.   These screws are made regularly in steel and brass with the four types of heads—*flat, round, oval,* and *fillister*—shown in Fig. 10.   The same style can be obtained also in the Phillips recessed heads.   Sizes are designated as to length in inches, from $\frac{1}{8}$ of an inch to 3 inches, and as to diameter, in numbers of American screw gauge for diameters less than $\frac{1}{4}$ inch, and in fractions of an inch for diameters $\frac{1}{4}$ of an inch and larger, Table III.

Machine screws are used to fasten butt hinges to metal jambs, lock cases, and door closers to their brackets.   They are available with both coarse and fine threads.

TABLE III. DIAMETER AND THREAD MACHINE SCREWS AND STOVE BOLTS

	Sizes of Screws and Bolts*											
Diameter	2	3	4	5	6	8	10	12	¼	⁵⁄₁₆	⅜	½
Coarse thread	56	48	40	40	32	32	24	24	20	18	16	13
Fine thread	64	56	48	44	40	36	32	28	28	24	24	—

*Machine screws both fine and coarse threads; stove bolts coarse threads only. Diameters of small screws indicated by number, larger sizes by fraction of an inch.

BOLTS

Bolts are another means of fastening one member to another. Let us consider the machine bolt, carriage bolt, lag bolt or screw, stove bolt and handrail bolt.

Machine bolts (Fig. 11) have square heads and like most bolts, come with a nut. Their lengths range from ¾ inch to 30 inches. They are used for heavy construction. The diameter of the bolt is the same as the thickness of the nut. Hexagon heads and nuts can usually be obtained by special order. One use of these bolts is the fastening of the beam to the stanchion in house construction.

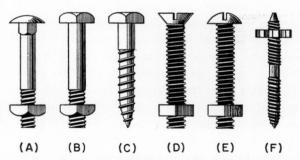

(A)   (B)   (C)   (D)   (E)   (F)

Fig. 11. Types of Commonly Used Bolts: (A) Carriage Bolt; (B) Machine Bolt; (C) Lag Bolt; (D) Flat Head Stove Bolt; (E) Round Head Stove Bolt; (F) Handrail Bolt

Carriage bolts (Fig. 11) have oval heads and a square shank just under the head to prevent the bolt from turning. Their lengths range from ¾ inch to 20 inches. They are sold with nuts and the threads are the same as those of machine bolts. When it is necessary to nail to a metal surface, a strip of wood known as a nailer is first fastened to the metal surface, and carriage bolts are often used for this purpose since the head is pulled into the wood, permitting other members to be nailed to the nailer without interference from the bolt head.

Lag bolts or screws (Fig. 11) do not have nuts, since the threads are self binding. They are used to fasten wood to metal, except when used as the medium with lag expansion shields. Their length ranges from 1 inch to 16 inches. They are used in heavy construction.

Stove bolts, with round or flat heads (Fig. 11) range in length from ⅜ inch to 6 inches. They have either round or flat heads, and are used in light construction. Stove bolts up to 2 inches in length are threaded to the head and those longer than 2 inches are threaded to a maximum of 2 inches.

Handrail bolts or screws (Fig. 11) are sold in one size only, $\frac{5}{16}$ inch in diameter and 3⅜ inches long. Handrail bolts are used to fasten sections of stair handrail together, and have self-binding threads on one end and nut on the other. These devices are supplied with the stair crooks.

ANCHORS

The following descriptions are not intended to be a complete list, but rather a representative cross-section of available devices.

The fastening of wood and other materials to concrete and masonry has always been a problem for the carpenter. Anchors for such work can be divided into three general categories; the first group including anchors used during the initial construction. The second group includes anchors used after the initial construction, in concrete or masonry. The third group are those anchors designed to be installed after initial construction in hollow masonry, or plaster which has a hollow space behind it in which the anchor can expand.

Anchors Used During Initial Construction. *Dovetail slot anchors* are used to connect masonry to concrete. The connecting medium is a dovetail brick anchor or a dovetail stone anchor, shown in Fig. 12. The anchor is available in ten foot lengths.

Plain inserts (Fig. 12) anchor metal to concrete. The connecting medium is a machine bolt, and the bolt head goes into the insert. This type of insert is mainly used in factories for the installation of pipes and conveyors in the ceiling. The size specification of the insert represents the bolt size. They are available for bolt sizes of ½, ⅝, ¾ and ⅞ of an inch.

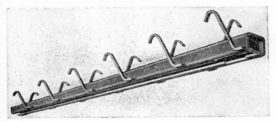

Slotted Insert

Tapped Insert   Wedge Insert   Dovetail Slot Anchor

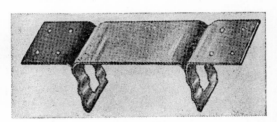

Plain Insert   Sleeper Clip

Fig. 12.   Anchors Used During Construction
All Except Sleeper Clip, Courtesy Gateway Engineering Co.

Tapped inserts (Fig. 12) also anchor metal to concrete, but in this case the insert is tapped and the threaded end of a machine bolt goes into this insert.   Two nailing lugs are provided for nailing the insert to the concrete form.   The size of tapped inserts is specified by the thread size.   They are available in ¼, ⅜, ½, and ⅝ of an inch standard thread.

Slotted inserts (Fig. 12) are also used for anchoring metal to concrete.   In this application, many machine bolts or hangers are used.

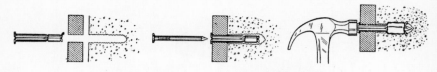

STAR DRYVIN EXPANSION DEVICE

FIBRPLUG ANCHOR

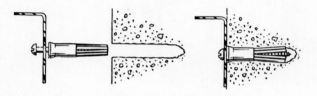

LEAD SCREW ANCHOR

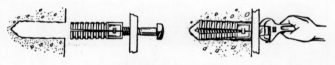

LAG EXPANSION SHIELD

MACHINE EXPANSION SHIELD

Fig. 13.   Anchors Used After Initial Construction
Star Expansion Co.

Standard lengths range from 1 foot to 5 feet. The slots are made for
½ inch, ⅝ inch or ¾ inch standard square head machine bolts.

Sleeper clips (Fig. 12) are used to embed and anchor wooden sleepers in concrete. These wooden sleepers are used to provide a base for

nailing. Sleeper clips are available 2, 3, and 4 inches wide.

Anchors Used After Initial Construction in Concrete or Solid Masonry. The *star dryvin expansion device* (Fig. 13) is furnished complete with either single or double head nail. Lengths range from $7/8$ inch to $3\frac{1}{2}$ inches. The shield holds the fixture, while the nail expands the lead wrapper on the bottom end.

A *rawlplug anchor* is a fiber anchor with a hollow metal core for use with wood screws. It can be used in almost any material, and is not affected by temperature, moisture, shock or vibration. Sizes run 6, 8, 10, 12, and 14. These size numbers refer to the size of screw for which they were designed although they will take one size smaller. Larger sizes are designed for use with lag screws.

Lead screw anchors (Fig. 13) are used in a similar way to rawlplugs, and take three different sizes of screw. Lengths range from $3/4$ inch to $1\frac{3}{4}$ inches.

Expansion screw anchors take a machine screw. The larger sizes take a machine bolt. They consist of two parts, the conical member is tapped, and a lead sleeve slides over it. A pilot setting punch which comes with this anchor sets the lead sleeve tight in the hole. Sizes range from $1/8$ inch machine screw to 1 inch machine bolt.

Machine expansion shields (Fig. 13) take a machine bolt, and are used in heavy construction. There is a tapered nut in the bottom which locks when the bolt is tightened, and thereafter will be securely anchored even if the bolt is removed. The smaller sizes are for $1/4$ inch bolts and the larger ones for up to 1 inch bolts.

Lag expansion shields (Fig. 13) take a lag bolt. There is no nut in these anchors. The lag bolt screws itself further in as it is tightened. Used in heavy construction, sizes vary from $1/4$ inch to $3/4$ inch.

Self-drilling expansion shields make their own holes. The sizes range from $1/4$ inch to $3/4$ inch. They can be used with a hammer (electric or air) in concrete or masonry.

Pin bolt drives need no bolt or screw. They are available with flat or round heads. The diameter is $1/4$ inch and the length ranges from $1/4$ inch to 2 inches. They are used in concrete or solid masonry. The fixture is inserted in a prepared hole, and then the furnished pin is driven in.

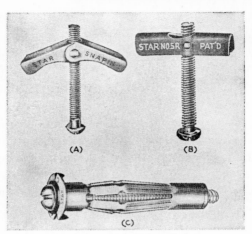

Fig. 14. Anchors Used in Hollow Masonry
Star Expansion Co.

Anchors Used in Hollow Masonry, or Plaster, Which Has a Clear Space Behind It. *Toggle bolts* (spring wing) (Fig. 14) have a wing head which is fitted with interior springs which cause the head to open after it has passed through the hole. An advantage of the spring wing toggle is that the constant tension on the machine screw helps to absorb vibration. Toggle bolts (tumble) (Fig. 14) are designed to be used horizontally and are not recommended for vertical use. The sizes for both types range from $\frac{1}{8}$ inch to $\frac{1}{2}$ inch machine screw.

Hollow wall screw anchors (Fig. 14) come with a machine screw. There is a nut set in the bottom which, when the screw is tightened, draws that end up tight to the back of the material in which it is used. The flange on the face remains on the outside surface of the wall, and once tightened, the screw may be removed without losing the anchor. Sizes range up to that designed for a wall $1\frac{3}{4}$ inches thick.

METAL WOOD CONNECTORS

Timber Connectors. Metal devices employed in the contact faces of lapped members to transfer loads from one member to another are known as *timber connectors*. The joints of these devices are held together by one or more bolts. Timber connectors were first developed in Europe but they are rapidly gaining favor in this country. They are valuable especially in heavy timber framing, such as trusses, towers, piers, and wharfs, where through their use the strength of the joints is increased many fold,[2] thus increasing the possibilities for the use of

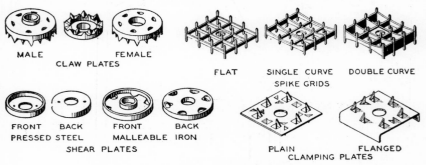

MALE   FEMALE
CLAW PLATES

FLAT   SINGLE CURVE   DOUBLE CURVE
SPIKE GRIDS

FRONT   BACK   FRONT   BACK
PRESSED STEEL   MALLEABLE IRON
SHEAR PLATES

PLAIN   FLANGED
CLAMPING PLATES

Fig. 15(A).   Timber Connectors Used in Connection with Bolts

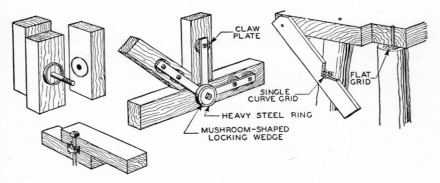

CLAW
PLATE

FLAT
GRID

SINGLE
CURVE GRID

HEAVY STEEL RING

MUSHROOM-SHAPED
LOCKING WEDGE

Fig. 15(B).   Timber Connectors, Showing Method of Installation

lumber. They also simplify the process of connecting timbers, doing away with the former interlocking wood joint, which required much more time for construction.

Two types of timber connectors designated according to application are *rings* and *plates,* Fig. 15(A). Grooves are cut in the wood to receive the rings and plates; the clamping plate and spike grids placed between the timbers are forced into the wood by drawing up the bolts. Fig. 15(B) illustrates the uses of timber connectors.

[2] Strength values for timber connectors have been established by the United States Forest Products Laboratory, Madison, Wisconsin, and the Timber Engineering Company, Washington, D.C.

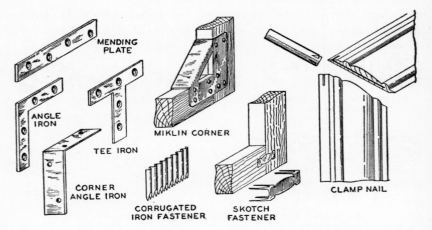

Fig. 16. Metal Fasteners Used in Cabinetmaking and other Light Construction Work

Metal Fasteners for Light Construction. The metal *mending plate, angle iron, tee iron, corner angle iron,* and *corrugated iron fasteners* need little explanation as they have been in general use for many years, Fig. 16. Also shown in this illustration is the *Skotch fastener,* which is a newer device. This has great holding power, is easily applied, and is available in two sizes. The *Miklin metal corner* is a great aid in making screens as it will insure a strong joint and eliminates the need of a mortise and tenon.

Mending plate (Fig. 16), sizes range from 2 to 12 inches; they are made of steel, or zinc plated steel. Screw holes are staggered for greater structural strength.

The *angle iron* or *plate* (Fig. 16), is made of the same materials as the mending plate and is ideal for bracing or reinforcing corner joints. Sizes are from 1½ inches to 8 inches.

T irons (Fig. 16), are made from the same materials as other plates, and are used for center bracing. Sizes range from 1 inch to 8 inches.

Corner angles (Fig. 16), are used for either inside or outside corners, depending upon which side of the angle is countersunk for the screw heads. Sizes range from 1 inch to 8 inches.

Corrugated fasteners (Fig. 16), are used to fasten two pieces of wood together. Their lengths range from 3 inches to 8 inches, and their depth or height, the choice of which is dictated by the thickness of the wood, ranges from ¼ inch to ⅞ of an inch.

Skotch fasteners (Fig. 16), are used for making or strengthening any type of wood joint. The curved prongs draw both sides of a joint firmly together. Skotch fasteners are available in two sizes.

Miklin metal corners (Fig. 16), are used on inside corners, and come in sizes for 1 inch and 1¼ inch wood stock. They are made of sheet metal and are nailed to the corner. A rigid corner results, because the Miklin corner acts as a diagonal brace.

Clamp nails (Fig. 16), consist of a steel spline with a clamp action that draws a joint together as it is driven into two saw kerfs; the wide end is driven in first. Clamp nails are used on elaborate stair parts, cabinets, furniture, sash and door trims.

HINGES

There are four basic hinge classifications:

Full mortise	Full surface
Half mortise	Half surface

Many different types of hinge are manufactured to meet various design requirements; however, the type of hinge which requires the most careful selection is the door hinge. The weight of the door, and the frequency of its use determine the weight of the hinge, and whether plain or ball bearing hinges are to be used. The width and thickness of the door determine the size of the hinge. A rule which can be applied to the selection of door hinges is as follows: *The width of the hinge for doors up to 2¼ inches is equal to twice the thickness of the door, plus the trim projection, minus ½ inch.* For doors from 2½ inches to 3 inches thick, the same rule applies, but ¾ of an inch should be subtracted instead of ½ inch. If the result of this calculation falls between regular sizes, the next larger size should be selected. Suggested rules for placement of door hinges are as follows:

Top hinge; 6–7 inches from jamb rabbet to the top of the hinge barrel. (Or as specified.)

Bottom hinge; 10–11 inches from bottom edge of barrel to finish door. (Or as specified.)

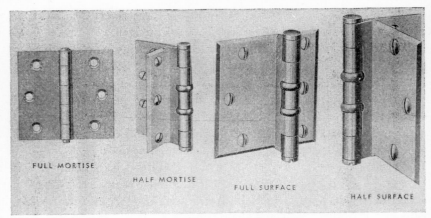

FULL MORTISE

HALF MORTISE

FULL SURFACE

HALF SURFACE

Fig. 17. A Selection of Door Hinges
Stanley Works

Third hinge; (although a third hinge is not always required, its use represents good construction practice) centered between top and bottom hinge. A selection of door hinges is shown in Fig. 17. The hinges should be set back at least ¼ inch from the edge of the door.

Ball bearing hinges (Fig. 18) are used for heavy doors, or on doors which are subjected to heavy use, such as doors in schools, office buildings and department stores.

Template hinges conform to government specifications. They will exactly fit the sinkage and screw hole locations in metal doors and jambs. They are also available with non rising pins.

Olive knuckle butt hinges (Fig. 18) have fixed pins with a loose leaf, and must be selected according to the way in which the door is to open. These hinges are longer than they are wide, and are used for cupboard and intercommunicating doors.

Parliament butt hinges (Fig. 18) have either a fixed or loose pin. They have a greater width than length and are used in churches on communion rails.

T *Hinges* in most cases have a fixed pin, and are classified as rough hardware. The size is measured by the length of the strap. They are obtainable in light, heavy or extra heavy metal, according to their application.

Double action spring floor hinge (Fig. 19), as its name implies, has

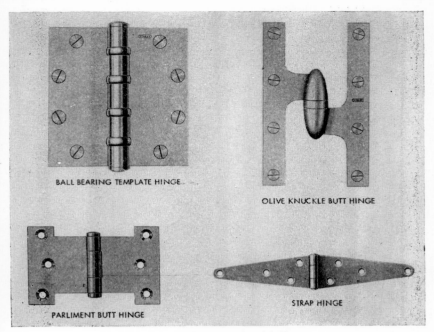

BALL BEARING TEMPLATE HINGE

OLIVE KNUCKLE BUTT HINGE

PARLIMENT BUTT HINGE

STRAP HINGE

Fig. 18. A Selection of Special Hinges
Stanley Works

a spring return action, which is effective in both directions. The spring action is generally concealed in the door in residential installations, and in the floor below the door in commercial installations. It is designed for doors which have a thickness between $1\frac{1}{8}$ inches and $1\frac{3}{4}$ inches.

The *double action spring butt* (Fig. 19) is used in commercial installations. Its design requires a hinge strip on the jamb. It is designed for use on doors that can be pushed open from either side and will close under spring action.

Invisible hinges (Fig. 19) are made so that no portion of the hinge is visible when the door is closed. They fit snugly into a mortise cut into the door and jamb, and because of this, much of the weight of the door is taken off the screws. Invisible hinges are made to open 180 degrees and are reversible.

Many kinds of *ornamental hinges* are manufactured, and find their main use in the construction of cupboards. Illustrated in Fig. 19 are

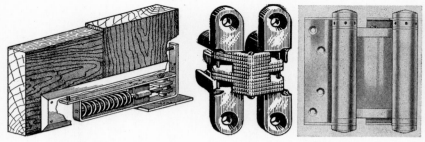

Spring Floor Hinge   Invisible Hinge   Spring Butt

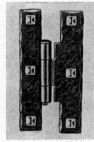

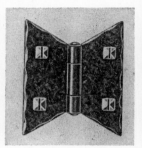

H-Hinge   HL-Hinge   Butterfly Hinge

Offset Hinge   Door Knocker

Fig. 19.   Special Hinges and Door Hardware
Ornamental Hinges, Courtesy Stanley Works

an "H" hinge, an "H-L" hinge, a butterfly hinge, and a ⅜ inch offset hinge for lip cupboard doors.

DOOR TRIM

Door knockers (Fig. 19) add to the appearance of a door, apart

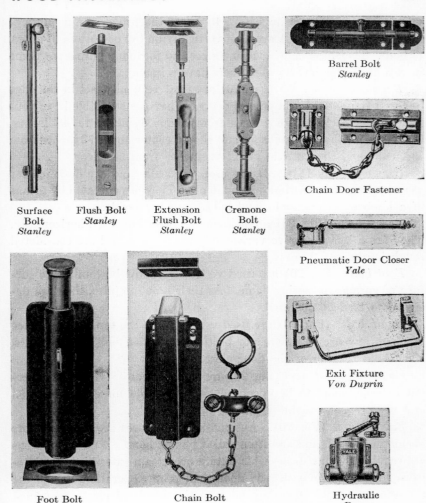

Surface Bolt
Stanley

Flush Bolt
Stanley

Extension Flush Bolt
Stanley

Cremone Bolt
Stanley

Barrel Bolt
Stanley

Chain Door Fastener

Pneumatic Door Closer
Yale

Exit Fixture
Von Duprin

Foot Bolt
Stanley

Chain Bolt
Stanley

Hydraulic Door Closer
Yale

Fig. 20. Selection of Bolts and Door Fixtures

from their function. They are available in a great number of designs and sizes, for exterior doors as well as in smaller sizes called guest room knockers, which are becoming increasingly popular.

Surface bolts (Fig. 20) are generally used vertically on doors, cupboards and casement windows. They are available in various weights and lengths, and it is important to select the proper strike plate.

Flush bolts (Fig. 20) are used vertically on top or bottom of doors, or both. They are made in various sizes and for many purposes. Some have a flush type lever, while others have a knob.

Extension flush bolts (Fig. 20) are used vertically, set in the edge of the inactive door of a pair of doors. They are available in various widths and their length ranges from about 5 inches to 48 inches. The lever for the top extension bolt should center about 72 inches from the floor, and the bottom, about 12 inches from the floor.

Cremone bolts (Fig. 20) are used vertically and are designed for use with large french windows and doors. They are operated by means of a knob or lever handle and open from the inside.

Barrel bolts (Fig. 20) are a surface type of bolt used horizontally. They are a less expensive variety of surface bolts and are considered rough hardware.

Foot bolts (Fig. 20) are used vertically on the bottom inside surface of garage and swing doors. As their name implies, they are designed to be foot operated.

Chain bolts (Fig. 20) are used vertically on the top inside surface of doors and are considered to be the companion bolt to foot bolts. They hold the top of the door closed.

Chain door fasteners (Fig. 20) are made in many styles. They permit exterior doors to be opened sufficiently wide for communication and yet prevent forcible entrance.

Exit fixtures (Fig. 20). Automatic exit fixtures are used on doors opening outward, and are often called "panic bars." Public buildings are required by law to use this fixture on certain exterior doors. Because human life may depend upon their proper operation, it is of the utmost importance that they be properly fitted. They are specified according to the hand of the door, for they cannot be reversed, and are obtainable in rim or mortise type.

Hydraulic door closers (Fig. 20) are mounted on the surface of the jamb, casing, or door bracket. The helical spring, either torsion or compression type, closes the door while the fluid checks it as it nears the door jamb and causes it to close slowly. The arm can be set to hold the door open if desired.

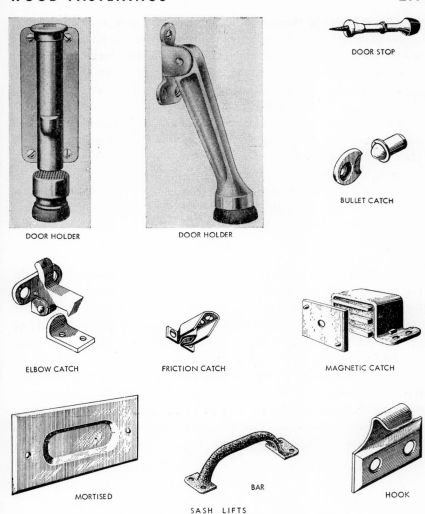

DOOR STOP

BULLET CATCH

DOOR HOLDER   DOOR HOLDER

ELBOW CATCH   FRICTION CATCH   MAGNETIC CATCH

MORTISED   BAR   HOOK

SASH LIFTS

Fig. 21.   Miscellaneous Small Building Hardware
Door Stop and Door Holder, Courtesy Stanley Works

Pneumatic door closers (Fig. 20) are used for the same purpose as hydraulic door closers, but on lightweight doors.   Their checking medium is air, and a set screw adjusts the time of closing.   They are used on screen and combination doors.

Other Building Hardware Used on Doors and Windows. *Door stops* (Fig. 21) vary in style, some are used on the baseboard, while others are used on the floor. They protect the door locks and the wall from being marred or damaged.

Door holders (Fig. 21) vary in design, their purpose is to hold the door open at a given point.

Catches (Fig. 21) are used on cabinets and cupboards. The bullet catch is mortised in the edge of the door top, bottom side, or even the frame, whereas friction and elbow catches are applied to the inside surface.

Sash lifts (Fig. 21) are used on the bottom rail of double-hung sashes. The flush sash lift is mortised into the rail while the bar and the hook are screwed to the rail.

GLUE

As a means of fastening joints, glue is not used as extensively by the carpenter as it is by the cabinetmaker or the millman. However, in small quantities, the use of glue is essential in the construction of stairs, some joints in interior trim, and such cabinetwork as is built on the job. The relatively new method of building beams, arches, and curved members of glued laminated construction has gained favor in this country in recent years. Large arches and rafters are now built to the correct size and shape by the carpenter on the job. Small units of material, casein glue, and nails are used.

There are approximately seven general types of glue used for wood joints currently available, and they are:

Liquid glue   Blood albumin glue
Casein glue   Vegetable glue
Animal glue   Synthetic resin glue
        Cellulose cement and rubber compounds

The properties, uses and methods of application of the different types of glue vary, and the selection of a glue depends upon such factors as the rate of setting, water resistance, and tendency to stain wood; as well as the strength factor.

Liquid Glue. Glue in liquid form is easily handled, which is one of its main assets. It is made from fish and animal products, and comes ready for use. There are many different kinds available on the market. Liquid glue is used chiefly for small jobs and repair work. Its holding power is not as great as that of some other forms of glue, and it also has a rather low resistance to water and moisture.

Casein Glue. After World War II, casein glue came prominently into use. It is made principally of casein which is mixed with caustic lime. Casein is the dried curd of cow's milk. Other ingredients used in the manufacture of casein glue are trade secrets. Casein glue is marketed in powder form and is prepared for use by the addition of water, mixing well, and allowing the mixture to stand for a short period of time before applying. One great advantage of casein glue is the fact that it is easily prepared, and another advantage is its relatively high water resistance. The better grades are highly waterproof, a quality which makes this glue desirable in construction work.

Animal Glue. There are some 21 grades of animal glue, which have been extensively used for many years. The best grade is that made from animal hides. However, animal glues are not very practical for construction work, because they are not water resistant. Another factor which makes their use for construction work impractical is that the glue must be heated carefully before it is applied to the wood, which must also be warmed. The necessary heating of the wood and glue demand shop facilities which are not usually available on the construction site.

Blood Albumin Glue. Glues made from a base of blood albumin have been in use for many years, but their main extensive use is in the making of plywood and other veneer work. They are mixed from the various ingredients at the time of use, and are applied by hand or with mechanical spreaders. They are quick setting, but most of them require hot setting, which imposes certain limitations upon their extensive use.

Vegetable Glue. Vegetable glues, vegetable protein glues, or vegetable starch glues as they are variously known, are used mainly for making plywood, and other veneer products for interior use. The glue is prepared by the user, by heating the vegetable-starch powder with water and then cooling the mixture to room temperature before use. Vegetable glues set at room temperature and develop their strength by loss of water to the surrounding wood. Vegetable glues are not very resistant to moisture or water.

Synthetic-Resin Glue. The synthetic-resin glues, or as they are more simply called, the resin glues, were introduced about 1935, but their development and acceptance on a large scale began during World War II and is still increasing. These resin glues originate from raw materials derived from coal, air, petroleum or natural gas, and water. Although the intermediate raw materials are available, the complex production methods required for the resins and the fact that some of them are covered by current patents makes the small scale production of resin glues by the individual user not ordinarily practical.

Synthetic resins are usually divided into two general groups, thermoplastic and thermosetting. The thermoplastic resins never harden permanently but soften or melt when the temperature is raised and harden again when it is lowered. This reversible hardening process involves no actual chemical change. The thermosetting resins however, undergo irreversible chemical change either at room temperature or at a higher temperature, to develop their strength and durability. After this reaction has taken place, the resin cannot be dissolved or melted again.

Some resins are sold in a single package, ready for use, or as a powder to be mixed only with water. Many others however, must be prepared for use by mixing resin, catalyst, filler, extender and water or other solvents at the time of use.

The principal advantages of some of the resins over other types of glue are the high degree of durability that they can impart to a wood joint when properly used, their adaptability to high volume production, and in some cases favorable cost.

Cellulose Cement and Rubber Compounds. Cellulose cement and rubber compounds are usually sold in liquid form ready to apply to wood. However, they have limited applications as woodworking glues. Cellulose cements are pressed cold, whereas most rubber compounds require heat. The relatively high cost of these compounds tends to impose further limits on their extensive use.

DOWELS

Dowels are pins made of hardwood, usually birch. These pins are used to fasten wood members together. Before nails came into use, dowels were used extensively in timber framing, and in pinning of boards to walls and floors. Today their chief use is found in manufacturing doors and furniture. In many instances dowels are used to replace the mortise and tenon joint.

WOOD JOINTS

A joint is formed when one piece of wood is fitted against another piece; the two pieces may only be butted against each other or they may be interlocked or secured in place with glue, dowel pins, nails, or other similar fastenings. The joints illustrated here are by no means the only types in use; however, those shown are the ones most commonly used. For convenience, these are divided roughly into three groups, as follows:

1. Joining timbers in framing.
2. Joining boards at an angle for change in direction.
3. Joining boards at the edge to increase the surface area.

Since there is some overlapping in such a grouping of joints, the carpenter's choice is governed by the nature of his work and the kind of joint suitable for the particular situation at hand.

A joint must be well made, carefully fitted and secured to give complete satisfaction and service; to accomplish this feat requires skill and experience. A mechanic's ability can be judged quickly by the strength and appearance of the joint he is able to produce.

1. Joining Timbers in Framing. In increasing the length of timbers, consideration must be given to the strains and stresses which the joint or splice must bear, such as tension, compression, or cross strain, or a combination of these factors. These needs can be met with splices similar to those shown in (A), (B), (C), and (D) of Fig. 22. For temporary structures timbers may be lengthened by use of the *lap joint* shown at (G), Fig. 22. Such a joint may be secured by use of bolts. Today, in timber framing, complicated joints seldom are made. Such joints have been replaced by metal connectors described earlier in this chapter.

The most simple of all joints is the *butt joint* which is made by merely placing two pieces of timber together with the end of one piece against the side of the other and nailing the pieces firmly together after

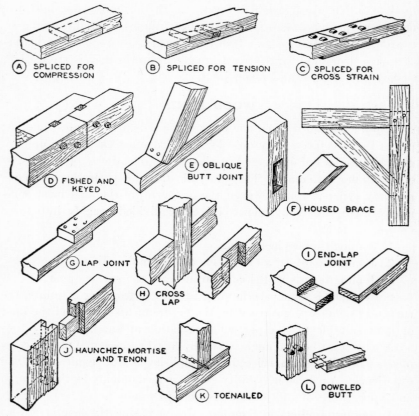

Fig. 22. Wood Joints Commonly Used in Timber Framing and Other Types of Woodworking

both have been trimmed square and true. In such a case the two pieces
are perpendicular to each other. When the two pieces are arranged
so as to form a *square butt joint* as shown at (*K*), Fig. 22, nails are
driven diagonally through both pieces, an operation known as *toenailing*. An *oblique butt joint* is formed when two pieces of timber are
not perpendicular to each other, but are trimmed to fit closely as illustrated at (*E*), Fig. 22. The *housed brace* shown at (*F*), Fig. 22, is a
common type of brace construction. The illustration shows how such
a joint is cut and fitted together. This type of construction gives additional strength to the joint, especially where there may be a tendency

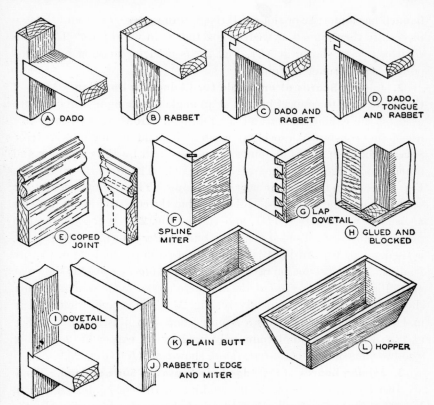

Fig. 23. Wood Joints Commonly Used in Cabinet Construction and Interior Trim

for one piece to slide along the other as in the case of a brace. Where timbers cross one another and are required to have one or both faces flush, both timbers are notched so as to fit over each other as shown in the *cross-lap joint* at (*H*), Fig. 22. Ends of heavy timbers or wall plates are usually cut so as to join as shown at (*I*), Fig. 22, and are known as *end-lap joints*. The cross-lap and end-lap joints are held together by spikes driven into the two pieces. A form of joint known as a *tenon joint* is shown at (*J*), Fig. 22. In some cases the tenon has an additional haunch which adds considerably to its strength. The *haunched mortise and tenon joint* is used extensively in the making of doors. The piece of timber which is to be joined to the tenon and haunch has a mortise or slot cut through it to receive the tenon; the two pieces are then pinned or wedged together with wood pins. The *doweled-butt joint* shown at (L), Fig. 22, is used for making both temporary and permanent joints.

2. Joining Boards at an Angle for Change in Direction. Most of the joints used to connect boards at an angle for changing direction are used by the cabinetmaker and the millman. However, the carpenter uses joints constantly, especially when fitting and placing interior trim. Several different types of joints commonly used by the carpenter and other woodworkers are illustrated in Fig. 23. The *dado* shown at (A), Fig. 23, is often used for interior door jambs. These joints usually are secured with glue and nails. Joints used in the construction of drawers are shown at (B), (C), (D), and (G) of Fig. 23. When joining two pieces at an evenly divided angle the *spline miter* shown at (F), Fig. 23, is used. This type of joint is commonly used in the making of picture frames. The construction used in a *glued and blocked joint* is shown at (H), Fig. 23. A *dovetail dado* and a *rabbeted ledge and miter* are shown at (I) and (J), respectively, Fig. 23. The type of joint used in making hoppers is known as a *hopper joint*. An illustration is shown at (L), Fig. 23. A joint commonly used by all carpenters and other woodworkers is the *plain-butt joint* shown at (K), Fig. 23.

3. Joining Boards at the Edge to Increase the Surface Area. There are two important factors in the making of the edge joints shown in Fig. 24. First, the boards must be selected according to grain; that is, the annual growth rings must run in opposite directions in adjacent boards. The curve of the annual rings must turn upward in one board and downward in the adjoining board as illustrated in the ends of the boards joined at (A), Fig. 24. This method of joining boards will insure a true surface in glued boards which generally will remain true. Second, the edges of the boards must be joined straight, true, and square with the surface to insure good continuous contact throughout the entire length of the board. A shaped edge adds little if any strength to a glued joint. Examples of such joints are the *splined, doweled*, or *tongued and grooved* joints shown at (B), (C), and (D), respectively, Fig. 24. The reason for the lack of added strength in such joints is due to the fact that, even though the surface area has been

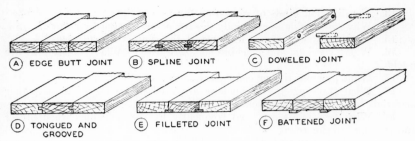

Fig. 24. Wood Joints Used in Edge Joining of Boards

increased, the contact usually is imperfect. However, the use of such joints has a tendency to line up the board which is an advantage in construction work. In all six of the methods of edge jointing illustrated in Fig. 24 the boards usually are secured with glue. Wood strips intended to cover or close an open joint are illustrated at (E) and (F), Fig. 24. Such joints are known as *filleted*, shown at (E), and *battened*, shown at (F).

CHECKING ON YOUR KNOWLEDGE

The following questions give you the opportunity to check up on yourself. If you have read the chapter carefully, you should be able to answer the questions. If you have any difficulty, read the chapter over once more so that you have the information well in mind before you read on.

DO YOU KNOW

1. All the general methods of fastening employed in carpentry?
2. How the length of a nail is specified, and the abbreviation of the term generally used as a unit of size?
3. The purpose of the duplex-headed nail?
4. What type of nail is used in concrete and masonry work?
5. The names of three kinds of wood screws?
6. In what laboratory successful experiments on improving wood construction have been performed?
7. The names of three kinds of bolts used in heavy construction work?
8. What the purpose of the sleeper clip is?
9. The basic hinge classifications?
10. The different finishes given to screws?
11. The advantages of the type of screw head known as the Phillips Recessed Head?
12. What fastenings are commonly used with metal trim?

13. The different kinds of glue used for wood joints?

14. Why casein glue is especially desirable for construction work?

15. The advantages offered by some of the synthetic-resin glues?

16. Where carriage and machine bolts are used? Where dowel pins are used?

17. What purpose timber connectors serve?

18. What three groups of anchors are used to fasten wood and other materials to concrete and masonry?

19. What two joints are used frequently by the carpenter when fitting and placing interior trim?

20. What wood fastenings were used by carpenters before nails came into use?

Essential Preparation
for Building a Home

QUESTIONS THIS CHAPTER WILL ANSWER

1. *What important factors are involved in the selection of a suitable location for a new residence?* 2. *In what way is it an advantage to a carpenter to be prepared to advise the prospective homeowner concerning existing zoning laws and building codes?* 3. *What precautions should the future homeowner take to prevent failure of his home-building project and to safeguard his investment?* 4. *What is the largest single item of expense in the cost of building a home?* 5. *Why is a lot survey important? Who should be engaged to make the survey?*

INTRODUCTION TO CHAPTER VIII

One of the most important undertakings in a man's life is the building of a home for his family. When the average man makes up his mind to build a home of his own, he knows little about the problems involved in home building. During the process of choosing a suitable location, informing himself concerning the local restrictions of city regulations, zoning laws, and building codes, and solving the numerous other problems that are encountered in connection with the actual construction of a house, the homeowner learns a great deal. However, after the house is completed and the family has moved in, it is too late to make use of the knowledge acquired through this new and often distressing experience. Few men have the opportunity to build more than one home during a lifetime. Hence, in case the new house proves to be inconvenient in location and arrangement or otherwise unsatisfactory, the family may have to be content with making the best of a bad situation.

As a carpenter you are more than a craftsman. It is your privilege to help the homeowner through this confusing and difficult labyrinth of details. You should be prepared to furnish him with all necessary information regarding zoning laws and building codes. Your knowledge of construction procedure should enable you to advise the prospective homeowner in regard to securing the assistance of an architect for preparing drawings and building specifications. You should be able also to give advice in connection with choosing a suitable location, drawing up of contracts, and in handling the financial problems involved in a home-building project. Your customer's satisfaction in his new home may depend to a great extent upon the advice you as a builder are able to give him. If your advice proves to be good you make a friend and build goodwill as well as homes in the community. One satisfied customer will bring others.

Usually the man who performs the greatest service to his fellowmen is the one who derives the greatest enjoyment from his work. However, it is a part of wisdom for the carpenter, as well as other men, to heed the admonition, "Let no man presume to give advice to others who has not first given good counsel to himself."

THE CARPENTER AS ADVISER TO THE HOME BUILDER

When building a house the largest single item of expense is the amount the carpenter receives; that is, the cost of labor. (See chart, Fig. 8, of the chapter on Carpentry as a Trade.) This is especially true of the small house. Because so large a share of the cost of a building goes to the carpenter, he is considered by many as the builder, and by others as a building expert. Hence, he is called upon frequently for counsel and advice on general building and homeownership problems. These may include legal and financial advice as well as matters regarding community and personal obligations of the homeowner. In many cases the prospective homeowner is so engrossed with the idea of homeownership and his future happiness in the new house that he does not give sufficient nor reasonable consideration to the many relatively important factors necessary in preparation for the actual construction of the home.

Building of a home is an undertaking which the average individual is not likely to repeat during his lifetime. Home building is an investment which perhaps will require all or at least most of the owner's savings. Should the venture prove to be a failure or one of disappointment, others might be discouraged by the failure. Therefore, a carpenter can render a service to a future homeowner by taking an interest in his building problems and by being prepared to give him helpful and much needed advice. This service will give the carpenter a good reputation in the community and will encourage others to undertake home building.

LOCATION AND TYPE OF HOME

Selection of Location. The type of family that is to occupy the home should govern the selection of a location. If there are one or more members of the family employed outside the home and there are growing children in the family, careful consideration should be given to accessibility to suitable employment areas, transportation, schools, and recreational facilities. A home always should be near market centers if possible.

Financial Investment. Family needs and the quality of the proposed house must be considered carefully, so that the investment will be in keeping with the owner's individual resources. Before beginning a building proposition, provision must be made for satisfactory financing of the project. The cost of maintaining the home after it is completed should be taken into account also. This item of expense is governed by the prospective annual income of the owner.

BUILDING CODES AND ZONING LAWS

Whenever people live together in a community certain regulations must be established which will work to the best interests of the majority. These regulations or laws are commonly called *city codes*. Those which are or should be of special interest to the contractor or builder are the *zoning laws* and *building codes*. These codes are written and passed upon by the people of the community to help make it a better and more desirable place in which to live. The codes are also intended to protect health, insure safety, to promote beauty and recreational facilities, and to assure the maintaining of reasonable property values for landowners.

Too frequently people look upon these zoning and building codes as restrictions upon their rights. It is true codes do restrict the individual who fails to take into account the rights of others. However, in reality codes are designed to give the greatest amount of freedom to the greatest number of people.

The primary purpose of the zoning law in a community is: to divide the city into districts, such as residential and apartment house, commercial and business, industrial and manufacturing, and recreational zones; to promote health and safety; to protect property values; to eliminate or minimize fire hazards; and to control density of population. Zoning laws also govern the height of buildings and the size of open spaces required around buildings in accordance with the type of occupancy classifications.

Building codes promote safe engineering practices in the use of materials and establish standards which have been proved the most effective. To insure safety, buildings should not only conform to the best-known practices for sturdy construction, but safety precautions must also be taken against fire hazards due to imperfect heating equipment, defective chimneys, oil burners, and electrical devices. As the amount of open space around a building decreases, the fire hazard increases and fire-resisting features of a building must be increased. This safety of construction and precaution against fire hazards is equally as important for the private dwelling as it is for a public assembling place, such as churches, theaters, and other auditoriums. Other important phases of building codes pertain to sanitation, control of plumbing in buildings, ventilation, amount of glass area in the windows, and the height of ceilings. All of these factors are vitally important to the general welfare of a community as well as to individual members of the community.

Many states also exercise some degree of control over the most densely populated areas through zoning and building laws; however, state laws are formulated mainly from the viewpoint of sanitation; because unsanitary conditions in one community may affect neighboring communities. The licensing of architects is controlled by state legislation. Some states have an architectural-practice law which demands that licensed architects be employed for all public buildings, and in residential construction which exceeds a value of $7,500.

As a rule, licensed architects become familiar with zoning and building laws during the process of training. However, the builder or contractor frequently is either unaware of, or minimizes the value of, existing building laws and codes. Ignoring of zoning laws and building codes may work a great hardship upon both the carpenter and owner of a building. Therefore, before beginning construction work a wise builder will inform himself regarding all prevailing laws or codes, including state laws, which might cause him trouble later. In addition, every carpenter should utilize the opportunities offered by the office of building commissioners, or building inspector, and obtain all possible information and assistance necessary for interpreting any laws or codes which would in any way affect a building enterprise which he is preparing to undertake. The prospective owner rarely is informed concerning various legal requirements and practices and usually depends upon the architect or builder to supply information essential for protecting their mutual interests.

Water and Sewerage. Adequate water supply, drainage, and sewerage disposal are extremely important, not only for household needs but also from the standpoint of health and sanitation. If city water is not available plans for a well must be made before building operations begin. If low land does not have natural drainage facilities, but otherwise is a desirable location for a home, consideration must be given to providing adequate drainage before a house is built. The sewer level should be checked with the city engineer to determine the height of the sewer, its adequacy, and record of performance. This information will be a great help in determining the depth the basement should be in order to insure proper drainage. Where sewers are not available attention must be given to septic tanks, and existing laws governing them and their drainage.

Electric, Gas, and Telephone Services. Public utility services must be checked as to their availability and the possibilities for connections with service lines. Sometimes building locations are selected so remote from such conveniences that special provisions must be made with the utility companies in order to secure and facilitate their services.

Title to Property. The foregoing discussion suggests the variety and nature of the problems which must be satisfactorily solved by the future property owner before purchasing a lot on which to build his new home. Acquiring a piece of property is a legal transaction which can best be handled by an experienced lawyer or a competent real-estate broker. An efficient lawyer or broker will check delinquent taxes, mortgages, liens, or any other irregularities which may be held against the property. Such a procedure will insure the buyer a clear and unquestionable title to the land he buys. This is not only a future protection to the purchaser but is also essential for the acquisition of a loan for financing of a building project.

Lot Survey. A lot survey should be made by a licensed civil engineer who is qualified to certify as to the accuracy of his report. The making of such a survey is strongly advised because it assures the property owner that the prospective building will be erected upon the right plot of ground and within the bounds of that plot. Due to the lack of such a survey many an individual has been plunged into costly legal entanglements. Court records show that buildings have been erected on the wrong lot or have extended partly onto an adjoining lot to which the owner of the building had no title. Such a situation places the builder or house owner at the mercy of the neighboring landowner who may sue for infringement of property rights. In case a building project is to be financed by a loan, a lot survey is imperative because financing companies demand a certified survey before lending money for the erection of a building on a plot of ground. Furthermore, before issuing a building permit, city building departments demand a lot survey.

Preparation in Drawing Up Specifications. Oftentimes a homeowner is disappointed in a new house because it has been erected without expert advice. Sometimes a carpenter must proceed with his construction work without definite instructions. In many cases the only specifications the builder receives is the meager information furnished him in a few sketchy drawings. These may have been made by someone totally ignorant of the varied and numerous details of a building project and the proper procedure to follow in dealing with them. Such laxity results invariably in costly changes during construction and gives rise to misunderstandings between the parties involved, especially between the builder and the homeowner. The drawings and building specifications, prepared by a competent architect, are well worth his fees. His expert knowledge of materials and methods of construction, as well as his training and experience, are valuable to a new homeowner unfamiliar with architectural procedure. A trained architect not only assumes responsibility for drawing up specifications and contracts but also takes over supervision of the work during the process of construction. In addition he is able to protect the owner's interests by his understanding of how to plan economically to avoid waste in time and materials. The average new homeowner is unfamiliar with all such details.

Frequently carpenters are competent architects with the ability required for looking after all details of construction and giving expert advice to their clients. Sometimes the owner has had training and experience which fits him to assume the responsibility for details himself. Regardless of how adequate drawings and building specifications are prepared, this is an important phase of home building which justifies the investment of ample time and effort in order to avoid misunderstandings between the builder and owner as to how the work is to be done.

Contracts. A prospective homeowner, or his agent, should draw up contracts and have them signed by all parties who sell or deliver materials for the construction job. Contracts should also be made with the architect, the builder, and with everyone else who performs services during the process of construction of a new house. Contracts may be verbal but, if carefully prepared, written contracts are more desirable. In case a question arises regarding either the material or the construction work, the evidence furnished in a written contract will remove all doubt as to the original agreement made between the owner and any contractor.

When competitive bids are called for on a construction job, it is advisable for a prospective homeowner to reserve the right to reject any or all bids and to investigate carefully the integrity, ability, and record of performance of every bidder. An important fact to remember is: *the lowest bid is not always the best bid.*

If complete, the contract figures will furnish the owner with definite assurance of the total cost of his home-building project, providing no changes in construction are made later. Such figures are not only a protection to the home builder but are necessary in making application for a loan to finance the proposed project.

Financing. The prospective homeowner should not obligate himself in any way by signing any contracts until final settlement has been made regarding financing of the new-building project. Before considering making a loan, financing companies demand adequate proof of a clear title to the property on which the building is to be erected. In addition these companies require several sets of drawings and building specifications together with figures showing the actual costs involved. When the loan has been granted, the owner or his agent can proceed to sign contracts; and construction work on the house may begin without undue risk.

All this preliminary preparation may appear to some to be a long and arduous procedure, which it is; but we must not forget that the erection of a house is an important and difficult enterprise. The suggestions given in this chapter furnish a foundation for a successful home-building venture. The builder, or carpenter, who wishes to perform a real and valuable service to the new homeowner, will give the foregoing suggestions careful consideration.

CHECKING ON YOUR KNOWLEDGE

If you have any difficulty answering the following questions read the chapter again. After the second reading you should be able to answer all of the questions. You should have the information given in this chapter well in mind before you go on with your study of the next chapter.

DO YOU KNOW

1. Why a home-building project is of special importance to the average man?

2. The most essential factors included in the preparations for building a new home?

3. Why some home-building projects are failures as financial investments?

4. Why a homeowner is sometimes disappointed in his new home after it is completed?

5. Why the average man is not qualified to handle all the difficult problems connected with the preparation of building a new home?

6. How a carpenter can be of service in helping the prospective homeowner to solve his home-building problems?

7. Why a licensed engineer should be engaged to make a lot survey of the land on which a new home is to be erected?

8. Why the proper drainage of such a lot is of first importance to the homeowner?

9. Why some states have laws regulating the location of homes in relation to industrial and manufacturing centers?

10. How certain factors connected with the location of a new home may affect various members of the family concerned and, therefore, are of vital importance to the property owner?

11. What factors are more important, when choosing a building location, than a pleasing view from the front porch?

12. Who should be engaged to prepare architectural drawings and building specifications?

13. How the prospective homeowner can protect himself when seeking legal advice?

14. Why financial companies are interested in the property owner having a clear title to his home?

15. The primary purpose of zoning laws? In what way zoning laws and building codes restrict the rights of an individual homeowner?

16. Why it is important for the property owner to be informed regarding existing zoning laws and building codes in his community before beginning a building project?

17. Why it is important for the prospective homeowner to study carefully all financial matters involved in connection with the cost of building a new house?

18. What financial problems, in addition to the actual cost of building a new house, should be considered in connection with the cost of building?

19. Why the location of public utilities in relation to a new home is important to the homeowner?

20. What precautions the home builder should take before signing contracts with an architect, carpenters, dealers in materials, and other interested parties? Why the lowest bid is not always the best bid?

CHAPTER IX

Blueprint Reading

QUESTIONS THIS CHAPTER WILL ANSWER

1. *What are blueprints?* 2. *Why is it important for the carpenter to be able to read and understand the directions given on architectural drawings, or blueprints?* 3. *What are the* elevation drawings *of a house?* 4. *Why is it important for the architect to know the* datum line *before he begins to draw the building plans for a new home?* 5. *What advantage is there in the use of symbols on blueprints? What information may be given by symbols?*

INTRODUCTION TO CHAPTER IX

In frame construction, if the foundation of the house is to be made of concrete, the carpenter begins the construction work by building the forms into which the concrete is later poured. When the foundation is ready for the superstructure, the carpenter also begins this part of the construction by framing the walls and roof. He must follow exactly the directions given on the blueprints and in the building specifications. If he fails to do this, the other tradesmen, whose work is done later, may make mistakes, or they may be delayed while corrections are made in the faulty framing. The carpenter, then, begins the construction of a new building. The success of the work of other tradesmen on the job, such as plumbers and electricians, depends largely upon the accuracy of the carpenter's work. The finishing of the building is also done by the carpenter who, by necessity, is the last workman to leave the job.

Since the carpenter is the first and the last workman on a construction job, it is necessary for him to have some knowledge of all the processes involved during the progress of erecting a new house, including work done by all the other tradesmen. The carpenter must not only be able to read and follow directions given on blueprints but he must also be able to explain these instructions to other tradesmen, who may not be able to read the directions. The responsibility which rests upon the carpenter is greater than that of any of the other tradesmen who have a share in the construction job. Therefore, the carpenter is often looked upon as the most important craftsman on the job.

However, in spite of such responsibility, some carpenters never take the trouble to learn to read blueprints. They depend upon the architect or some other tradesman to tell them what is to be done. Such workmen are never able to reach a high level in their trade. The ambitious young carpenter who wants to become a high-class tradesman, perhaps a foreman or contractor, must learn how to read blueprints. If you will apply yourself to mastering the details connected with blueprint reading you will be amply repaid for your trouble.

The ability to read blueprints takes you "behind the scenes," giving you an opportunity to see how a new building is conceived. First, as an idea, then as

a mental image which takes shape in the mind of an architect, or builder.   Later
this picture is transferred, by means of blueprints and building specifications,
to the minds of the carpenter and other tradesmen.   Then, finally, the original
idea becomes a reality in the form of a new building.

This chapter gives basic information and instructions which you should
learn.   Study carefully the architectural drawings given in Chapter X.   Be
sure you understand the various symbols and other information which you
will find on these drawings.   The effort you make to master these details will
be well worth while.

ARCHITECTURAL DRAWINGS

An important qualification of an efficient carpenter is his ability to
read and understand drawings commonly called *blueprints*.   *Architectural drawings* usually are in the form of blueprints which are white
photographic prints on a bright-blue background.   These prints are prepared by transferring drawings to paper or cloth which has been sensitized to light by chemical treatment.   The drawings or prints are developed by exposure to sunlight or electric light.

The carpenter must not only know his own trade but must be
familiar also with the work performed by other trades in the process of
erecting a new building.   The carpenter is the most important mechanic
on a construction job because he must frame the building so that the
other tradesmen can put their work in place properly.   In the framing
of a modern house, the carpenter's knowledge of the requirements of the
other trades is especially important because of the danger due to the
improper installing of such features as the heating, lighting, water, and
plumbing systems.   Although it is true that the foreman on a construction job reads and interprets the drawings while an ordinary carpenter
merely follows instructions, yet the ambitious young carpenter who
wishes to advance himself to the position of foreman or contractor must
learn to read and understand the directions given on blueprints.   There
are many carpenters who are skillful in the use of tools and are able to
read floor plans but become confused when they attempt to read instructions for elevations, sections, and other details.

In this text, space does not permit detailed instructions for blueprint
reading.   However, an attempt is made to point out some of the most
important facts which every carpenter should know in order to be able
to find, on the drawings for a small house, the various dimensions which
will indicate the size and shape of the building.   He should be able to
properly locate partitions, windows, and doors; to find the sizes of

windows and doors, and the heights of the ceilings for the different floors. He should be able to determine the different kinds and sizes of materials needed not only for his own trade but also for that of other trades involved. He must know also where to look for information necessary for working out details. If he can find this information on a simple set of drawings he has a good beginning knowledge of how to read blueprints or drawings for more complicated building construction.

One method of learning how to read blueprints is to study and analyze a set of drawings. To assist you in doing this a set of drawings for a typical small American home has been reproduced in Chapter X of this text. As will be pointed out, these blueprints, reduced in size, are the drawings made for a building which actually has been erected. In fact, the design and layout of this little cottage have become so popular that this same type of home has been erected many times in different parts of the country.

A set of questions relating to these drawings is included in this chapter. If you will go to the trouble of taking a sheet of paper and writing out answers to these questions, it will help you to fix the various important points in your mind and will also help you to analyze the drawings. After you have written answers to the questions given at the end of this chapter, turn to the Appendix at the back of the book where you will find the correct answers to the questions. Check your answers with the correct answers, then find your score.

DRAWINGS OR BLUEPRINTS

The purpose of a set of drawings or blueprints is to furnish definite information on what the building is to be like when it is finished. The drawings, together with the written specifications, are instruments whereby the architect, the builder, the dealer who furnishes the materials, and the owner of the house may have a thorough understanding of what is wanted for the house while it is in the process of construction. If the blueprints and the written specifications are carefully prepared there can be no grounds for any disagreements.

SCALE

Because of the large size of a house, full-sized drawings would be inconvenient, expensive, and impractical. Therefore, the drawings are made to *scale;* that is, reduced proportionately to a size which can be made and handled conveniently. House drawings usually are drawn to a one-fourth inch scale, indicated as $\frac{1}{4}''=1'0''$. This means that every $\frac{1}{4}''$ on the drawing will equal one foot on the building, or the building will be 48 times larger than the drawing. To reduce the size of the drawings for larger buildings, the $\frac{1}{8}''$ scale ($\frac{1}{8}''=1'0''$) is frequently used. Some parts of a building are more complicated than others and to show the details better these parts are drawn to a larger scale, $\frac{1}{2}''=1'0''$, or $\frac{3}{4}''=1'0''$, or $1\frac{1}{2}''=1'0''$. Certain complicated details are sometimes drawn full size; for example, the plaster cornice and head of the entrance.

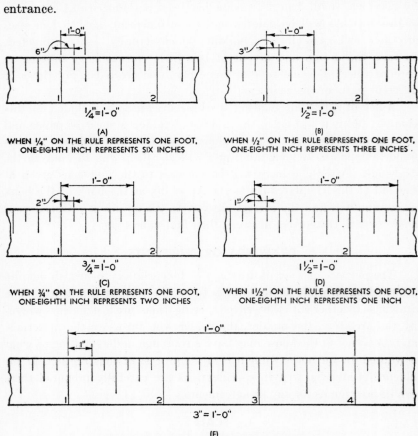

(A) WHEN ¼" ON THE RULE REPRESENTS ONE FOOT, ONE-EIGHTH INCH REPRESENTS SIX INCHES

(B) WHEN ½" ON THE RULE REPRESENTS ONE FOOT, ONE-EIGHTH INCH REPRESENTS THREE INCHES .

(C) WHEN ¾" ON THE RULE REPRESENTS ONE FOOT, ONE-EIGHTH INCH REPRESENTS TWO INCHES

(D) WHEN 1½" ON THE RULE REPRESENTS ONE FOOT, ONE-EIGHTH INCH REPRESENTS ONE INCH

(E) WHEN 3 INCHES ON THE RULE REPRESENTS ONE FOOT, ONE-FOURTH INCH REPRESENTS ONE INCH

Fig. 1. Scales Showing Method of Reducing Dimensions on Architectural Drawings

By using these various scales, Fig. 1, the architect makes it possible for the builder to use his own rule to make scaled measurements on drawings such as those for the building shown in Chapter X (Fig. 1). Therefore, it is essential that the builder find out the scale to which the drawings are made before he begins taking any measurements with his rule.

TYPES OF LINES

Full or Visible Lines. Border lines and the outline, or visible parts, of the house are always represented by *full*, or *visible lines*, Fig. 2.

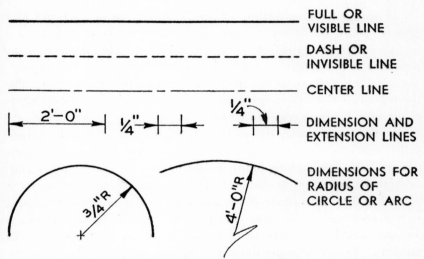

FULL OR VISIBLE LINE

DASH OR INVISIBLE LINE

CENTER LINE

DIMENSION AND EXTENSION LINES

DIMENSIONS FOR RADIUS OF CIRCLE OR ARC

Fig. 2. Various Types of Lines Used on Architectural Drawings

Dash Lines. The outline of hidden, or invisible, parts of a house are shown by *dash lines*, Fig. 2. These represent the outline of parts which may be hidden under floors, within walls, or occur beyond or behind elevations.

Center Lines. Fine, alternate long and short lines used to show the center of the axis of an object are called *center lines*, Fig. 2. The center of a round object is shown by two intersecting center lines.

Extension Lines. Fine lines which show the extreme limits of a dimension are called *extension lines*, Fig. 2.

Dimension Lines. Fine solid lines, terminated by arrowheads and used to indicate distances between points and lines, are called *dimension*

lines, Fig. 2. The radius of a circle is indicated by a dimension line drawn from the center of the circle and terminating with an arrow at the circumference of the circle. The length of the radius is expressed by the dimension and the letter R; that is, ¾″R means the center of the circle is three-fourths of an inch from the circumference of the circle, Fig. 2.

The *ceiling lines* and *floor lines* are shown as heavy, alternate long and short lines in the elevation drawings, Chapter X (Figs. 2, 3, 4, and 5).

PLANS

Drawings for architectural construction may be divided into four groups: *plans, elevations, details,* and *sections.* The drawings for a building often are called *the plans.* However, this is incorrect as the *plan view* is that part of the drawings which shows the floor plan only, looking directly down on the flat surface of any particular floor. The terms *plan view* and *floor plan* mean exactly the same and are used interchangeably by architects and builders.

A *plan view* shows the room arrangement, chimneys, fireplaces, stairs, and closets. The plan view also shows the location of various devices, such as plumbing fixtures, lighting outlets, heating apparatus, and other mechanical appliances. The average set of drawings for a house has three floor plans—basement with footing, a first-floor, and a second-floor plan. Sometimes in addition a *lot plan* is furnished to show lot lines, location of the house on the lot, trees, and the contour of the grounds. For complicated buildings, special plans are shown of the footings, joists, and rafter layouts.

ELEVATIONS

Elevation drawings show the outside of the finished building in true proportion. When the architect designs a house he thinks of the elevations in terms of the location of the house on the lot. Therefore, he names them the *south, east, north,* and *west elevation.* Sometimes the front of the building is known as the *front elevation.* As one observes the house from the front, the side to the right of the observer is called the *right elevation;* the side to the left, *left elevation;* and the one showing the back of the house, the *rear elevation.*

Elevation drawings also show the floor levels and grade lines, story and window heights, and the various materials to be used. Together with the architectural drawings and building specifications, an architect usually is provided with a survey of the lot on which the new building is to be erected. A typical lot survey shows the contour lines of the land on which the building will stand as specified in the location plans. Lines on a map, or chart, representing imaginary lines connecting points having the same elevation above sea level on a land surface are known as *contour lines*. When the contour lines show that a piece of land has a gradual slope this particular area is a suitable spot for a house unless other circumstances enter into the problem and make the location undesirable. Thus, with a lot survey at hand, an architect can easily select the best location for a new house.

In any large city or town, the records kept in the city building show the *city datum line* or *datum point*. A *datum line* is a level from which heights and depths are measured or calculated; that is, any base or fundamental line or point, from which dimensions are taken or graphic calculations are made, is known as a *datum line* or *datum point*. A city datum line is determined by the distance above sea level of the contour lines of an area within the city limits. Therefore, the city datum line is used as a basis for measuring elevation heights of new buildings. On architectural drawings for city homes or other buildings, the elevation measurements must be calculated from the city datum point, to insure proper drainage from water and sewerage systems.

In the architectural drawings for the house, shown in Chapter X, an elevation of 100'0" is used to indicate the height of the finished first floor above the city datum point. The basement-floor level is shown as elevation 92'0", which means that it is 8'0" below the level of the first floor. The elevation of the finished second floor is 109'0", which means that it is 9'0" above the level of the first floor.

Some architects use elevation 0'0" as the first-floor level and any level below that is shown as a minus number, for example —8'0"; and any level above 0'0" is shown as a plus number, for example +9'0".

DETAILS

The plans and elevations are usually drawn to a scale which is too small to show accurately the character or construction of certain parts. To show these parts more clearly, larger scale drawings are made.

Details are shown in elevations, floor plans, and sections, Chapter X (Figs. 2-8).

SECTIONS

A *section view* is one in which a part of the building or object has been cut away, exposing the construction, size, and shape of materials which need further clarification. Examples of sectional views are detailed drawings for the fireplace and kitchen cabinets shown in Chapter X (Fig. 3) and wall sections shown in Chapter X (Fig. 9).

Construction details of the wall sections *A–A* and *B–B*, Chapter X (Fig. 9) show size of joists, studs, and rafters; sills, headers, plates, window cornice, floor construction, and other important details. Such detailed sectional views are important as an aid to the carpenter in framing the building. A vertical section provides more information than can be given on floor plans. Details of the stairs and of doors *C* and *D* are shown in Chapter X (Fig. 4); detailed vertical sections of the bay window, porch beams, and interior trim are shown in Chapter X (Fig. 5); detailed vertical sections and elevations of the entrance doorway are shown in Chapter X (Fig. 8).

Molding and various interior-trim members usually are shown in full-size sections to bring out intricate lines more clearly. These detailed drawings often are spread around on different plan views or elevations wherever the architect can find room to show the section view. Sometimes all the details are grouped together on one or more sheets called *detail sheets*. Before proceeding with this work an architect frequently demands, through specifications, that the manufacturers submit drawings of certain materials produced in mills. Millwork of standard construction, such as flush or lip cabinet doors and sash do not demand details; indications given on the drawings or mentioned in the specifications are sufficient.

TRANSVERSE OR LONGITUDINAL SECTIONS

Transverse or longitudinal sections frequently are shown. These elevation sections show the interior of a building along a certain line. The transverse section is across the building while the longitudinal section is lengthwise through the building. Different floor levels and interior views of stairs can be illustrated more clearly with this type of sectional view.

SCHEDULES

Separate schedules for doors and windows are shown with the first-floor plans, Chapter X (Fig. 7). References to window openings are indicated by numbers and references to doors by letters, Chapter X (Figs. 6–8). This practice helps to keep the drawings from becoming cluttered with too many details which often make the instructions difficult to read.

SPECIFICATIONS

When a builder undertakes the construction of a new house all the information he will need cannot possibly be given on the architectural drawings; even though the set is complete and includes, in addition to the floor plans, elevation drawings and section views. Therefore, in order that the carpenter may have a thorough understanding of what is wanted in the building, it is necessary that the drawings be supplemented by written specifications. Carpentry specifications for a typical American home are given in Chapter X. The questions on blueprint reading at the end of this chapter apply also to the building specifications given in Chapter X.

Anyone interested in learning to read blueprints should study carefully both the architectural drawings and the building specifications which supplement them. If the finished building is to be entirely satisfactory to everyone concerned, including the architect, builder, and owner, then the carpenter must have a thorough understanding of what is needed and desired by the owner in his new home. During the process of constructing a new house, whenever the information in the specifications appears to conflict with the instructions shown on the drawings, before proceeding with his work, the carpenter should consult the architect in order to find out exactly what is wanted.

SYMBOLS

Drawings are simplified by the use of symbols. Various materials, such as wood, stone, brick, and concrete, are represented by certain symbols. Examples of material symbols commonly used in the building trade are shown in Fig. 3. Mechanical devices also are represented by symbols which indicate where heating, lighting, and plumbing appliances are to be installed in a new building. Mechanical symbols commonly used are shown in Fig. 4. The elevation of windows and their

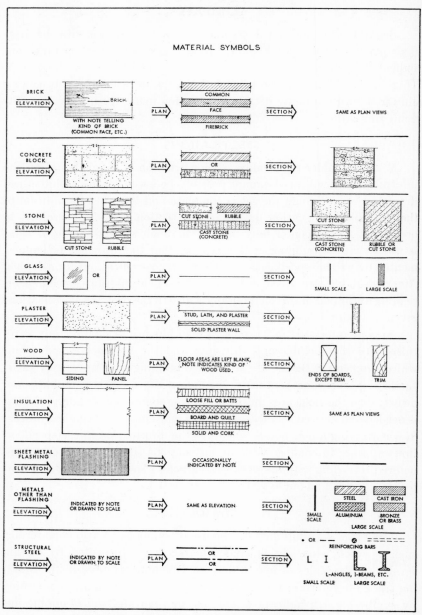

Fig. 3. Various Material Symbols Used by Builders

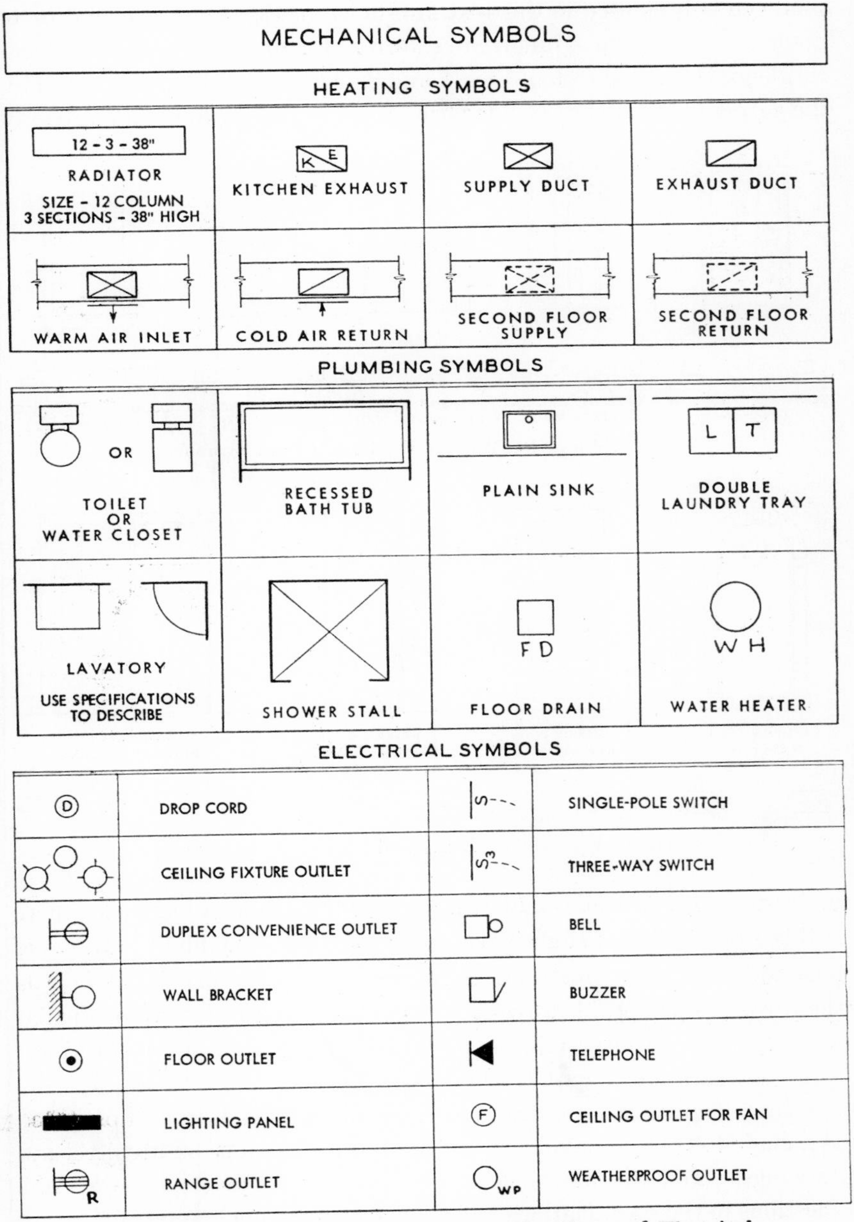

MECHANICAL SYMBOLS

HEATING SYMBOLS

12 - 3 - 38" RADIATOR SIZE - 12 COLUMN 3 SECTIONS - 38" HIGH	KITCHEN EXHAUST	SUPPLY DUCT	EXHAUST DUCT
WARM AIR INLET	COLD AIR RETURN	SECOND FLOOR SUPPLY	SECOND FLOOR RETURN

PLUMBING SYMBOLS

OR TOILET OR WATER CLOSET	RECESSED BATH TUB	PLAIN SINK	DOUBLE LAUNDRY TRAY
LAVATORY USE SPECIFICATIONS TO DESCRIBE	SHOWER STALL	F D FLOOR DRAIN	W H WATER HEATER

ELECTRICAL SYMBOLS

D	DROP CORD	S	SINGLE-POLE SWITCH
	CEILING FIXTURE OUTLET	S³	THREE-WAY SWITCH
	DUPLEX CONVENIENCE OUTLET		BELL
	WALL BRACKET		BUZZER
	FLOOR OUTLET		TELEPHONE
	LIGHTING PANEL	F	CEILING OUTLET FOR FAN
R	RANGE OUTLET	WP	WEATHERPROOF OUTLET

Fig. 4. Mechanical Symbols—Heating, Plumbing, and Electrical

plan symbols as used in this text are shown in Fig. 5. The elevation of doors and their plan symbols are shown in Fig. 6. Miscellaneous structural symbols are shown in Figs. 7 and 8. Although the symbols used by the carpentry trade are standardized to some extent and can be readily

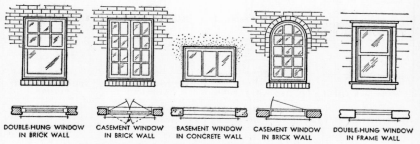

DOUBLE-HUNG WINDOW IN BRICK WALL   CASEMENT WINDOW IN BRICK WALL   BASEMENT WINDOW IN CONCRETE WALL   CASEMENT WINDOW IN BRICK WALL   DOUBLE-HUNG WINDOW IN FRAME WALL

Fig. 5. Elevation Windows and Their Plan Symbols

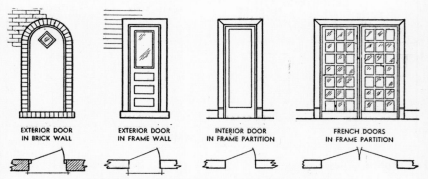

EXTERIOR DOOR IN BRICK WALL   EXTERIOR DOOR IN FRAME WALL   INTERIOR DOOR IN FRAME PARTITION   FRENCH DOORS IN FRAME PARTITION

Fig. 6. Elevation of Doors and Their Plan Symbols

understood by any tradesman, regardless of the language he speaks, there still is a possibility of slight variations in the use of symbols. To avoid misunderstanding of instructions, architects usually provide a *key* on the drawings as an aid in reading the symbols used for any particular job. Symbols for materials and mechanical devices, for a typical American home, are shown with the first-floor plans, Chapter X (Fig. 7).

The blueprint reading test on the adjoining page has been prepared as a guide to help you read and understand instructions on architectural drawings. You will find all the information required to answer these questions in the specifications and drawings given in Chapter X. Write out answers to the questions. Number each answer to correspond with the number of the question. When you have answered all of them, or as many as possible, turn to the Appendix at the back of the text and check your answers for correctness with those given there.

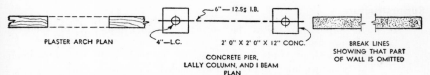

Fig. 7. Miscellaneous Construction Symbols on Working Drawings

Fig. 8. Structural Steel Sections

TEST YOUR KNOWLEDGE OF BLUEPRINT READING BY ANSWERING THESE QUESTIONS

General

1. What names are given to the four elevations shown on the working drawings for A Typical American Home?
2. Name the three floor plans of the house shown in Chapter X.
3. Through what parts of the building are the wall sections *A–A* and *B–B* taken?
4. To what scales are the various dimensions of this house drawn?

Foundation and Basement

5. What material is used for the outside foundation walls? What is the thickness of the outside walls?
6. (*a*) What material is used for the wall between the recreation and furnace rooms? (*b*) What is the thickness of this wall?
7. What is the length and width of the main section of the building? What is the length and width of the addition?
8. What is the total distance around the outside of the building not including the porch or chimney? (Allow 3′ 2″ for each side of the bay window.)
9. What is the thickness and width of the *footings*? (*Footings* are that part of the foundation built under and wider than the foundation or basement wall.)
10. How high are the foundation walls? (The first-floor construction is 1′ 2″ in thickness.)
11. How thick is the basement floor? Is it level with, or above, the top of the footings?

12. *(a)* What is the height of the foundation wall under the porch? *(b)* What is the thickness of this wall?

13. What size **I** beam is specified to carry the first-floor joists?

14. Give the *(a)* number; *(b)* kind of sash; and *(c)* size of the basement windows.

Superstructure

15. Is the superstructure of the house, shown in Chapter X, of wood or brick, or some other material?

16. What length of studs is required for the main-wall rear elevation? (The two top plates and the sill are each 1⅝" in thickness.)

17. What is the required thickness and width of the joists, and distance **O.C.**, for the living-room floor? (The length of these joists is 14'.)

18. Do the floor joists run in the same direction under and above the living room?

19. What is the width and thickness of the joists above the living room?

20. What is the size of the living room?

21. What is the thickness and width of the ceiling, or attic, joists? Distance on center?

22. What thickness and width will be required for the rafters for the front roof? Distance on center?

23. *(a)* How high are the tops of the windows set on the first floor, front? *(b)* How many panes are there in the basement windows? *(c)* What is the size of the glass used in the basement windows and in the bay window?

24. How high are the interior doors?

25. What is the ceiling height for the first floor? For the second floor?

26. How much does the main roof rise per foot of rafter run? What is the rise per foot run on the rear dormer? What is the rise per foot run of the roof of the addition?

27. What kind of insulation is specified for the exterior side walls?

28. In what detail drawing are the fire stops shown? What size are the fire stops?

29. What size bolts are required to anchor the plate to the foundation? How close are they set to each other?

30. What kind and size of bridging is required?

31. What is the width of the chimney at the fireplace?

32. How many flues has the chimney in the basement? At the second floor level? (*Flues* are the openings in the chimney through which the smoke and gases pass.)

33. What materials are to be used for the fireplace hearth?

34. What size is specified for the rear door? For the front door?

35. What size is specified for the doors (*H*)? Where are these doors located?

36. What kind of door is specified between the living room and hall?

37. What width counter is shown for the kitchen cabinets? What is the counter height?

38. What is the depth of the kitchen cabinet above the counter?

39. How many doors are there in the kitchen cabinet on each side of the window above the sink? What kind of doors are specified?

Mechanical Equipment

40. How many bath tubs are there in the house, shown in Chapter X? What is the length of each tub?
41. How many toilets, or water closets, are shown in the plans for this house?
42. How many lavatories, or wash basins, are indicated on the drawings for this house?
43. What is the thickness of the wall which carries the soil stack, or pipe?
44. Are there any floor drains in the basement? If so, where?
45. Is there a cabinet under the sink in the kitchen?
46. How many three-way switches are there in the building?
47. How many ceiling outlets are there in the basement? First floor? Second floor?
48. What kind of lighting is specified for the front door?
49. How many wall receptacles are there in the building? How many wall brackets?
50. Where would you look for information not given on the drawings?

CHECKING ON YOUR KNOWLEDGE

The following questions give you the opportunity to check up on yourself. If you have read the chapter carefully, you should be able to answer the questions. If you have any difficulty, read the chapter over once more so that you have the information well in mind before you go on with your reading.

DO YOU KNOW

1. Where to find the answers to the foregoing questions?
2. How disputes between the architect, carpenter, dealer in materials, and the homeowner can be prevented?
3. Why blueprints are drawn to scale?
4. The names of five different building materials which may be indicated on blueprints with standard symbols?
5. The difference between *floor plans* and a *plan view?*
6. What the *datum line* is?
7. What parts of a house are indicated on blueprints by: full or visible lines; dash lines; and heavy broken long and short lines?
8. How the end of a dimension is indicated on a blueprint?
9. Why sectional views are drawn on a larger scale than the main part of the house?
10. What is meant by the terms *window* and *door schedules?*

HOUSE IN PROCESS OF CONSTRUCTION SHOWING TWO DIFFERENT TYPES OF SCAFFOLDING

Courtesy of American Builder

A Typical American Home

QUESTIONS THIS CHAPTER WILL ANSWER

1. *In addition to the actual construction work, in what way is the carpenter an important factor in the building of a home?* 2. *What responsibilities must he assume in connection with the work done by other craftsmen on the job?* 3. *Before beginning construction of a house, what picture must the carpenter have in mind?* 4. *What method of procedure makes possible the creating of such a mental image?* 5. *Why is it necessary for the carpenter to be able to transfer his mental image to the minds of his fellow workmen? What important features are included in such a picture?*

INTRODUCTION TO CHAPTER X

You will find this a remarkable chapter; one that suggests the great variety of activities connected with the building of a house. You are told how the construction of a house really begins. Drawings and plans, such as those you will now read about, were used in the construction of the house shown in the picture (top), Fig. 1. This chapter also tells you what preliminary plans are necessary before beginning the construction of a building, and the part you as a carpenter will play as the work proceeds.

Construction begins with the study of the architectural drawings, building plans, and the carpenter's specifications. The details contained in this chapter should be read more than once. You should become familiar with the facts given here and learn the importance of knowing how to follow such drawings and specifications. Notice particularly the complete and detailed instructions given in the carpenter's specifications. When reading such statements as these, you will realize the importance of your obligations and responsibilities as a carpenter.

The carpenter must have a knowledge and understanding of building plans or drawings as well as of tools and materials. Since everything cannot be shown on the drawings, a word picture of the work and materials, called *specifications,* must be made available to the builder. The drawings, then, together with the specifications, will help both the builder and the owner to understand each other better and to know how and what is to be built.

A good carpenter is more than a mere craftsman, more than a man who works skilfully with his hands. He must be capable also of imagination; and as you read this chapter you should be able to visualize, or get a mental picture, of the house to be constructed. The three views shown in Fig. 1 will help you to visualize the finished house.

Front and West-Side
View

Front and East-Side View

Rear View

Fig. 1. A Typical American Home

After reading this chapter you will have a better understanding than before of how the work of the carpenter must be co-ordinated and harmonized with the work of other skilled craftsmen on the job. You will appreciate how essential it is for men, each doing the work assigned to him, to co-operate in bringing together materials, supplies, and equipment with which to fashion and construct the dwelling. This co-operation and harmony in working together is necessary if the construction of the house is to be a final success.

Since "houses are built to live in," the type of civilization attained by any race, or people, is judged today by the kind and variety of houses, or shelters, in which they live and carry on their everyday activities. Therefore, it pays to build well.

VISUALIZING THE HOUSE

Since carpentry is the subject under consideration in this text, only the work of the carpenter is dealt with in detail. The activities of other tradesmen are considered only when they may affect the work of the carpenter. The preceding chapters deal largely with preparatory steps in the process of learning the carpentry trade, including discussions and illustrations of: the carpenter's tools and their uses; the growth of woods, their physical characteristics and use in the carpentry trade; building insulations and methods of their application; numerous wood fastenings; and builders' hardware. In an early chapter instructions are given for building various small devices, such as a workbench, stepladder, and toolboxes. Also included in these preliminary chapters are several tables containing information valuable to the carpenter as timesavers.

In this chapter you will learn how to interpret plans used in the actual construction of a new house. The subject of your study is a typical American home, shown in Fig. 1. The architectural drawings and building plans used in the construction of this house have been used in the building of numerous American homes. In any building project, floor plans are especially important. Such plans must be prepared carefully and be exact in every detail.

The floor plans presented in this chapter will help you as a student to understand how to go about the construction work of a new house. When you look at the floor plans for a proposed new building, you should be able to form a mental picture of the work to be done and the appearance and arrangement of the rooms after the building is finished. This visualizing process requires a knowledge of several important principles, as well as familiarity with the special language and symbols used in the building trade.

The drawings, of course, have to be made much smaller than the portion of the house they represent. However, this does not affect their usefulness since they are drawn accurately to scale and contain all the necessary measurements. For instance, illustrations of articles of clothing or pictures of household furnishings, when used for advertising purposes in newspapers and magazines, or in merchandise catalogues, represent articles much larger than the pictures shown. Yet, we are able to visualize the articles as they appear in actual full size. The same holds true for floor plans of a building.

Because floor plans are proportionately so small, it is not possible to show all details exactly as they will appear in full size. For example, walls contain many parts and it would be impossible to show all of the parts on such a small scale. Hence, we use symbols; each symbol having a definite meaning either as to structure, or material, or both.

BUILDING PLANS

The success of any construction job depends to a great extent upon the builder's foreknowledge of the various problems involved in the project to be undertaken and in his ability to solve these problems as they arise. In order to achieve the results desired, a carpenter must have in mind a clear picture of the completed building before he begins any part of the construction work. In addition to being able to visualize the finished house himself, the builder, or architect, must also be able to convey his mental picture to others, including the various mechanics and tradesmen, as well as the prospective homeowner. This transfer of the mental image of the new house can be accomplished only by means of *drawings*, or *building plans*. Such plans must be prepared by a competent architect and copies, or *blueprints*, given to every individual who is in any way responsible for any part of the construction work. It is only by the use of such drawings that all possibility of misunderstanding regarding construction details can be eliminated.

When a carpenter speaks of *drawings* or *plans* for a house, he refers to a specific group of architectural drawings which show every detail of the particular job to be undertaken. These plans show the exterior appearance of the completed building, including front view, rear view, and each side view. (See Figs. 1, 3, and 5.) The drawings also show the location of windows, doors, and the division of the interior space into rooms, together with other details. Such details must be shown in a standard manner on the drawings so that everyone who reads them will form the same mental picture of the finished structure and will understand what work is to be done before the project is completed. In visualizing floor plans, we must remember that the plans are drawn as though we were looking directly down into the rooms. Then, once we understand the symbols used, we can easily form a mental picture of each room.

To the trade, building plans are known by various names. The term *working drawings* is sometimes used because the drawings show the work that is to be done. Many people engaged in the building industry refer to architectural drawings as *plans*, since, to most of us, a plan is the outline of something we expect to do. In this text the term *architectural drawings* is applied to a set of building plans showing the front, rear, and side views of a typical American home, with floor plans showing the arrangements into rooms and the numerous details of the interior of the building. Also shown are the locations of doors, windows, and stairs. Various other details shown include dimensions, material symbols, design of the fireplace, layout of the kitchen and bathrooms, also the sizes and kind of materials to be used throughout the building. Every detail must be noted carefully by the carpenter and other mechanics. All such details are a part of the actual planning for a new house.

A complete set of working drawings for a typical American home, such as are prepared by any competent architect, are found on the following pages. The south elevation, or front of the house, is shown in Fig. 2. The east elevation, or right side, is shown in Fig. 3; details of the fireplace, together with the kitchen cabinets, also are shown in Fig. 3. The north elevation, or rear, is shown in Fig. 4; the details of the stairs, together with the details of doors *C* and *D*, also are shown in Fig. 4. The west elevation, or left side, is shown in Fig. 5; details of the bay-window construction of the dining room, together with the interior trim details, and the beam-construction details for the porch are shown also in Fig. 5.

The basement plan, with its room arrangement and foundation requirements, is shown in Fig. 6. The main, or first-floor, plan is shown in Fig. 7. The window and door schedules, the key to the various materials, and the symbols used for electric and other outlet requirements

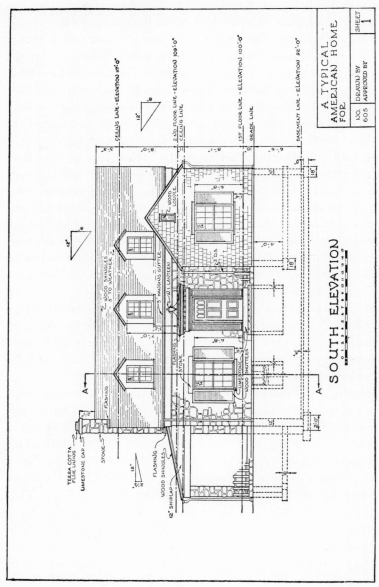

Fig. 2. South, or Front, Elevation of a Typical American Home

The plans for the south elevation were originally drawn to a scale of ¼ inch equal to one foot, but when the plans were reduced to the page size of this text, the scale was correspondingly reduced.

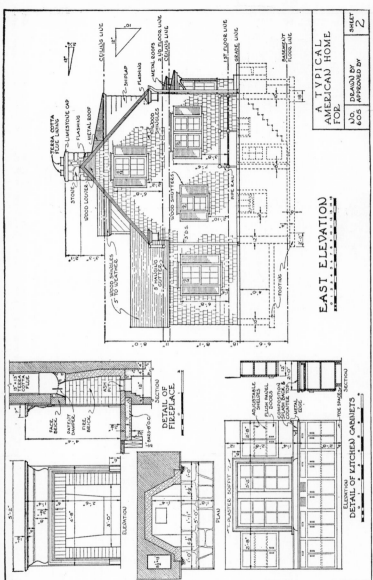

Fig. 3. East, or Right. Elevation of a Typical American Home, Together with Details of the Fireplace and Kitchen Cabinets

The plans for the east elevation were originally drawn to a scale of ¼ inch equal to one foot; details of the fireplace were drawn to a scale of ¾ inch equal to one foot; and details of the kitchen cabinets were drawn to a scale of ½ inch equal to one foot, but when the plans were reduced to the page size of this text, the scales were correspondingly reduced.

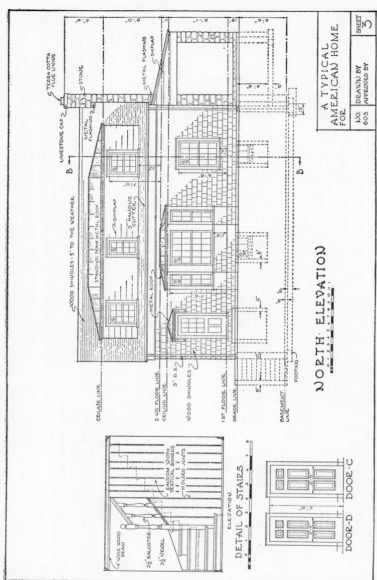

Fig. 4. North, or Rear, Elevation of a Typical American Home, Together with Details of Stairs and Doors *C* and *D*

The plans for the north elevation were originally drawn to a scale of ¼ inch equal to one foot; and details of the stairs were drawn to a scale of ½ inch equal to one foot, but when the plans were reduced to the page size of this text, the scales were correspondingly reduced.

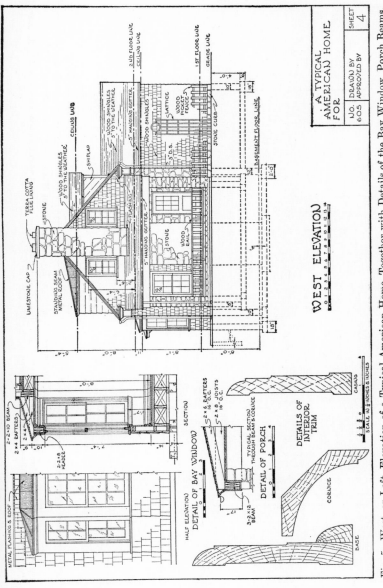

Fig. 5. West, or Left, Elevation of a Typical American Home, Together with Details of the Bay Window, Porch Beams, and Interior Trim

The plans for the west elevation originally were drawn to a scale of ¼ inch equal to one foot; details of the bay window and porch beams were drawn to a scale of ½ inch equal to one foot; and the details of the interior trim were drawn to a scale of 1 inch equal to one foot, but when the plans were reduced to the page size of this text the scales were correspondingly reduced.

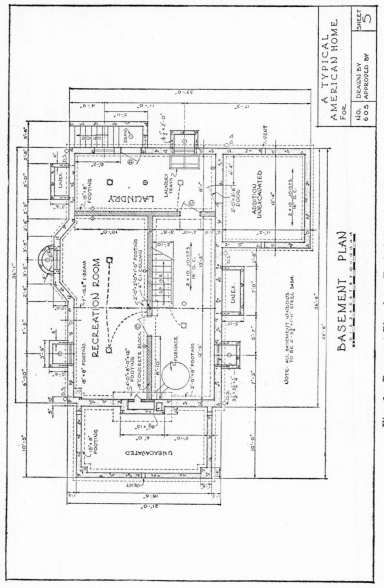

Fig. 6. Basement Plan for a Typical American Home

The basement-floor plans were originally drawn to a scale of ¼ inch equal to one foot, but when the plans were reduced to the page size of this text, the scale was correspondingly reduced.

also are shown in Fig. 7. The second-floor plans are shown in Fig. 8. Entrance features are important and demand more careful detailing than is shown in the south-elevation drawing; these details are found in Fig. 8.

The details of these drawings bring out certain important construction information which would be difficult to show in the elevation or floor-plan drawings. Details for the typical wall construction for the south wall in the living room is shown at *A–A* and for the north wall at *B–B*, Fig. 9.

CARPENTRY SPECIFICATIONS

Since it is impossible to show every minute detail on drawings, additional explanations are often given in the *carpentry specifications* which supplement the drawings. These specifications are written, telling in words what cannot be shown graphically on the architectural drawings. The information furnished by the specifications include directions regarding concrete mixtures; grades of lumber, bricks, and other materials; quality and catalogue number of mechanical appliances, and detailed instructions as to how the work is to be performed. The best method of giving all such detailed information is by means of *written specifications* similar to those presented in the following pages. These specifications may be defined as *instructions to the builder,* and as such they must be simple and complete. The primary aim of the written specifications is to make perfectly clear to the builder every item that cannot be shown on the *drawings* or *blueprints.*

In addition to their primary purpose, specifications have other important uses. Estimators, including general contractors, subcontractors, manufacturers, and material dealers make use of building specifications when calculating cost of materials and labor. If carefully written, specifications make it possible for estimators to price material and labor exactly. The specifications also serve as a guide to all the trades in carrying out their specific parts of a construction job. Well-prepared specifications save time, reduce waste in both material and labor, and assure better workmanship. They also serve as a guide in the purchase of all types of fixtures, especially millwork and built-in furnishings. Another important use of specifications is the preventing of disputes between the owner and the general contractor, also between the general

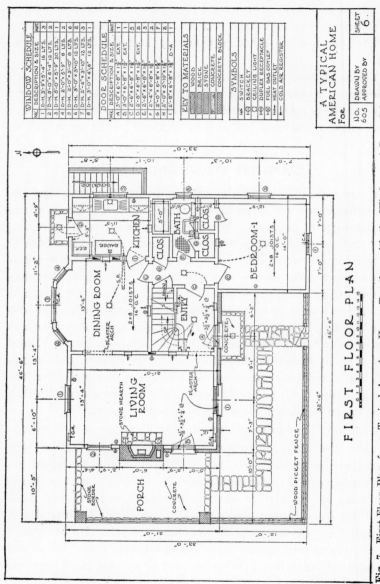

Fig. 7. First-Floor Plan for a Typical American Home, Together with the Window and Door Schedules, Key to Materials, and Mechanical Symbols

The first-floor plans originally were drawn to a scale of ¼ inch equal to one foot. but when the plans were reduced to the page size of this text, the scale was correspondingly reduced.

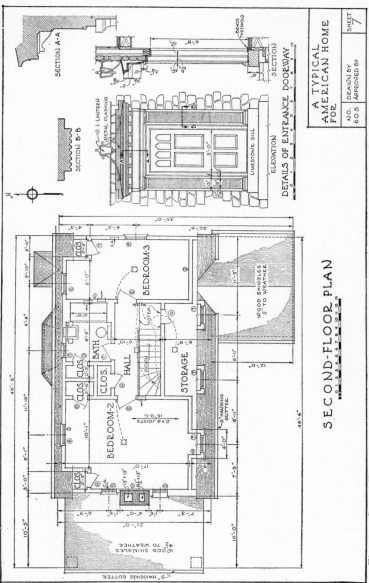

Fig. 8. Second-Floor Plan for a Typical American Home, Together with Details for Front Entrance Doorway

The plans for the second floor originally were drawn to a scale of ¼ inch equal to one foot; the details for the entrance doorway were originally drawn to a scale of ½ inch equal to one foot, but when the plans were reduced to the page size of this text, the scales were correspondingly reduced.

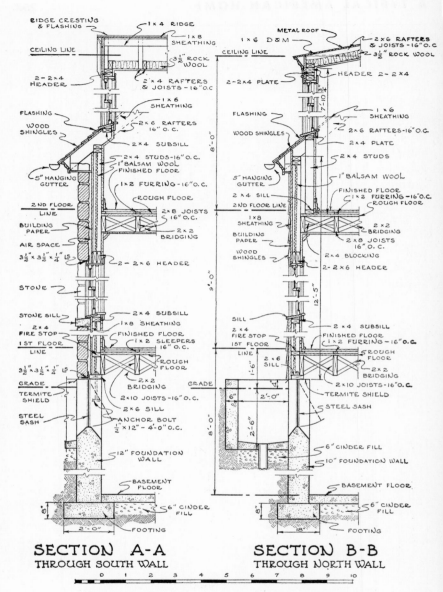

SECTION A-A
THROUGH SOUTH WALL

SECTION B-B
THROUGH NORTH WALL

Fig. 9. South Wall, Section *A-A*; North Wall, Section *B-B*

The plans for the sections of the south and north walls originally were drawn to a scale of ½ inch equal to one foot, but when the plans were reduced to the page size of this text, the scale was correspondingly reduced.

contractor and the subcontractor. If all necessary items are amply covered by the specifications, there can be no grounds for a dispute. Contracts are made in accordance with specifications.

Complete specifications deal with every phase of the building under construction, including carpentry, masonry, tile work, concrete work, electric wiring and fixtures, heating and ventilating, plumbing, lathing and plastering, painting, papering, roofing, insulation, weather stripping, and various miscellaneous items peculiar to every specific construction job. In addition, building specifications give general information regarding building permits for various trades, contract payments, insurance, liabilities, provisions for changes from original plans, drawings, or specifications, and supervision of construction work. However, in this text, we are interested only in the carpentry phase of the work. The purpose of the examples given in this chapter is to present a set of typical specifications so the student will understand their importance and know how to use them to the best advantage.

SPECIFICATIONS

1. WORK REQUIRED. The contractor shall furnish and erect all woodwork mentioned in the building specifications or indicated on the drawings, including all framing and finishing woodwork both outside and inside. He is to co-operate with and do any necessary carpentry required by other trades for completing their work.

No finished woodwork or finish flooring is to be put in place or stored in the building until the plastering is finished and thoroughly dry.

2. DIMENSION LUMBER. Unless otherwise specified, all dimension lumber shall be No. 1 yellow pine or fir, thoroughly seasoned. All lumber shall be straight and free from any defects that would weaken the stick.

3. WOOD JOISTS. Joists shall be framed properly with a clearance of 2 inches around the chimney masonry, except where 8 inches of masonry is used outside the flue lining, in which case the framing may be built flush with the chimney masonry. The 2-inch space thus formed shall be filled with fire-resistant material to form a fire stop. Framing necessary around stair wells and other similar places shall be of trimmers and headers, consisting of double joists well spiked together.

The cutting of floor joists to facilitate the installation of piping and duct work will be permitted, with the following limitations:

a) The top or bottom edges of joists may be notched not to exceed 1/6 of the joist depth. Notching the top or bottom edge of joists will not be permitted in the middle third of any joist span.

b) If cutting of a floor joist more than 1/6 of its depth is found necessary, a header the full depth of the joist shall be cut in to support the end of the joist.

c) Where location of pipes necessitates their passing through the joists, holes shall be drilled to receive the pipes. The diameter of the holes shall not be more than $\frac{1}{2}$ inch greater than the outside diameter of the pipe and in no case shall the diameter of the holes be greater than $2\frac{1}{2}$ inches. The edge of the holes shall not be located nearer than 2 inches from the top or bottom edge of the joist.

No stud shall be cut more than half its depth to receive piping and duct work. If more depth is required, the partition studs shall be increased accordingly. Where the running of pipes and ducts necessitates the cutting of plates, proper provision shall be made for tying together and supporting all structural members affected by such cutting.

4. ROOF. The wood-shingled roof is to be sheathed with No. 2, 6-inch boards laid with 1-inch spacing between boards. The sheathing for the metal roof to be 6-inch D & M (dressed and matched).

5. EXTERIOR WALL COVERING. All exterior sheathing is to be covered with one layer of asphalt waterproof building paper before finished material is applied. Paper is to be placed horizontally with at least 2-inch lap.

a) Exterior walls, where indicated, to be covered with the best grade of clear vertical grain Royal (4/2" 24") shingles laid 10 inches to the weather.

Note: A double starting row shall be used in shingle installation.

b) Exterior walls on the small dormers, porch ends, to be clear cypress shiplap.

c) All exterior trim, including roof cornice, porch, and bay window shall be clear white pine or cypress, carefully fitted and thoroughly nailed.

6. ROOF COVERING. Roof covering to be the best-grade vertical grain clear shingles (5/2" 16") where shingles are indicated. These shingles to be laid 5 inches to the weather except on the porch roof where they are to be laid $4\frac{1}{2}$ inches to the weather, double coursing all first courses.

7. INSULATION. Furnish and install wall thickness ($3\frac{1}{2}$") rock-wool blanket in all ceilings and roof as indicated and 1-inch balsam wool blanket in all exterior walls. The insulation to be inclosed in a vapor-proof paper covering with a spacer flange on the 1-inch blanket. All insulation to be installed according to manufacturers' instructions.

8. PARTITIONS. All studding partitions and outside walls shall be constructed as shown of 2x4's or 2x6's, with plates well spiked. All studs to be spaced 16 inches O.C. (on center). Cut 1x6 ribbons into studdings for supporting joists. Double studding around all openings, at all corners, and properly trussed across all openings. Corners for all rooms should be framed solid for lath or other interior finish.

9. WOOD FLOORS. Subfloor. Joists shall be floored with No.2, 8-inch sheathing laid close and double-nailed at each joist; straight on first floor, diagonally, on second floor.

Finished wood floors shall be hardwood as noted in the finish schedule and shall be laid on furring strips. Between all finished wood floors and subfloors provide single layer of building paper or deadening felt.

All flooring shall be well drawn together, joints broken and sanded, ready to receive finish as specified in painting instructions.

10. WEATHERSTRIPS. Furnish and install spring bronze

weatherstrips, for all windows and exterior doors, complete with interlocking sills for all exterior doors.

11. CALKING. All exterior doors and window frames set in masonry and all other intersections of wood and masonry shall be calked with an approved standard brand of calking paste.

12. WOOD DOOR AND WINDOW FRAMES. The parts of the frames exposed outside shall be made of strictly clear white pine or cypress. Pulley stiles to be $\frac{7}{8}$ of an inch in thickness and to have pockets for access to weights. Frame to be complete with blind stop, beads, sills, casings, and pulleys, all as shown on drawings.

13. WOOD SASH. All exterior sash shall be $1\frac{3}{8}$ inches thick unless otherwise indicated, made of kiln-dried white pine or cypress. All shall be mortised and tenoned and divided as shown on drawings. Basement windows to be steel sash.

14. STAIRS. Basement stairs to have $\frac{7}{8}$-inch mitered yellow pine risers and $1\frac{5}{8}$-inch treads, well supported on 2x12 stringers, 16 inches O.C., all as detailed on drawings. The main stairway shall be housed, properly glued, wedged, and blocked. The risers to be of white pine and the treads of oak. This stairway shall have not less than 6 feet 8 inches continuous clear head room measured vertically from the front edge of the tread to a line parallel to the stair run.

15. DOORS. All doors to be sandpapered, scraped, and hand smoothed. For sizes, thickness, and design, see drawings. Interior doors in finished rooms to be veneered on both sides to match trim of room.

16. CLOSETS. In all closets the trim and base shall be $\frac{5}{8}$ of an inch in thickness without moldings. Each closet to have 12-inch shelves and hook strips. Include $\frac{3}{4}$-inch gas pipe across back for hangers.

17. CUPBOARDS AND CASES. Build as shown and indicated, with $1\frac{1}{8}$-inch flush doors and $\frac{7}{8}$-inch adjustable shelves. All cupboards and other cases in the kitchen to have a birch face; cabinets in the rest of the house the same as the trim in the room.

18. MEDICINE CABINETS. Built-in toilet and bathroom medicine cabinets of steel.

19. PICTURE MOLD. Picture mold to be furnished and applied for the dining room and bedroom on the first floor as detailed, and material is to match the woodwork of the room.

20. CASINGS. All casings shall be detailed.

21. THRESHOLDS. Where two different kinds of flooring join, cover the joint with a neat threshold.

22. SCREENS. Furnish and fit for all exterior windows and doors full screens, frames $1\frac{1}{8}$-inch thick of white pine or cypress with mortise-and-tenon joints. All netting shall be best copper wire applied with tacks and covered with molding.

23. STORM SASH AND DOORS. Furnish and fit for all exterior windows and doors storm sash and doors, $1\frac{1}{8}$-inch thick, glazed with D.S.A. (double strength grade A) glass. Doors to match entrance doors of house.

24. CORNICE. Furnish and install wood cornice in rooms as detailed on drawings.

25. WOOD BASE. Furnish and install wood base in all rooms as detailed on drawings.

26. FIREPLACE MANTEL. Furnish and install as detailed, fireplace mantel and shelf.

27. ROUGH AND FINISH HARDWARE. Furnish all necessary rough hardware, such as nails, wall ties, sash weights, sash cord, and other builders' hardware, to complete the job.

a) Finish Hardware. All finish hardware, such as locks, butts, door checks, and similar finish hardware, except as otherwise specified, will be purchased by the owner and delivered to the building where the contractor shall receipt for it and properly install it.

b) Contractor shall include in his bid an allowance of $100.00 for finish hardware which owner will select and deliver to the building. Saving in this shall revert to owner, any extra cost to be borne by him. Contractor shall replace, at his own expense, any hardware that is lost or damaged.

SCHEDULE FOR WOOD TRIM AND FLOORING

BASEMENT. Wood trim around doors to be yellow pine.
FIRST FLOOR. Wood trim, grade B* or better white pine, except the kitchen and bathroom where it is to be select birch. Living room and entry walls to be covered with shiplap—molded knotty pine placed vertically; boards are to be 4-, 6-, and 8-inch widths. Flooring material to be grade A, 2¼-inch, straight-grain red oak in all rooms and hall except the kitchen and bathroom, which are to be in 4-inch flat-grain fir flooring. All flooring to be machine-sanded to a smooth finish ready for stain and filler. Kitchen and bathroom floors to be covered either by linoleum or asphalt tile which will be installed by owner.
SECOND FLOOR. Wood trim, grade B or, better, white pine, except bathroom, which is to be select birch. All floors to be 2¼-inch straight-grain red oak except bathroom, which is to be 4-inch flat-grain fir flooring.

CHECKING ON YOUR KNOWLEDGE

The following questions give you the opportunity to check up on yourself. If you have read the chapter carefully, you should be able to answer the questions. If you have any difficulty, read the chapter over until you have the information well in mind before you go on with your reading.

DO YOU KNOW

1. What is meant by the terms *architectural drawings, working drawings,* and *building plans?*
2. How working drawings reveal construction information, such as certain details for a typical wall construction?
3. Why it is important for building specifications to be exact?
4. What items of information the carpenter usually finds in the building specifications?
5. Why contracts are made in accordance with building specifications?
6. How the term *architectural drawings* is used in this text?
7. Why it is important to show such details as the location of windows and doors in a standard manner in drawings?
8. How the carpenter gets a mental image of the finished house before he begins work?
9. What other tradesmen and mechanics must also have a mental image of the finished house before construction work begins?
10. How the carpenter transfers his mental image of the completed house to the minds of the other tradesmen who are to work on the same job?

* For American Standard Lumber Grades, see Tables III and IV, Chapter V, on Principal Woods, Their Uses, Grades. and Classifications.

APPENDIX

ANSWERS TO QUESTIONS ON BLUEPRINT READING

CHAPTER IX

When checking your answers to the questions, given at the end of Chapter IX, with the following correct answers, draw a line through any of your answers which are wrong. If there are two or more parts to a question, mark each part separately. If you have answered one part correctly cross out only that part of your answer which is wrong.

1. The names of the four elevations are: *South, East, North,* and *West.*

2. The floor plans shown are: *basement, first floor,* and *second floor.*

3. The wall sections shown in detail are: *A—A* through the south window of the living room; and *B—B* through the north window of the living room.

4. The scales used in the original blueprints for the house, shown in Chapter X, are as follows: for the elevation drawings and floor plans, ¼" equals one foot; for details of the fireplace, ¾" equals one foot; for details of the kitchen cabinets, stairs, bay window, porch beams, and the wall sections, *A—A* and *B—B,* ½" equals one foot; for details of the interior trim, 1" equals one foot

Note: The original blueprints, reduced to conform to the page size of this text, are reproduced in Chapter X. For your convenience the scales, correspondingly reduced, are shown in connection with the working drawings to which they apply.

5. Concrete. The thicknesses of the outside foundation walls are 12" and 10". See *Basement Plan.*

6. *(a)* Concrete blocks; *(b)* the thickness is 8".

7. The main section of the house, shown in Chapter X, is 36' 6" in length (front) and 21' in width. The addition is 12'x14.'

8. The total distance around the building, not including the porch (nor chimney), but allowing 3' 2" for each side of the bay window, is 139' 11".

9. Two different widths are used for footings. Under the 12" walls the footings are 2' 0"; under other walls the footings are 1' 6". All wall footings are 8" in thickness. Chimney footings are 12".

10. The foundation walls of the main section are 7' 2" in height. The difference between the elevation 100' 0" and 92' is 8'. This distance minus the thickness of the first-floor construction (1' 2") plus 4" the thickness of the basement floor gives the height of the foundation walls.

11. The basement floor is 4" thick. It is above the footing.

12. *(a)* The height of the foundation wall under the porch is 4' 4"; *(b)* the thickness of this wall is 8".

13. The size of the I beam specified, as shown in the basement-floor plan, is 7", weight 15.3 pounds per foot.

14. *(a)* There are five windows in the basement; *(b)* steel sashes; *(c)* size of all basement windows to be 2' 9¾"x1' 11".

15. The superstructure of the house, shown in Chapter X, is of wood frame construction with stone veneer, wood shingles, and shiplap siding finish.

16. For the main-wall rear elevation, the studs are 12' 5" minus two top plates and one sill (each 1⅝" in thickness), or 12' ⅛".

17. For the living-room floor, the required size for the joists is 2x10, spaced 16″ on center (O.C.).

18. Yes, the floor joists run in the same direction under and above the living-room floor. See detail sections of walls *A—A* and *B—B*.

19. The joists above the living room are 2x8.

20. The living room is 12′ 7″ wide and 19′ 6″ long. *Note:* The dimensions shown on the first-floor plan give the length of the living room as 21′ 0″. From this subtract the width, or thickness, of the outside front wall (12″) and the thickness of the rear wall (6″) which leaves 19′ 6″. The width of the living room shown on the plans, including the thickness of the west wall (6″) and one-half of the partition wall (3″) is 13′ 4″. From this subtract 9″, the sum of the outside wall and half of the partition which gives 12′ 7″.

21. The ceiling or attic-floor joists are: 2x6 spaced 16″ O.C.

22. The rafters on the front roof are 2x6 spaced 16″ O.C.

23. *(a)* Measured from the top of the sash, the height of the windows on the first floor front is 6′ 8″. (See *South Elevation* plan.) *(b)* There are three panes in each of the basement windows. *(c)* The size is 10″ x 20″. The size of lights in the bay window is 10″x16″. (See *North Elevation* drawing.)

24. According to the door schedule all interior doors are 6′ 8″ in height, except two of the closet doors *(H)* on the second floor.

25. The ceiling height for the first floor is 8′ 1″. (The difference between elevation 100′ 0″ and 109′ 0″ is 9′ 0″. This figure minus the total thickness of the construction for the second floor, which is 11″, gives height of first-floor ceiling.) The second-floor ceiling height is 8′ 0″.

26. The rise per foot of rafter run for the main roof is 10″ per foot. For the rear dormer windows, the rise per foot of rafter run is 2¼″ per foot. For the addition the rise per foot of rafter run is 8″ per foot.

27. For the exterior walls the insulation used is 1″ balsam wool.

28. Fire stops are shown in the detail sections *A—A* and *B—B*, Chapter X (Fig. 9). The fire stops are 2x4s.

29. The size of the anchor bolts for the foundation walls is ½″x12″. The bolts are set at a distance from each other of 4′ 0″, O.C.

30. The bridging is of wood, size 2x2.

31. The width of the chimney at the fireplace is 6′ 0″.

32. The chimney has one flue in the basement; two flues on the second floor.

33. Stone is used for the fireplace hearth.

34. The specifications for the rear door call for size 2′ 8″x6′ 8″ with a thickness of 1¾″. The specifications for the front door call for size 3′ 0″ x 6′ 8″, with a thickness of 1¾″.

35. The size specified for doors *H* is 2′ 0″x5′ 10″ with 1⅜″ thickness. These are two closet doors on second floor.

36. There is no specification given for the door between the living room and hall; the plans show a plastered archway here.

37. The kitchen cabinets are to have a counter of a little more than 2′ 0″ in width. (See detail drawing.) The counter height is 3′ 0″.

38. The depth of the cabinet above the counter is 12″.

39. There are two doors on each side of the window above the kitchen sink. Flush panel doors are specified.

40. There are two bath tubs, each 5′ 0″ in length.

41. There are two toilets.

42. There are two lavatories.

43. The stack wall (see first-floor plan) is 8″ thick, to allow for the hub of the pipe.

44. There are two floor drains in the basement: one in the furnace room and one in the laundry.

45. Yes.

46. There are four three-way switches in the building.

47. There are five ceiling outlets in the basement; six on the first floor; and four on the second floor.

48. The front door has a wall lantern above it.

49. There are twenty wall receptacles and six wall brackets, making a total of twenty-six.

50. Information not given in the drawings can be found in the specifications, Chapter X.

When you have finished checking your answers with the correct answer given here, add up the number of answers you had wrong, if any, then find your score. Each complete question rates 2 per cent. If the question is divided into two parts and you had one part correct and the other part wrong, give yourself credit for 1 per cent. If your score is less than 25 per cent, you should spend more time in study of the material given in this text. When you have thoroughly mastered the information presented here, you should be able to make a high score.

Right ——

Wrong ——

Score ——

TABLE I. WEIGHTS OF WOODS GROWN IN THE UNITED STATES—
COMMERCIALLY IMPORTANT[1]

| SPECIES | WEIGHT PER CUBIC FOOT | | WEIGHT PER 1,000 BOARD FEET (NOMINAL SIZE) AIR DRY (12 PER CENT MOISTURE CONTENT) |
	Green	Air Dry (12 Per Cent Moisture Content)	
	Pound	Pound	Pound
Alder, red..............................	46	28	2,330
Ash, black.............................	52	34	2,830
Ash, commercial white*..................	48	41	3,420
Ash, Oregon............................	46	38	3,160
Aspen.................................	43	26	2,170
Basswood..............................	42	26	2,170
Beech.................................	54	45	3,750
Birch†................................	57	44	3,670
Birch, paper...........................	50	38	3,160
Butternut.............................	46	27	2,250
Cedar, Alaska..........................	36	31	2,580
Cedar, eastern red......................	37	33	2,750
Cedar, incense.........................	45	—	—
Cedar, northern white...................	28	22	1,830
Cedar, Port Orford......................	56	29	2,420
Cedar, southern white...................	26	23	1,920
Cedar, western red......................	27	23	1,920
Cherry, black..........................	45	35	2,930
Chestnut..............................	55	30	2,500
Cottonwood, eastern....................	49	28	2,330
Cottonwood, northern black.............	46	24	2,000
Cypress, southern......................	51	32	2,670
Douglas fir (coast region)...............	38	34	2,830
Douglas fir (*Inland Empire* region)........	36	31	2,580
Douglas fir (Rocky Mountain region).......	35	30	2,500
Elm, American.........................	54	35	2,920
Elm, rock.............................	53	44	3,670
Elm, slippery..........................	56	37	3,080
Fir, balsam............................	45	25	2,080
Fir, commercial white‡..................	46	27	2,250
Gum, black............................	45	35	2,920
Gum, red..............................	50	34	2,830
Gum, tupelo...........................	56	35	2,920
Hackberry.............................	50	37	3,080
Hemlock, eastern.......................	50	28	2,330
Hemlock, western.......................	41	29	2,420

[1]United States *Wood Handbook*.
*Average of biltmore white ash, blue ash, green ash, and white ash.
†Average of sweet birch and yellow birch.
‡Average of lowland white fir and white fir.

TABLE 1. WEIGHTS OF WOODS GROWN IN THE UNITED STATES—
COMMERCIALLY IMPORTANT (Continued)

SPECIES	WEIGHT PER CUBIC FOOT		WEIGHT PER 1,000 BOARD FEET (NOMINAL SIZE) AIR DRY (12 PER CENT MOISTURE CONTENT)
	Green	Air Dry (12 Per Cent Moisture Content)	
	Pound	Pound	Pound
Hickory, pecan*..........................	62	45	3,750
Hickory, true†...........................	63	51	4,250
Honey locust.............................	61	—	——
Larch, western...........................	48	36	3,000
Locust, black............................	58	48	4,000
Magnolia, cucumber.......................	49	33	2,750
Magnolia, evergreen......................	59	35	2,920
Maple, bigleaf...........................	47	34	2,830
Maple, black.............................	54	40	3,330
Maple, red...............................	50	38	3,170
Maple, silver............................	45	33	2,750
Maple, sugar.............................	56	44	3,670
Oak, red‡................................	64	44	3,670
Oak, white§..............................	63	47	3,920
Pine, lodgepole..........................	39	29	2,420
Pine, northern white.....................	36	25	2,080
Pine, Norway.............................	42	34	2,830
Pine, ponderosa..........................	45	28	2,330
Pines, southern yellow:			
loblolly............................	53	36	3,000
longleaf............................	55	41	3,420
shortleaf...........................	52	36	3,000
Pine, sugar..............................	52	25	2,080
Pine, western white......................	35	27	2,250
Poplar, yellow...........................	38	28	2,330
Redwood..................................	50	28	2,330
Spruce, eastern‖.........................	34	28	2,330
Spruce, Engelmann........................	39	23	1,920
Spruce, Sitka............................	33	28	2,330
Sugarberry...............................	48	36	3,000
Sycamore.................................	52	34	2,830
Tamarack.................................	47	37	3,080
Walnut, black............................	58	38	3,170

*Average of bitternut hickory, nutmeg hickory, water hickory, and pecan.
†Average of bigleaf shagbark hickory, mockernut hickory, pignut hickory, and shagbark hickory.
‡Average of black oak, laurel oak, pin oak, red oak. scarlet oak, southern red oak, swamp red oak, water oak, and willow oak.
§Average of bur oak, chestnut oak, post oak, swamp chestnut oak, swamp white oak, and white oak.
‖Average of black spruce, red spruce, and white spruce.

TABLE II. SOFTWOODS—EASE OF WORKING WITH HAND TOOLS[1]

EASY TO WORK	MEDIUM TO WORK	DIFFICULT TO WORK
Cedar, incense	Cedar, eastern red	Douglas fir
Cedar, northern white	Cypress, southern	Larch, western
Cedar, Port Orford	Fir, balsam	Pine, southern yellow
Cedar, southern white	Fir, white	
Cedar, western red	Hemlock, eastern	
Pine, northern white	Hemlock, western	
Pine, ponderosa	Pine, lodgepole	
Pine, sugar	Redwood	
Pine, western white	Spruce, eastern	
	Spruce, Sitka	

[1]United States *Wood Handbook*.

Paint as a Preservative of Wood. When examined under a microscope, a piece of wood appears to be made up of a great many small fibers. These fibers, if further examined in cross section, are found to be composed of small cells held together in a complicated manner, according to the kind of wood. Since these cells act as pores and absorb moisture from the air, the wood will decay rapidly when exposed to the weather. However, a good quality of paint, when properly applied, will fill these pores and act as a preservative agent. Some woods are naturally more resistant to decay than others. Woods such as cedar, redwood, and white pine are more absorbent than yellow pine or Douglas fir. The following table gives a classification of woods which will serve as a guide to the builder.

TABLE III. SOFTWOODS—CLASSIFICATION FOR PAINTING

GROUP 1*	GROUP 2†	GROUP 3‡	GROUP 4§
Alaska cedar	Northern white pine	Commercial white fir	Douglas fir
Incense cedar	Western white pine	Eastern hemlock	Western larch
Northern white cedar	Sugar pine	Western hemlock	Norway pine
Port Orford cedar	————	Ponderosa pine	Southern yellow pine
Southern white cedar	————	Lodgepole pine	Tamarack
Western red cedar	————	Eastern spruce	————
Southern cypress	————	Engelmann spruce	————
Redwood	————	Sitka spruce	————

*Woods that hold paint longest and suffer least when protection against weathering becomes inadequate.

†Woods that hold white-lead paint as long as those of Group 1, but do not hold mixed-pigment paints quite so long and suffer more than those of Group 1, if protection becomes inadequate.

‡Woods that do not hold either white-lead paint or mixed-pigment paints so long as woods of Group 1, and suffer more than woods of Group 1, if protection becomes inadequate.

§Woods that do not hold paint coatings so long as woods of Group 3.

TABLE IV. WOODS—CLASSIFICATION FOR DECAY RESISTANCE[1]

Heartwood durable even when used under conditions that favor decay	Cedar, Alaska Cedar, eastern red Cedar, northern white Cedar, Port Orford Cedar, southern white Cedar, western red Chestnut Cypress, southern Locust, black Osage-orange Redwood Walnut, black Yew, Pacific
Heartwood of intermediate durability but nearly as durable as some of the species named in the high-durability group	Douglas fir (dense) Honey locust Oak, white Pine, southern yellow (dense)
Heartwood of intermediate durability	Douglas fir (unselected) Gum, red Larch, western Pine, southern yellow (unselected) Tamarack
Heartwood between the intermediate and the nondurable group	Ash, commercial white Beech Birch, sweet Birch, yellow Hemlock, eastern Hemlock, western Hickory Maple, sugar Oak, red Spruce, black Spruce, Engelmann Spruce, red Spruce, Sitka Spruce, white
Heartwood low in durability when used under conditions that favor decay	Aspen Basswood Cottonwood Fir, commercial white Willow, black

Practically all native species of wood will be free from decay, indefinitely, if kept either constantly dry or continuously submerged in water. The principal factors affecting the rate of decay are moisture and temperature. The heartwood of all species is more resistant to decay than the untreated sapwood. The rate of decay varies in each species and even in each tree. The decay-resistant grouping of common native species made by the United States Department of Agriculture (Table IV) is based upon estimates made from service records and general experience with the heartwood.

[1] United States *Wood Handbook.*

TABLE V. DEPRECIATION OF WOOD FRAME HOUSE—LIFE OF PARTS[1]

BUILDING PARTS	AVERAGE LIFE YEARS	ANNUAL DEPRECIATION PER CENT
Plastering	20	5
Painting, outside	5	20
Painting, inside	7	14
Shingles	16	6
Cornice	40	2½
Weatherboarding	30	3½
Sheathing	50	2
Flooring	20	5
Flooring (entirely carpeted)	40	2½
Doors, complete	30	3½
Windows, complete	30	3½
Stairs and newels	30	3½
Base	40	2½
Building hardware	20	5
Outside blinds	16	5
Sills and floor joists	15	4
Dimension lumber	50	2
Porches	20	5

[1]From *American Builder*.

TABLE VI. BOARD MEASURE

Size	LENGTH IN FEET											
	12	14	16	18	20	22	24	26	28	30	32	34
1x 2	2	2⅓	2⅔	3	3⅓	3⅔	4	4⅓	4⅔	5	5⅓	5⅔
1x 3	3	3½	4	4½	5	5½	6	6½	7	7½	8	8½
1x 4	4	4⅔	5⅓	6	6⅔	7⅓	8	8⅔	9⅓	10	10⅔	11⅓
1x 6	6	7	8	9	10	11	12	13	14	15	16	17
1x 8	8	9⅓	10⅔	12	13⅓	14⅔	16	17⅓	18⅔	20	21⅓	22⅔
1x10	10	11⅔	13⅓	15	16⅔	18⅓	20	21⅔	22⅓	25	26⅔	28⅓
1x12	12	14	16	18	20	22	24	26	28	30	32	34
2x 4	8	9	11	12	13	15	16	17	19	20	21	23
2x 6	12	14	16	18	20	22	24	26	28	30	32	34
2x 8	16	19	21	24	27	29	32	35	37	40	43	45
2x10	20	23	27	30	33	37	40	43	47	50	53	57
2x12	24	28	32	36	40	44	48	52	56	60	64	68
2x14	28	33	37	42	47	51	56	61	65	70	75	80
3x 8	24	28	32	36	40	44	48	52	56	60	64	68
3x10	30	35	40	45	50	55	60	65	70	75	80	85
3x12	36	42	48	54	60	66	72	78	84	90	96	102
3x14	42	49	56	63	70	77	84	91	98	105	112	119
4x 4	16	19	21	24	27	29	32	35	37	40	43	45
4x 6	24	28	32	36	40	44	48	52	56	60	64	68
4x 8	32	37	43	48	53	59	64	69	75	80	85	91
4x10	40	47	53	60	67	73	80	87	93	100	107	113
4x12	48	56	64	72	80	88	96	104	112	120	128	136
4x14	56	65	75	84	93	103	112	121	131	140	149	159
6x 6	36	42	48	54	60	66	72	78	84	90	96	102
6x 8	48	56	64	72	80	88	96	104	112	120	128	136
6x10	60	70	80	90	100	112	120	130	140	150	160	170
6x12	72	84	96	108	120	132	144	156	168	180	192	204
6x14	84	98	112	126	140	154	168	182	196	210	224	238
8x 8	64	75	85	96	107	117	128	139	149	160	171	181
8x10	80	93	107	120	133	147	160	173	187	200	213	227
8x12	96	112	128	144	160	176	192	208	224	240	256	272
8x14	112	131	149	168	187	205	224	243	261	280	299	317
10x10	100	117	133	150	167	183	200	217	233	250	267	283
10x12	120	140	160	180	200	220	240	260	280	300	320	340
10x14	140	163	187	210	233	257	280	303	327	350	373	397
12x12	144	168	192	216	240	264	288	312	336	360	384	408
12x14	168	196	224	252	280	308	336	264	392	420	448	476
14x14	197	229	261	294	327	356	392	425	457	490	523	555

TABLE VII—WIRE NAILS—KINDS AND QUANTITIES REQUIRED

Length, in inches	Am. Steel & Wire Co.'s Steel Wire Gauge	Approx. No. to lbs.	Nailings	Sizes and Kinds of Material	Trade Names	Pounds per 1000 feet B. M. on center as follows:				
						12″	16″	20″	36″	48″
						Pounds				
2½	10¼	106	2	1x 4	8d common...	60	48	37	23	20
2½	10¼	106	2	1x 6	8d common...	40	32	25	16	13
2½	10¼	106	2	1x 8	8d common...	31	27	20	12	10
2½	10¼	106	2	1x10	8d common...	25	20	16	10	8
2½	10¼	106	3	1x12	8d common...	31	24	20	12	10
4	6	31	2	2x 4	20d common...	105	80	65	60	33
4	6	31	2	2x 6	20d common...	70	54	43	27	22
4	6	31	2	2x 8	20d common...	53	40	53	21	17
4	6	31	3	2x10	20d common...	60	50	40	25	20
4	6	31	3	2x12	20d common...	52	41	33	21	17
6	2	11	2	3x 4	60d common...	197	150	122	76	61
6	2	11	2	3x 6	60d common...	131	97	82	52	42
6	2	11	2	3x 8	60d common...	100	76	61	38	34
6	2	11	3	3x10	60d common...	178	137	110	70	55
6	2	11	3	3x12	60d common...	145	115	92	58	46
2½	12½	189	2	Base, per 100 ft. lin...	8d finish......	....	1			
2½	10¼	106	2	Byrket lath..........	8d common......	....	48			
2½	12½	189	1	Ceiling, ¾x4.........	8d finish......	18	14			
2	13	309	1	Ceiling, ½ and ⅝.....	6d finish......	11	8			
2½	12½	189	2	Finish, ⅞.........	8d finish......	25	12			
3	11½	121	2	Finish, 1⅛........	10d finish....	12	10			
2½	10	99	1	Flooring, 1x3........	8d floor brads.	42	32			
2½	10	99	1	Flooring, 1x4........	8d floor brads.	32	26			
2½	10	99	1	Flooring, 1x6........	8d floor brads.	22	18			
4	6	31	⎰	Framing, 2x4 to 2x16.	20d common..	20	16	14		
3½	8	49	⎬	requires 3 or more sizes	16d common..	10	10	8		
3	9	69	⎱	and varies greatly.	10d common..	8	6	5		
6	2	11		Framing, 3x4 to 3x14.	60d common..	30	25	20		
2½	11½	145	2	Siding, drop, 1x4.....	8d casing.	45	35			
2½	11½	145	2	Siding, drop, 1x6.....	8d casing.	30	25			
2½	11½	145	2	Siding, drop, 1x8.....	8d casing.	23	18			
2	13	309	1	Siding, bevel, ½x4....	6d finish.	23	18			
2	13	309	1	Siding, bevel, ½x6....	6d finish.	15	13			
2	13	309	1	Siding, bevel, ½x8....	6d finish.	12	10			
				Casing, per opening...	6d and 8d casing......	About ½ pound per side.				
1¼	14	568	12″ o.c.	Flooring, ⅜x2......	3d brads......	About 10 pounds per 1000 square feet.				
1⅛	15	778	16″ o.c.	Lath, 48″...........	3d sterilized blued lath...	6 pounds per 1000 pieces.				
⅞	12	469	2″ o.c.	Ready roofing........	Barbed roofing.	¾ of a pound to the sq.				
⅞	12	469	1″ o.c.	Ready roofing........	Barbed roofing.	1½ pounds to the square.				
⅞	12	180	2″ o.c.	Ready roofing........ (⅝ heads)	American felt roofing......	1½ pounds to the square.				
⅞	12	180	1″ o.c.	Ready roofing........ (⅝ heads)	American felt roofing.....	3 pounds to the square.				
1¼	13	429	....	Shingles*...........	3d shingle....	4½ pounds; about 2 nails to each 4 inches.				
1½	12	274	....	Shingles............	4d shingle.....	7½ pounds; about 2 nails to each 4 inches.				
⅞	12	180	4	Shingles............	American felt roofing	12 lbs., 4 nails to shingle.				
⅞	12	469	4	Shingles............	Barbed roofing.	4½ lbs., 4 nails to shingle.				
1	16	1150	2″ o.c.	Wall board, around entire edge.....	Plaster board nails flat head	5 pounds, per 1,000 square feet.				
1	15½	1010	3″ o.c.	Wall board, intermediate nailings.......	2d...........	2½ lbs., per 1,000 square feet.				

Note in center column: I. Used square edge, as platforms, floors, sheathing, or shiplap. II. When used D. & M., blind nailed, only ½ quantity named required.

Note in Trade Names column (siding rows): or 7d Siding Nails

*Wood shingles vary in width; asphalt are usually 8 inches wide. Regardless of width 1000 shingles are the equivalent of 1000 pieces 4 inches wide.

Courtesy American Steel & Wire Co.

TABLE VIII. SCREW GAUGES, WIRE GAUGES, AND DECIMAL EQUIVALENTS

SCREW GAUGE AMERICAN		WIRE GAUGE OLD STANDARD BIRMINGHAM		DECIMAL EQUIVALENTS			
No.	Inch	No.	Inch	Fraction	Dec. Equiv.	Fraction	Dec. Equiv.
0	.060	17	.058	$\frac{1}{64}$	.015625	$\frac{33}{64}$	.515625
1	.073	16	.065	$\frac{1}{32}$	.03125	$\frac{17}{32}$	.53125
2	.086	15	.072	$\frac{3}{64}$	.046875	$\frac{35}{64}$	.546875
3	.099	14	.083	$\frac{1}{16}$	.0625	$\frac{9}{16}$	.5625
4	.112	13	.095	$\frac{5}{64}$	.078125	$\frac{37}{64}$	.578125
5	.125	12	.109	$\frac{3}{32}$	.09375	$\frac{19}{32}$	.59375
6	.138	11	.120	$\frac{7}{64}$	.109375	$\frac{39}{64}$	.609375
7	.151	10	.134	$\frac{1}{8}$	.125	$\frac{5}{8}$	.625
8	.164	9	.148	$\frac{9}{64}$	.140625	$\frac{41}{64}$	.640625
9	.177	8	.165	$\frac{5}{32}$	.15625	$\frac{21}{32}$	.65625
10	.190	7	.180	$\frac{11}{64}$	.171875	$\frac{43}{64}$	.671875
11	.203	6	.203	$\frac{3}{16}$	.1875	$\frac{11}{16}$	.6875
12	.216	5	.220	$\frac{13}{64}$	.203125	$\frac{45}{64}$	.703125
13	.229	4	.238	$\frac{7}{32}$	.21875	$\frac{23}{32}$	.71875
14	.242	3	.259	$\frac{15}{64}$	.234375	$\frac{47}{64}$	.734375
15	.255	2	.284	$\frac{1}{4}$	.25	$\frac{3}{4}$	.75
16	.268	1	.300	$\frac{17}{64}$	.265625	$\frac{49}{64}$	.765625
17	.281	0	.340	$\frac{9}{32}$	.28125	$\frac{25}{32}$	.78125
18	.294	00	.380	$\frac{19}{64}$	.296875	$\frac{51}{64}$	.796875
20	.320	000	.425	$\frac{5}{16}$	.3125	$\frac{13}{16}$	.8125
22	.346	0000	.454	$\frac{21}{64}$	.328125	$\frac{53}{64}$	.828125
24	.372	——	——	$\frac{11}{32}$	.34375	$\frac{27}{32}$	.84375
26	.398	——	——	$\frac{23}{64}$	.359375	$\frac{55}{64}$	.859375
28	.424	——	——	$\frac{3}{8}$	.375	$\frac{7}{8}$	.875
30	.450	——	——	$\frac{25}{64}$	.390625	$\frac{57}{64}$	.890625
—	——	——	——	$\frac{13}{32}$	.40625	$\frac{29}{32}$	.90625
—	——	——	——	$\frac{27}{64}$	.421875	$\frac{59}{64}$	.921875
—	——	——	——	$\frac{7}{16}$	.4375	$\frac{15}{16}$	.9375
—	——	——	——	$\frac{29}{64}$	.453125	$\frac{61}{64}$	.953125
—	——	——	——	$\frac{15}{32}$	.46875	$\frac{31}{32}$	.96875
—	——	——	——	$\frac{31}{64}$	.484375	$\frac{63}{64}$	.984375
—	——	——	——	$\frac{1}{2}$	.5	1	1.00

TABLE IX. MENSURATION—LINES, CIRCLES, CUBES AND SQUARES[1]

LINEAR MEASURE

1 hair's breadth	=	1/48 inch
3 barleycorns (lengthwise)	=	1 inch
7.92 inches	=	1 link
12 inches	=	1 foot = 0.3048 meter
3 feet	=	1 yard = 0.91438 meter
5½ yards	=	1 rod, perch, or pole
4 poles or 100 links	=	1 chain
10 chains	=	1 furlong
8 furlongs	=	1 mile = 1.6093 kilometers = 5280 feet
3 miles (nautical)	=	1 league
1 line	=	1/12 inch
1 nail (cloth measure)	=	2¼ inches
1 palm	=	3 inches
1 hand (used for height of horses)	=	4 inches
1 span	=	9 inches
1 cubit	=	18 inches
1 pace (military)	=	2½ feet
1 pace (common)	=	3 feet
1 Scotch ell	=	37.06 inches
1 vara (Spanish)	=	33.3 inches
1 English ell	=	45 inches
1 fathom	=	6 feet
1 cable's length	=	120 fathoms
1 "knot"	=	6082.66 feet
1 degree of equator	=	69.1613 statute miles
1 degree of equator	=	60 geographical miles
1 degree of meridian	=	60.046 statute miles
1 degree of meridian	=	59.899 geographical miles
1.1527 statute miles	=	1 geographical mile
6086.07 feet	=	1 minute of longitude = 1 nautical mile
5280 feet	=	1 statute mile

CIRCULAR MEASURE

60 seconds	=	1 minute
60 minutes	=	1 degree
30 degrees	=	1 sign
12 signs	=	1 circle or circumference

CUBIC MEASURE

1,728 cubic inches	=	1 cubic foot
27 cubic feet	=	1 cubic yard

[1] From *American Builder.*

TABLE IX. MENSURATION—LINES, CIRCLES, CUBES, AND SQUARES—*Continued*

SQUARE MEASURE

144 square inches	= 1	square foot
9 square feet	= 1	square yard
30¼ square yards	= 1	square rod
40 square rods	= 1	rood
4 roods	= 1	acre
640 acres	= 1	square mile
36 square miles	= 1	township

SURVEYORS' SQUARE MEASURE

625 square links	= 1	square rod
16 square rods	= 1	square chain
10 square chains	= 1	acre
640 acres	= 1	square mile
36 square miles or 6 miles square	= 1	township

SURVEYORS' LONG MEASURE *

7.92 inches	= 1	link
25 links	= 1	pole
100 links	= 1	chain
10 chains	= 1	furlong
8 furlongs	= 1	mile

RULES PERTAINING TO A CIRCLE

To find circumference:

Multiply diameter by	3.1416
or divide diameter by	0.3183

To find diameter:

Multiply circumference by	0.3183
or divide circumference by	3.1416

To find radius:

Multiply circumference by	0.15915
or divide circumference by	6.28318

To find side of an inscribed square:

Multiply diameter by	0.7071
or multiply circumference by	0.2251
or divide circumference by	4.4428

To find side of an equal square:

Multiply diameter by	0.8862
or divide diameter by	1.2840
or multiply circumference by	0.2821
or divide circumference by	3.5450

---

* Used by surveyors, civil engineers, and others in measuring distances.

Square:

A side multiplied by 1.4142 equals diameter of its circumscribing circle.

A side multiplied by 4.443 equals circumference of its circumscribing circle.

A side multiplied by 1.128 equals diameter of an equal circle.

A side multiplied by 3.547 equals circumference of an equal circle.

Square inches multiplied by 1.273 equal circle inches of an equal circle.

To find the area of a circle:

Multiply circumference by one-quarter of the diameter,
or multiply the square of diameter by   0.7854
or multiply the square of circumference by   0.07958
or multiply the square of one-half the diameter by   3.1416

To find the surface of a sphere or globe:

Multiply the diameter by the circumference,
or multiply the square of the diameter by   3.1416
or multiply four times the square of the radius by   3.1416

FRAMEWORK AND SHEATHING OF HOUSE IN PROCESS OF CONSTRUCTION
Courtesy of American Builder

abrasive: A substance used for wearing away or polishing a surface by friction. A grinding material, such as emery, sand, and diamond. Other abrasives include: crushed garnet and quartz, pumice or powdered lava, also decomposed limestone, known as *tripoli*. There are other abrasives which are made artificially and sold under various trade names.

abrasive paper: Paper, or cloth, covered on one side with a grinding material glued fast to the surface, used for smoothing and polishing. Materials used for this purpose include: crushed flint, garnet, emery or corundum.

abrasive tools: All implements, used for wearing down materials by friction or rubbing, are known as *abrasive tools;* these include: grindstones which are made of pure sandstone, whetstones, emery wheels, sandpaper, emery cloth, and other abrading tools.

abreuvoir: In masonry, the mortar joint between stones in a wall or between two arch stones.

abutment: That part of a pier or wall from which an arch is suspended; specifically the support at either end of an arch, beam, or bridge which resists the pressure due to a load.

accelerator: Material added to Portland cement concrete during the mixing to hasten its natural development of strength.

acoustics: Science of sound. A study of the effects of sound upon the ear. The sum of the qualities that determine the value of an auditorium as to distinct hearing. The acoustics are said to be *good* or *bad* according to the ease of clearness with which sounds can be heard by the audience. The main factors influencing acoustical conditions are reverberation, extraneous noises, loudness of the original sound and the size and shape of the auditorium.

adjustable clamp: Any type of clamping device that can be adjusted to suit the work being done, but particularly clamps used for holding column forms while concrete is poured. See Fig. 53.

adobe: An aluminous earth from which unfired brick are made, especially in the western part of the United States; an unfired brick dried in the sun; a house or other structure built of such materials or clay.

adz: A cutting tool resembling an ax. The thin arched blade is set at right angles to the handle. The adz is used for rough-dressing timber.

adze-eye hammer: A claw hammer with the eye extended. This gives a longer bearing on the handle than is the case in hammers not having an extended eye. See Fig. 17.

aerated concrete: A lightweight material made from a specially prepared cement, and used for subfloors. Due to its cellular structure, this material is a retardant to sound transmission.

African mahogany: A large tree remotely related to the mahogany family. The tree is found principally in Africa and produces exceptionally fine figured timber of unusual lengths and widths. The wood is used for fine furniture.

aggregate: A collection of granulated particles of different substances into a compound, or conglomerate mass. In mixing concrete, the stone, or gravel, used as a part of the mix is commonly called the *coarse aggregate,* while the sand is called the *fine aggregate.*

aiguille: In masonry, an instrument for boring holes in stone or other masonry material.

air brick: A hollow or perforated brick specially prepared for ventilating purposes; also, a box of brick size made of metal with grated sides which allow air to enter a building where ventilation is otherwise restricted.

air conditioning: The process of heating or cooling, cleaning, humidifying or dehumidifying, and circulating air throughout the various rooms of a house or public building. This term has been erroneously used many times and before installing air-conditioning equipment it should be carefully investigated.

air-cooled slag: The product of relatively slow-cooling molten blast-furnace slag, resulting in a solid mass of tough, durable material which is excavated, crushed, and screened for commercial purposes, such as concrete and bituminous aggregate.

air-dried lumber: Any lumber which is seasoned by drying in the air instead of being dried in a kiln or oven.

air pocket: An airspace which accidentally occurs in concrete work.

air slaking: In masonry, the process of exposing quicklime to the air, as a result of which it will gradually absorb moisture and break down into a powder.

air space: A cavity or space in walls or between various structural members.

aisle: A passageway by which seats may be reached, as the *aisle* of a church.

alcove: Any recess cut in a room. An *alcove* is usually separated from the main room by an archway.

all-rowlock wall: In masonry, a wall built so that two courses of stretchers are standing on edge, alternating with one course of headers standing on edge.

aluminum nails: Nails made of this metal are lightweight, stainless, rustless, and sterilized.

American bond: A method of bonding brick in a wall whereby every fifth, sixth, or seventh course consists of headers, the other courses being stretchers. This type of bond is used extensively because it is quickly laid.

anchor blocks: Blocks of wood built into masonry walls, to which partitions and fixtures may be secured.

anchor bolts: Large bolts used for fastening or anchoring a wooden sill to a masonry foundation, floor, or wall. See Fig. 12. Also, any of several types of metal fasteners used to secure wood construction to masonry. See Fig. 1.

anchors: In building construction, devices used to give stability to one part of a structure by securing it to another part; metal ties, such as concrete inserts or toggle bolts, used to fasten any structural wood member to a concrete or masonry wall. See Fig. 1.

angle bead: A molded strip used in an angle, usually where two walls meet at right angles. See *corner bead*.

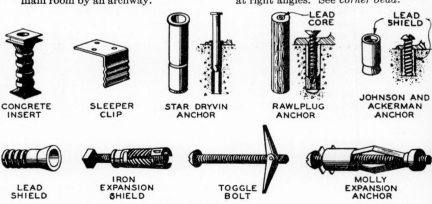

CONCRETE INSERT   SLEEPER CLIP   STAR DRYVIN ANCHOR   RAWLPLUG ANCHOR   JOHNSON AND ACKERMAN ANCHOR

LEAD SHIELD   IRON EXPANSION SHIELD   TOGGLE BOLT   MOLLY EXPANSION ANCHOR

Fig. 1. Anchors

angle bonds: In masonry work, brick or metal ties used to bind the angles or corners of the walls together.

angle bracket: A type of support which has two faces usually at right angles to each other. To increase the strength, a web is sometimes added.

angle closer: In masonry, a portion of a whole brick which is used to close up the bond of brickwork at corners. See *closer*.

angle dividers: A tool primarily designed for bisecting angles. It can also be used as a try square.

angle gauge: A tool used to set off and test angles in work done by carpenters, bricklayers, and masons.

angle iron: A section of a strip of structural iron bent to form a right angle.

anhydrous lime: Unslacked lime which is made from almost pure limestone. Same as *quicklime*. Also called *common lime*.

annual ring: The arrangement of the wood of a tree in concentric rings, or layers, due to the fact that it is formed gradually, one ring being added each year. For this reason the rings are called *annual rings*. The rings can easily be counted in cross section of a tree trunk. If a tree is cut close to the ground, the age of the tree can be estimated by the number of annual growth rings. See Fig. 2.

anta: A rectangular pier or pilaster formed by thickening a wall at its extremity; often furnished with a capital and base; also, a special type of pier formed by thickening a wall at its termination. A pilaster opposite another, as on a door jamb.

apex stone: A triangular stone at the top of a gable wall, often decorated with a carved trefoil. Sometimes called a *saddle stone*.

apron: A plain or molded finish piece below the stool of a window; put on to cover the rough edge of the plastering. See Fig. 20.

arbor: A type of detached latticework, or an archway of latticework. See *trellis*.

arc: Any part of the *circumference* of a circle.

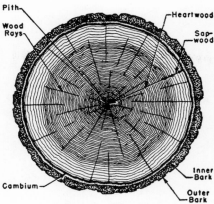

Fig. 2. Annual Rings

arcade: An arched roof, or covered passageway; a series of arches supported either on piers or pillars. An *arcade* may be either attached to a wall or detached from the wall.

arch: A curved or pointed structural member supported at the sides or ends. An *arch* is used to bridge or span an opening, usually a passageway or open spaces. An arch may also be used to sustain weight, as the arch of a bridge.

arch bar: A support for a flat arch. The support may be either a strip of iron or a flat bar.

arch brick: Special wedge-shaped brick used in the building of an arch; also suitable for other circular work; a term also applied to brick which have been overburned by being placed in contact with the fire in the arch of the kiln.

architect: One who designs and oversees the construction of a building; anyone skilled in methods of construction and in planning buildings; a professional student of architecture.

arch stone: A stone shaped like a wedge for use in an arch. Same as *voussoir*.

archway: The passageway under an arch.

area: An uncovered space, such as an open court; also, a sunken space around the basement of a building, providing access and natural lighting and ventilation. Same as *areaway*. See Fig. 3.

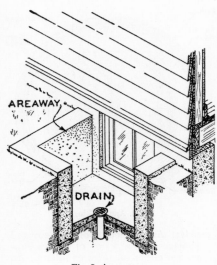

Fig. 3. Areaway

area drain: A drain set in the floor of a basement areaway, any depressed entryway, a loading platform, or a cemented driveway which cannot be drained otherwise. See Fig. 3.

areaway: An open subsurface space around a basement window or doorway, adjacent to the foundation walls. An *areaway* provides a means of admitting light and air for ventilation, and also affords access to the basement or cellar. See *prefabricated areaway*, Figs. 3 and 46.

armored concrete: Concrete which has been strengthened by reinforcing with steel rods or steel plates. See *reinforced concrete*.

arris: An edge or ridge where two surfaces meet. The sharp edge formed where two moldings meet is commonly called an arris.

artificial stone: A special kind of manufactured product resembling a natural stone. A common type is made from pulverized quarry refuse mixed with Portland cement (sometimes colored) and water. After being pressed into molds, the mixture is allowed to dry out, and then is seasoned in the open air for several months before being used.

artisan: A skilled craftsman; an artist; one trained in a special mechanical art or trade; a handicraftsman who manufactures articles of wood or other material.

asbestos cement: A fire-resisting, waterproofing material made by combining Portland cement with asbestos fibers.

asbestos shingles: A type of shingle made for fireproof purposes. The principal composition of these shingles is *asbestos,* which is incombustible, nonconducting, and chemically resistant to fire. This makes *asbestos shingles* highly desirable for roof covering.

ashlar: One of the studs or uprights between floor beams and rafters in a garret. A short stud cutting off the

THIN JOINTS

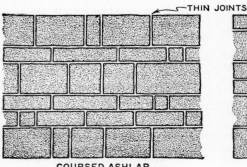

COURSED ASHLAR

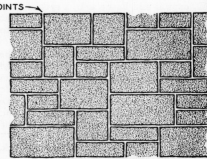

RANDOM ASHLAR

Fig. 4. Ashlar

angle between floor and roof in an attic, thus affording a wall of some height. Also, squared stone used in foundations and for facing of certain types of masonry walls. See Fig. 4.

ashlar brick: A brick that has been rough-hackled on the face to make it resemble stone.

ashlar masonry: Masonry work of sawed, dressed, tooled, or quarry-faced stone with proper bond. See Fig. 4.

aspen: A tree common in many parts of the United States. It is especially noted for the trembling of its leaves which are never still. The wood has little commercial value except as pulp for the manufacture of paper. For paper pulp, aspen wood ranks in importance next to spruce and hemlock. The aspen tree grows to a height of 50 feet and the wood weighs 25 pounds per cubic foot.

asphalt cement: A cement prepared by refining petroleum until it is free from water and all foreign material, except the mineral matter naturally contained in the asphalt. It should contain less than one per cent of ash.

assize: In masonry, a cylinder-shaped block of stone which forms part of a column, or of a layer of stone in a building.

astragal: A small semicircular molding, either ornamental or plain, used for covering a joint between doors. For decorative purposes it is sometimes cut in the form of a string of beads.

atrium: A large hallway or lobby with galleries at each floor level on three or more sides.

attic: A garret; the room or space directly below the roof of a building. In modern buildings the *attic* is the space between the roof and the ceiling of the upper story. In classical structures the *attic* is the space, or low room, above the entablature or main cornice of a building.

auger: A wood-boring tool used by the carpenter for boring holes larger than can be made with a gimlet. The handle of an *auger* is attached at right angles to the tool line. There are several dif-

ferent types of augers made for various purposes.

auger bit: An auger without a handle to be used in a brace. Such a bit has square tapered shanks made to fit in the socket of a common brace. This combination tool is known as a *brace and bit.*

automatic grouter: A pressurized steel form, faced with foam rubber, which forces grout in and around stones, or brick, after it has been poured in from the top of stonework.

avoirdupois weight: A system of weights in common use in English-speaking countries for weighing all commodities except precious stones and metals, also precious drugs. In this system 16 ounces equal one pound; 2,000 pounds equal one *short ton;* a *long ton* contains 2,240 pounds.

awl: A small sharp-pointed instrument used by the carpenter for making holes for nails or screws. The carpenter often uses an *awl* to mark lines where pencil marks might become erased.

awl haft: The handle of an *awl.*

awning window: A type of window in which each light opens outward on its own hinges, which are placed at its upper edge. Such windows are often used as ventilators in connection with fixed picture windows. See Fig. 5.

Fig. 5. Awning Window

axhammer: A type of cutting tool, or ax, having two cutting edges, or one cutting edge and one hammer face, used for dressing or spalling the rougher kinds of stone.

B

back band: The exterior finish, or outside member, of a door or window casing.

back filling: Coarse dirt, broken stone, or other material used to build up the ground level around the basement or foundation walls of a house to provide a slope for drainage of water away from the foundation.

backing hip rafter: The beveling arris as at corners of hip rafters to tie up with adjacent roof surfaces.

backing of a joist or rafter: The blocking used to bring a narrow joist up to the height of the regular width joists. The widths of joists or rafters may vary, and in order to assure even floors or roofs some of the joists or rafters must be blocked up until all the upper surfaces are of the same level.

backing of a wall: The rough inner face of a wall; the material which is used to fill in behind a retaining wall.

backing tier: In masonry, the tier of rough brickwork which backs up the *face tier* of an exterior wall for a residence or other well-built brick structure. This part of a brick wall

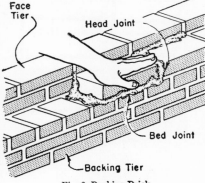

Fig. 6. Backing Brick

is often of a cheaper grade of brick than that used for the face tier. See Fig. 6.

back plastering: The application of a ⅜″ thick mortar coat on the back of the facing tier for purposes of moisture-proofing and air-proofing; also called *parging*. See Fig. 41.

backsaw: Any saw with its blade stiffened by an additional metal strip along the back. The *backsaw* is commonly used in cabinet work as a bench saw.

badger: An implement used to clean out the excess mortar at the joints of a drain after it has been laid.

badigeon: In building, a kind of cement or paste made by mixing suitable materials for filling holes or covering defects in stones or wood.

balk: A large squared timber, or beam.

balloon framing: A type of building construction in which the studs extend in one piece from the foundation to the roof; in addition to being supported by a ledger board, the second-floor joists are nailed to the studs. See Fig. 7.

ball peen hammer: A hammer having a peen which is hemispherical in shape; used especially by metal workers and stonemasons.

baluster: One of a series of small pillars, or units, of a balustrade; an upright support of the railing for a stairway. See *closed-string stair,* Fig. 50.

balustrade: A railing consisting of a series of small columns connected at the top by a coping; a row of balusters surmounted by a rail.

band saw: A saw in the form of an endless serrated steel belt running on revolving pulleys; the saw is used in cutting woodwork; also used for metal work.

banister: The balustrade of a staircase; a corruption of the word *baluster.*

banker: In masonry, a type of workbench on which bricklayers and stonemasons work when shaping arches or other construction requiring shaped materials.

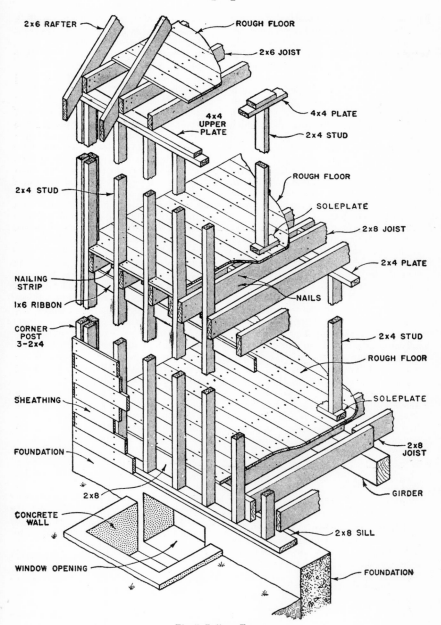

Fig. 7. Balloon Frame

bar clamp: A device consisting of a long bar and two clamping jaws, used by woodworkers for clamping large work.

bargeboard: The decorative board covering the projecting portion of a gable roof; the same as a *verge board;* during the late part of the nineteenth century, bargeboards frequently were extremely ornate.

barge course: A part of the tiling which usually projects beyond the principal rafters or *bargeboards,* along the sloping edge of a *gable roof;* also, a course of brick laid on edge to form the coping of a wall. See *bargeboard.*

bark pocket: A patch of bark nearly, or wholly, enclosed in the wood is known as a *bark pocket.*

base: The lowest part of a wall, pier, monument, or column; the lower part of a complete architectural design.

baseboard: A board forming the base of something; the finishing board covering the edge of the plastered wall where the wall and floor meet; a line of boarding around the interior walls of a room, next to the floor.

base course: A footing course, as the lowest course of masonry of a wall or pier; the foundation course on which the remainder rests.

basement: The story of a building next below the main floor; a story partly or wholly below the ground level; the finished portion of a building below the main floor, or section; also, the lowest division of the walls of a building.

base molding: The molding above the plinth of a wall, pillar, or pedestal; the part between the shaft and the pedestal, or if there is no pedestal, the part between the shaft and the plinth.

base trim: The finish at the base of a piece of work, as a board or molding used for finishing the lower part of an inside wall, such as a *baseboard;* the lower part of a column which may consist of several decorative features, including various members which make up the base as a whole; these may include an ornate pedestal and other decorative parts.

bastard tuck pointing: In masonry, a type of pointing of joints whereby a wider ridge is formed along the center of the joints than in true tuck pointing of mortar joints. See *tuck pointing.*

bat: A piece of brick with one end whole, the other end broken off.

batten: A thin, narrow strip of board used for various purposes; a piece of wood nailed across the surface of one or more boards to prevent warping; a narrow strip of board used to cover cracks between boards; a small molding used for covering joints between sheathing boards to keep out moisture. When sheathing is placed on walls in a vertical position and the joints covered by battens, a type of siding is formed known as *boards and battens.* This form of siding is commonly used on small buildings, farm structures, and railroad buildings. A cleat is sometimes called a *batten.* Squared timbers of a special size used for flooring are also known as *battens.* These usually measure 7 inches in width, 2½ inches in thickness, and 6 feet, or more, in length.

batten door: A door made of sheathing boards reinforced with strips of boards nailed crossways and the nails clinched on the opposite side.

batter: A receding upward slope; the backward inclination of a timber or wall which is out of plumb; the upward and backward slope of a retaining wall which inclines away from a person who is standing facing it. A wall is sometimes constructed with a sloping outer face while the inner surface is perpendicular; thus the thickness of the wall diminishes toward the top.

batter board: Usually, one of two horizontal boards nailed to a post set up near the proposed corner of an excavation for a new building. The builder cuts notches or drives nails in the boards to hold the stretched building cord which marks the outline of the structure. The boards and strings are used for relocating the exact corner of the building at the bottom of the finished excavation. See Fig. 8.

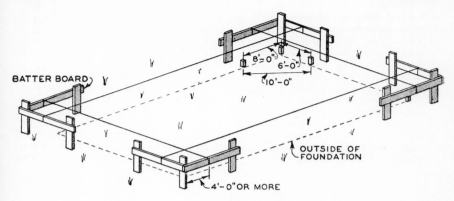

Fig. 8. Batter Board

bead: A circular or semicircular molding; a beaded molding is known as *beading;* when the beads are flush with the surface and separated by grooves, this type of molding is called *quirk bead.*

bead plane: A special type of plane used for cutting beads.

B & C B: An abbreviation for the term *beaded on the edge and center.*

beam: Any large piece of timber, stone, iron, or other material, used to support a load over an opening, or from post to post; one of the principal horizontal timbers, relatively long, used for supporting the floors of a building.

beam ceiling: A type of construction in which the beams of the ceiling, usually placed in a horizontal position, are exposed to view. The beams may be either true or false, but if properly constructed the appearance of the ceiling will be the same, whether the beams are false or true.

beam fill: Masonry or concrete used to fill the spaces between joists; also, between a basement or foundation wall and the framework of a structure, to provide fire stops in outside walls for checking fires which start in the basement of a building.

bearing: That portion of a beam or truss which rests upon a support; that part of any member of a building that rests upon its supports.

bearing plate: A plate placed under a heavily loaded truss beam, girder, or column, to distribute the load so the pressure of its weight will not exceed the bearing strength of the supporting member.

bearing wall or **partition:** A wall which supports the floors and roof in a building; a partition that carries the floor joists and other partitions above it.

bed: In masonry, a layer of cement or mortar in which the stone or brick is embedded, or against which it bears; either of the horizontal surfaces of a stone in position, as the *upper* and *lower beds;* the lower surface of a brick, slate, or tile.

bed dowel: A dowel placed in the center of a stone bed.

bed joint: In brickwork, the horizontal joint upon which the bricks rest (Fig. 6); also, the radiating joints of an arch.

bed molding: Finish molding used where the eaves of a building meet the top of the outside walls; the moldings, in any architectural order, used as a finish immediately beneath the corona and above the frieze; any molding in an angle, as between the projection of the overhanging eaves of a building and the sidewalls.

bed of a stone: The under surface of a stone; when the upper surface is prepared to receive another stone, it is called the *top bed,* and the natural stratification of the stone is called the *natural bed.*

bedplate: A foundation plate used as a

support for some structural part; a metal plate used as a bed, or rest, for a machine; a foundation framing forming the bottom of a furnace.

bed stone: A large foundation stone, as one used to support a girder.

belt courses: A layer of stone or molded work carried at the same level across or around a building. Also, a decorative feature, as a horizontal band around a building, or around a column. Two types of belt courses are shown in Fig. 9.

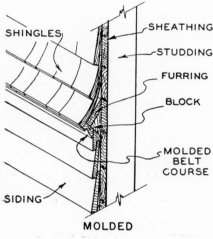

MOLDED

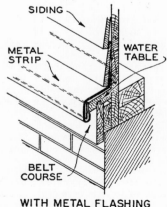

WITH METAL FLASHING

Fig. 9. Belt Courses

bench dog: A wooden or metal peg placed in a hole near the end of a workbench to prevent a piece of work from slipping out of position or off from the bench.

bench hook: A hook-shaped device used to prevent a piece of work from slipping on the bench during certain operations; a flat timber or board with cleats nailed on each side and one on each end to hold a piece of work in position and to prevent slipping which might cause injury to the top of the workbench.

bench marks: A basis for computing elevations by means of identification marks or symbols on stone, metal, or other durable matter, permanently fixed in the ground, and from which differences of elevations are measured.

bench plane: Any plane used constantly and kept handy on the bench; a plane used on the bench as a jack plane, a truing plane, or a smoothing plane.

bench stop: An adjustable metal device, usually notched, attached near one end of a workbench, to hold a piece of work while it is being planed.

bench table: A course of projecting stones forming a stone seat running around the walls at the base of a building such as a large church; a projecting course around the base of a pillar sufficient to form a seat.

bent: A framework transverse to the length of a structure usually designed to carry lateral as well as vertical loads.

bevel: One side of a solid body which is inclined in respect to another side, with the angle between the two sides being either greater or less than a right angle; a sloping edge. See T bevel, Fig. 51.

bevel siding: A board used for wall covering, as the shingle, which is thicker along one edge. When placed on the wall the thicker edge overlaps the thinner edge of the siding below to shed water. The face width of the bevel siding is from 3½" to 11¼" wide

bid: An offer to furnish, at a specified price, supplies or equipment for performing a designated piece of work;

an offer to pay a specified sum for goods sold at auction.

biscuit: A term applied to unglazed tile or ware after first firing in a biscuit oven, but before glazing.

bit brace or bit stock: A curved device used for holding boring or drilling tools; a bit stock, with a curved handle, designed to give greater leverage than is afforded by a boring tool with a straight handle. See Fig. 13.

blade: The longer of the two extending arms of the *framing square,* usually 24 inches long and 2 inches wide. The *tongue* of the square forms a right angle with the *blade. Rafter framing tables* and *essex board measure tables* appear on the faces of the blade of the square. Also called *body.*

blank flue: If the space on one side of a fireplace is not needed for a flue, a chamber is built in and closed off at the top in order to conserve material and labor, and to balance the weight.

bleeder tile: The pipe placed in the foundation walls of a building, to allow the surface water accumulated by the outside tile drain to pass into the drain provided on the inside of the foundation wall. Sometimes called bleeder pipe. See Fig. 10.

blemish: Any imperfection which mars the appearance of wood.

blind header: In masonry work, stones or bricks having the appearance of headers; they really are only short blocks of stone or the ends of bricks.

block: In building construction, a small piece of wood glued into the interior angle of a joint to strengthen and stiffen the joint (Fig. 30); a piece of wood placed back of a wainscot for support and to hold it away from the wall; a building unit of terra cotta or cement which differs from brick in being larger and sometimes hollow; also, a small piece of stone which has been cut down, usually for attaching a rope for lifting purposes.

block-in-course: A kind of masonry used for heavy engineering construction,

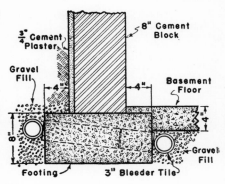

Fig. 10. Bleeder Tile

in which the stones are carefully squared and finished to make close joints, and the faces are dressed with a hammer.

block-in-course bond: In masonry, a bond used for uniting the concentric courses of an arch by inserting transverse courses, or *voussoirs,* at intervals.

blocking course: In masonry, a finishing course of stones on top of a cornice, showing above the cornice, and crowning the walls, usually serving as a sort of solid parapet, forming a small architectural attic.

block plane: A tool used for working end grain. This type of plane is usually small in size, measuring from 5 to 7 inches in length. The cutting bevel is placed up instead of down, and has no cap iron. Designed to use in one hand when in operation.

bloom: An efflorescence which sometimes appears on masonry walls, especially on a brick wall. Also a defect on a varnished surface usually caused by a damp atmosphere.

blueprint: A working plan used by tradesmen on a construction job; an architectural drawing made by draftsmen, then transferred to chemically treated paper by exposure to sunlight, or strong artificial light. The sensitized paper, to which the drawing is transferred, turns blue when exposed to light.

blue stain: A discoloration of lumber due

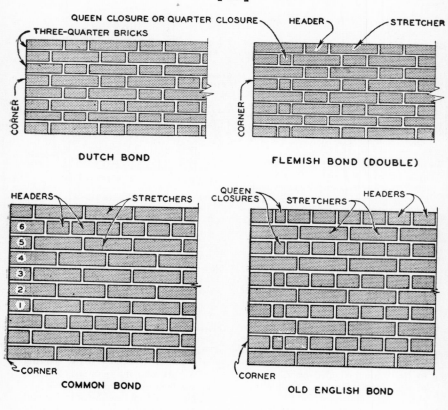

QUEEN CLOSURE OR QUARTER CLOSURE   HEADER   STRETCHER

THREE-QUARTER BRICKS

CORNER

DUTCH BOND   **FLEMISH BOND (DOUBLE)**

HEADERS   STRETCHERS

6
5
4
3
2
1

CORNER

COMMON BOND

QUEEN CLOSURES   STRETCHERS   HEADERS

CORNER

OLD ENGLISH BOND

QUEEN CLOSURES

CORNER

STRETCHERS

HEADERS

ENGLISH CROSS BOND

Fig. 11. Common Bonds

to a fungus growth in the unseasoned wood. Although *blue stain* mars the appearance of lumber, it does not seriously affect the strength of the timber.

bluestone: A grayish-blue sandstone quarried near the Hudson River; much used in the East as a building stone, especially for window and door sills; also used for lintels.

board measure: A system of measurement for lumber. The unit of measure being one board foot which is represented by a piece of lumber 1 foot square and 1 inch thick. Quantities of lumber are designated and prices determined in terms of *board feet.*

board rule: A measuring device with various scales for finding the number of board feet in a quantity of lumber without calculation; a graduated scale used in checking lumber to find the cubic contents of a board without mathematical calculation.

boasted work: In masonry, a dressed stone having a finish on the face similar to tooled work. *Boasting* may be done by hand or with a machine tool.

boaster: In stone masonry, a chisel used to smooth the surface of hard stone or to remove tool marks.

body: Same as the *blade* of a *framing square.*

bolster: A crosspiece on an arch centering, running from rib to rib; the bearing place of a truss bridge upon a pier; a top piece on a post used to lengthen the bearing of a beam.

bond: In masonry and bricklaying, the arrangement of brick or stone in a wall by lapping them upon one another, to prevent vertical joints falling over each other. As the building goes up, an inseparable mass is formed by tying the face and backing together. Various types of bond are shown in Fig. 11.

bondstones: In masonry, stones running through the thickness of a wall at right angles to its base to bind the wall together.

bossage: In masonry, stones which are roughly dressed, such as corbels and

quoins, built in so as to project, and then finish-dressed in position.

Boston hip roof: A method of shingling used to cover the joint, or hip, of a hip roof. To insure a watertight job, a double row of shingles or slate is laid lengthwise along the hip.

boulder wall: In masonry, a type of rustic wall composed of boulders, usually undressed, and mortar.

bow: Any part of a building which projects in the form of an arc or of a polygon.

bow saw: A special type of saw used for making curved cuts. The blade which is thin and narrow is held in tension by the leverage obtained through the twisting of a cord, or by means of rods and turnbuckle.

box column: A type of built-up hollow column used in porch construction; it is usually square in form.

box frame: A window frame containing boxes for holding the sash weights.

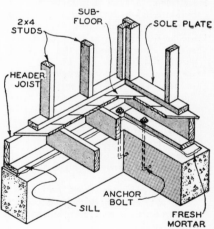

Fig. 12. Box Sill

box sill: A header nailed on the ends of joists and resting on a wall plate. It is used in frame-building construction. See Fig. 12.

brace: A piece of wood or other material used to resist weight or pressure of loads; an inclined piece of timber used as a support to stiffen some part of a structure; a support used to help hold parts of furniture in place, giving strength and durability to the entire piece. A term also applied to a tool with which *auger bits* are turned for boring holes in wood. A bit brace is shown in Fig. 13.

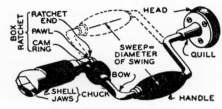

Fig. 13. Brace

brace bit: A tool used for boring holes in wood. An ordinary bit has square, tapered shanks to fit into the socket of a common brace.

brace frame: A type of framework for a building in which the corner posts are braced to sills and plates.

brace jaws: The parts of a bit brace which clamp around the tapered shank of a bit. See Fig. 13.

brace measure: A table which appears on the *tongue* of a *framing square*. This table gives the lengths of common 45° braces plus the length of a brace with a run of 18″ to 24″ of rise. Limited in use to braces conforming to these specifications.

bracing: The ties and rods used for supporting and strengthening the various parts of a building.

bracket: A projection from the face of a wall used as a support for a cornice, or some ornamental feature; a support for a shelf.

brad: A thin, usually small, nail made of wire with a uniform thickness throughout and a small head.

bradawl: A short straight awl with a chisel or cutting edge at the end; a nontapering awl.

break: A lapse in continuity; in building, any projection from the general surface of a wall; an abrupt change in direction as in a wall.

breaking of joints: A staggering of joints to prevent a straight line of vertical joints. The arrangement of boards so as not to allow vertical joints to come immediately over each other.

break iron: An iron fastened to the top of the bit of a plane. The purpose of the iron is to curl and break the shavings.

breast drill: A small tool used for drilling holes by hand in wood or metal. A hand-turned crank transmits power through bevel gears to the drill chuck.

breastsummer: A heavy timber, or summer, placed horizontally over a large opening; a beam flush with a wall or partition which it supports; a lintel over a large window of a store, or shop, where the lintel must support the superstructure above it.

breeze concrete: A concrete composed of coke breeze, sand, and Portland cement. It is a relatively cheap concrete and nails can be driven into it,

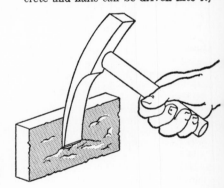

Fig. 14. Brick Hammer

but it has inferior fire-resistive properties. Also called *coke breeze concrete.*

breezeway: A covered passage, open at each end, which passes through a house or between two structures, increasing ventilation and adding an outdoor living effect.

brick: Block of material used for building or paving purposes. The brick are made from clay or a clay mixture molded into blocks which are then hardened by drying in the sun or baking in a kiln. American-made brick average 2½ x 4 x 8 inches in size.

brick beam: A lintel made of brick, with iron straps.

brick cement: A waterproofed masonry cement employed for every kind of brick, concrete brick, tile, or stone masonry, and also in stucco work.

brick facing: The same as *brick veneer.*

bricklayer's hammer: A tool used by bricklayers for dressing brick. It has both a sharpened peen and a hammer head. See Fig. 14.

brick nogging: In a wood-framed wall or partition, brickwork used to fill in the spaces between studs or timbers; also called brick-and-stud work.

brick pier: A detached mass of masonry which serves as a support.

brick set: In masonry, a tool used to cut bricks when exact surfaces are required. The *bricklayer's hammer* is used to force the chisel-like brick set into the brick.

brick trimmer: An arch built of brick between trimmers in the thickness of an upper floor to support a hearth and to guard against fire.

brick trowel: In masonry, a flat triangular-shaped trowel used by bricklayers for picking up mortar and spreading it on a wall. See *buttering trowel.*

brick veneer: A brick facing applied to the surface of the walls of a frame structure, or other types of structures.

bridging: An arrangement of small wooden pieces between timbers, such as joists, to stiffen them and hold them in place; a method of bracing partition studding and floor joists by the use of short strips of wood; cross bridging used between floor joists; usually a piece of 1x3, 2x2, or 2x4 Solid bridging used between partition studs is the same size as the studding.

British thermal unit: The quantity of heat required to raise the temperature of one pound of pure water one degree Fahrenheit at or near the temperature of maximum density of water 39 degrees Fahrenheit. Abbreviation B.t.u.

broached work: In masonry, broad grooves which give a finish to a building stone, made by dressing the stone with a punch.

brush or spray coat: A waterproofing application of one or more coats of asphalt, or a commercial waterproofing, on the exterior of the foundation, below grade line, with a brush, trowel, or by spraying. May be used where subgrade moisture problems are not severe.

builders' tape: Steel measuring tape usually 50 or 100 feet in length, contained in a circular case. *Builders' tape* is made sometimes of fabricated materials.

building: A structure used especially for a dwelling, barn, factory, store, shop, or warehouse; the art, or work, of assembling materials and putting them together in the form of a structure; the act of one who or that which builds.

building block: Any hollow rectangular block of burned clay, terra cotta, concrete, cement, or glass, manufactured for use as building material.

building line: The line, or limit, on a city lot beyond which the law forbids the erection of a building; also, a second line on a building site within which the walls of the building must be confined; that is, the outside face of the wall of the building must coincide with this line.

building paper: A form of heavy paper prepared especially for construction work. It is used between rough and finish floors, and between sheathing and siding, as an insulation and to keep out vermin. It is used, also, as an undercovering on roofs as a protection against weather.

building stone: An architectural term applied in general to any kind of stone which may be used in the construction of a building, such as limestone, sandstone, granite, marble, or others.

bull header: In masonry, a brick having one rounded corner, usually laid with the short face exposed to form the brick sill under and beyond a window frame; also used as a *quoin* or around doorways.

bull nose: An exterior angle which is rounded to eliminate a sharp or square corner. In masonry, a brick having one rounded corner; in carpentry, a stair step with a rounded end used as a starting step. Also called *bull's nose*.

bull-nose plane: A small plane which can be used in corners or other places difficult to reach. The mouth can be adjusted for coarse or fine work.

Fig. 15. Butterfly Roof

bull's-eye arch: An arch forming a complete circle.

bull stretcher: A brick with one corner rounded and laid with the long face exposed, as a *quoin.*

bungalow: A one-story house with low sweeping lines and a wide veranda; sometimes the attic is finished as a second story. This type of dwelling was first developed in India. In the United States, the *bungalow* has become especially popular as a country or seaside residence.

burl: An abnormal growth on the trunks of many trees; an excrescence often in the form of a flattened hemisphere; veneer made from these excrescences, an especially beautiful *burl* veneer is cut from the stumps of walnut trees.

Burnett's process: The infusion of timber with chloride of zinc as a preservative.

burnisher: A tool, of hardened steel, used for finishing and polishing metal work by friction. The *burnisher* is held against the revolving metal piece which receives a smooth polished surface due to the compression of the outer layer of the metal. This tool is used, also, to turn the edge of a scraper.

burrs: In brick making, lumps of brick which have fused together during the process of burning; often misshapened and used for rough walling.

butt: A hinge of any type except a strap hinge.

butterfly roof: A roof constructed so as to appear as two shed roofs connected at the lower edges. See Fig. 15.

buttering: In masonry, the process of spreading mortar on the edges of a brick before laying it.

buttering trowel: In masonry, a flat tool similar to, but smaller than, the brick trowel; used for spreading mortar on a brick before it is placed in position.

butt hinge: A hinge secured to the edge of a door and the face of the jamb it meets when the door is closed, as distinguished from the strap hinge. Usually mortised into the door and jamb.

butt joint: Any joint made by fastening two parts together end to end without overlapping. See Figs. 29 and 30.

buttress: A projecting structure built against a wall or building to give it greater strength and stability.

buzz saw: A circular saw.

C

cabinet: A piece of furniture, fitted with shelves or drawers, sometimes both, and enclosed with doors, as a *kitchen cabinet* for holding small kitchen equipment; a case with shelves or drawers used as a depository for various articles, such as jewels or precious stones. The doors for such cases are often made of glass, especially when the cases are used for display purposes.

cabinet latch: A name applied to various kinds of catches. These range from the type of catch used on refrigerator doors to the horizontal spring-and-bolt latch operated by turning a knob, as on kitchen cabinets.

cabinet scraper: A tool, made of a flat piece of steel, designed with an edge in such a shape that when the implement is drawn over a surface of wood any irregularities, or uneven places, will be removed, leaving the surface clean and smooth. The *cabinet scraper* is used for final smoothing of surfaces before sandpapering.

cabinetwork: The work of one who makes fine furniture, or beautifully finished woodwork of any kind.

cabin hook: A type of fastener, consisting of a small hook and eye, used on the doors of cabinets.

caisson: A deeply recessed panel sunk in a ceiling or soffit; also, a watertight box used for surrounding work involved in laying a foundation of any structure below water.

caisson pile: A type of pile which has been made watertight by surrounding it with concrete.

calcining: A term applied to the process of producing lime by the heating of limestone to a high temperature. The same as *lime-burning.*

calking: The process of driving tarred oakum or other material into the seams between planks to make the joints watertight, airtight, or steam tight; to fill seams of a ship to prevent leaking; to fill or close seams or crevices with rust cement.

calking tool: A tool used for driving tarred oakum, cotton, and other materials into seams and crevices to make joints watertight and airtight. The *calking tool* is made of steel and in appearance somewhat resembles a chisel.

calyon: In building, flint or pebble stone used in wall construction.

camber: A slight arching or convexity of a timber, or beam; the amount of upward curve given to an arched bar, beam, or girder to prevent the member from becoming concave due to its own weight or the weight of the load it must carry.

canopy: A rooflike structure projecting from a wall or supported on pillars, as an ornamental feature.

cant: To incline at an angle; to tilt; to set up on a slant, or at an angle; also a molding formed of plain surfaces and angles rather than curves.

cant brick: In masonry, a purpose-made brick with one side beveled. See *splayed brick.*

cant hook: A stout wooden lever with an adjustable steel, or iron, hook near the lever end. The *cant hook* is used for rolling logs and telephone, or telegraph, poles.

cantilever: A projecting beam supported only at one end; a large bracket, usually ornamental, for supporting a balcony or cornice; two bracketlike arms projecting toward each other from opposite piers or banks to form the span of a bridge making what is known as a *cantilever bridge.*

canting strip: A projecting molding near the bottom of a wall to direct rain water away from the foundation wall; in frame buildings, the same as a *water table.*

cap: The top parts of columns, doors, and moldings; the coping of a wall; a cornice over a door; the lintel over a door or window frame; a top piece.

capping: The uppermost part on top of a piece of work; a crowning, or topping part.

capping brick: In masonry, brick which are specially shaped for capping the exposed top of a wall. Same as *coping brick.*

cap stone: Stone used for the crown or top part of a structure.

Carborundum: A trade-mark for an abrasive made from a combination of carbon and silicon, and sometimes used instead of emery.

carborundum cloth or **paper:** An abrasive cloth or paper made by covering the material with powdered carborundum held in place by some adhesive, such as glue.

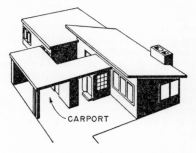

Fig. 16. Carport

carcase: The frame of a house; the unfinished framework, or skeleton, of a building or ship. Also *carcass*.

carpet strip: A piece beneath a door attached to the floor.

carport: A garage, built into a house, which has a roof but only one or two side walls. Generally found in mild climates. See Fig. 16.

carriage: The support for the steps of a wooden stairway; these supports may be either of wood or steel.

casement window: Windows with sash that open on hinges; a window sash made to open by turning on hinges attached to its vertical edge.

casing: The framework around a window or door.

caster: A wheel, or set of wheels, mounted in a swivel frame attached to the feet or base of a piece of furniture, trucks, and portable machines. Casters help in the moving of furniture without injury to the floor.

catch basin: A cistern, or depression, at the point where a gutter discharges into a sewer to catch any object which would not readily pass through the sewers; a reservoir to catch and retain surface drainage; a receptacle at an opening into a sewer to retain any matter which would not easily pass through the sewer; a trap to catch and hold fats, grease, and oil from kitchen sinks to prevent them from passing into the sewer.

caul: A tool used in forming veneer to the shape of a curved surface.

cavetto: A quarter round, concave molding; a concave ornamental molding opposed in effect to the ovolo—the quarter of a circle called the *quarter round*.

cavil: In masonry, a kind of heavy sledge hammer, having one blunt end and one pointed end, used for rough dressing of stone at the quarry; a term also applied to a small stone ax resembling a *jedding ax*.

cavity wall: A hollow wall, usually consisting of two brick walls erected a few inches apart and joined together with ties of metal or brick. Such

walls increase thermal resistance and prevent rain from driving through to the inner face. Also called *hollow wall*. See Fig. 36.

cellar: A room, or set of rooms, below the surface of the ground, used especially for keeping provisions and other stores; a room beneath the main portion of a building. In modern homes, the heating plant is usually located in the *cellar*.

cement: In building, a material for binding other material or articles together; usually plastic at the time of application but hardens when in place; any substance which causes bodies to adhere to one another, such as Portland cement, stucco, and natural cements; also mortar or plaster of Paris.

cement colors: A special mineral pigment used for coloring cement for floors. In addition to the natural coloring pigment obtained from mineral oxides, there are manufactured pigments produced especially for cement work.

cement gun: A mechanical device used for spraying fine concrete or cement mortar by means of pneumatic pressure. Same as *Cement Gun,* the trade-mark for a machine used to apply *Gunite*.

cementing trowel: A trowel similar to the plasterer's trowel, but often of a heavier gauge stock.

cement joggle: In masonry construction, a key which is formed between adjacent stones by running mortar into a square-section channel which is cut equally into each of the adjoining faces, thus preventing relative movement of the faces.

cement mortar: A building material composed of Portland cement, sand, and water.

center: A fixed point about which the radius of a circle, or of an arc, revolves; the point about which any revolving body rotates or revolves, as the middle, or center, of activity.

centering: The frame on which a brick or stone arch is turned; the false work over which an arch is formed. In concrete work the *centering* is known as the *frames*.

center line: A broken line, usually indicated by a dot and dash, showing the center of an object and providing a convenient line from which to lay off measurements.

centerpiece: An ornament placed in the middle of a ceiling.

centimeter: A measure of length in the metric system equal to the one-hundredth part of a meter, or .3937 inch.

ceramic mosaic: A collective term applied to floor tiles which are marketed in sheet units. The individual units are properly spaced and mounted on sheets of paper. The tiles are produced in a variety of sizes, shapes, and colors and used extensively for shower-bath floors, also for regular bathroom floors.

ceramic tile: A thin, flat piece of fired clay, usually square. These pieces of clay are attached to walls, floors, or counter tops, with cement or other adhesives, creating durable, decorative, and dirt-resistant surfaces. Tiles may be plastic process (formed while clay is wet) or dust-pressed process (compressed clay powder). They may be glazed (vitrified coating); unglazed (natural surface); non-vitrified; semivitrified, and vitreous (porous, semiporous, or relatively nonporous).

chain bond: In masonry, the bonding together of a stone wall by the use of a built-in chain or iron bar.

chamfer: A groove, or channel, as in a piece of wood; a bevel edge; an oblique surface formed by cutting away an edge or corner of a piece of timber, or stone. Any piece of work that is cut off at the edges at a 45 degree angle so that two faces meeting form a right angle are said to be *chamfered*.

channel: A concave groove cut in a surface as a decorative feature; a grooved molding used for ornamental pur-

poses; a decorative concave groove on parts of furniture.

channel iron: A rolled iron bar with the sides turned upward forming a rim, making the *channel iron* appear like a channel-shaped trough. In sectional form, the *channel iron* appears like a rectangular box with the top and two ends omitted.

chase: In masonry, a groove or channel cut in the face of a brick wall to allow space for receiving pipes; in building, a trench dug to accommodate a drainpipe; also, a recess in a masonry wall to provide space for pipes and ducts.

chasing: The decorative features produced by grooving or indenting metal.

check: An ornamental design composed of inlaid squares; a blemish in wood caused by the separation of wood tissues.

checking of wood: Blemishes or cracks in timber due to uneven seasoning.

check rail: The middle horizontal member of a double-hung window, forming the lower rail of the top sash and the top rail of the lower sash.

chevron: The meeting place of rafters at the ridge of a gable roof; a zigzag pattern used as an ornamentation in Romanesque architecture.

chimney: That part of a building which contains the flues for drawing off smoke or fumes from stoves, furnaces, fireplaces, or some other source of smoke and gas.

chimney blocks: Cement blocks designed to form a continuous round flue when placed in position, one on top of another.

chimney bond: In masonry, a form of bond commonly used for the internal division walls of domestic chimneys, as well as for the outer walls. The surface of this type of wall is made up of stretchers which break joints at the center, with a header on each alternate course at the corner.

chimney breast: That part of a chimney which projects from a wall where the chimney passes through a room.

When the chimney is a part of a fireplace, the breast of the chimney is usually built much wider than the chimney itself to provide for a mantel or to improve the appearance of the room.

chimney lining: Rectangular or round tiles placed within a chimney for protective purpose. The glazed surface of the tile provides resistance to the deteriorating effects of smoke and gas fumes.

chip ax: Small sharp cutting tool used in the building trades for cutting and shaping structural stone or timbers.

chipping: The process of cutting off small pieces of metal or wood with a cold chisel and a hammer.

chisel: A cutting tool with a wide variety of uses. The cutting edge on the end of the tool usually is transverse to the axis. The cutting principle of the *chisel* is the same as that of the wedge.

cinder blocks: Building blocks in which the principal materials are cement and cinders.

cinder concrete: A type of concrete made from Portland cement mixed with clean, well-burned coal cinders which are used as coarse aggregate.

cinder fill: A fill of cinders, from three to six inches deep, under a basement floor as an aid in keeping the basement dry; also, a fill of cinders outside of a basement wall to a depth of twelve inches, over drain tile, to facilitate drainage. Pebble gravel is sometimes used instead of cinders.

circular and angular measure: A standard measure expressed in degrees, minutes, and seconds, as follows:

60 seconds ($''$)	= 1 minute ($'$)
60 minutes	= 1 degree ($°$)
90 degrees	= 1 quadrant
4 quadrants	= 1 circle or circumference

circular saw: A saw with teeth spaced around the edge of a circular plate, or disk, which is rotated at high speed upon a central axis, or spindle, used for cutting lumber or sawing logs.

circumference: The perimeter of a circle; a line that bounds a circular plane surface.

circumscribe: The process of drawing a line to enclose certain portions of an object, figure, or plane; to encircle; to draw boundary lines; to enclose within certain limits.

clamp: A device for holding portions of work together, either wood or metal; an appliance with opposing sides or parts that may be screwed together to hold objects or parts of objects together firmly.

clamp brick. In masonry, stock bricks which have been burned in a clamp.

clamping screw: A screw used in a clamp; a screw used to hold pieces of work together in a clamp.

clapboard: A long thin board, graduating in thickness from one end to the other, used for siding, the thick end overlapping the thin portion of the board.

clap post: The upright post of a cupboard where the door *claps,* or closes.

classical: Pertaining to a style of architecture in accordance with ancient Greek and Roman models, or later styles of architecture modeled upon principles embodied in the early types of Greek and Roman structures.

classic molding: A type of molding similar to that used in classic orders of architecture.

claw hammer: A carpenter's tool having one end curved and split for use in drawing nails by giving leverage under the heads. See Fig. 17.

claw tool: A stonemason's tool having teeth or claws; used for dressing soft stone. Sometimes called *tooth chisel.*

clay shale: Clay which has a laminated structure; used as one of the ingredients in making clay tile.

cleat: A strip of wood or metal fastened across a door or other object to give it additional strength; a strip of wood or other material nailed to a wall usually for the pupose of supporting some object or article fastened to it.

clinch: The process of securing a driven nail by bending down the point; to fasten firmly by bending down the ends of protruding nails.

clockwise: Moving in the same direction as the rotation of the hands of a clock; with a right-hand motion.

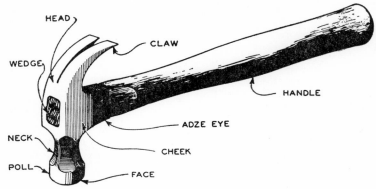

Fig. 17. Claw Hammer

closed cornice: A cornice which is entirely enclosed by the *roof, fascia,* and the *plancher;* same as *boxed cornice.* See Fig. 18.

closer: In constructing a masonry wall, any portion of a brick used to close up the bond next to the end brick of a course; the last stone, if smaller than the others, in a horizontal course, or a piece of brick which finishes a course; also, a piece of brick in each alternate course to enable a bond to be formed by preventing two headers from exactly superimposing on a stretcher; same as *closure.*

coarse aggregate: Crushed stone or gravel used to reinforce concrete; the size is regulated by building codes. See *rubble concrete.*

cob: A small mixture of unburned clay, usually with straw as a binder. Used in building walls known as *cob walls.*

cob wall: A wall built of clay blocks made of unburned clay or chalk mixed with straw; also, a wall constructed of *cobs,* such as clay bats.

cocobolo: A tropical wood, which is extremely hard and tough, used for the heads and handles on high-priced tools. It takes a beautiful finish.

code: Any systematic collection or set of rules pertaining to one particular subject, and devised for the purpose of securing uniformity in work or for

maintaining proper standards of procedure, as a *building code.*

coffer: An ornamental sunken panel in a ceiling, or soffit; a deeply recessed panel in a dome.

cofferdam: A watertight enclosure usually built of piles or clay, within which

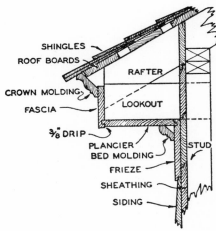

Fig. 18. Closed Cornice

excavating is done for foundations; also, a watertight enclosure fixed to the side of a ship for making repairs below the water line.

cold chisel: A name applied to a chisel made of tool steel of a strength and temper that will stand up under the hardest usage. A chisel suitable for cutting and chipping cold metal.

collar: In carpentry, an encircling band resembling a *collar;* a molding extending around a leg of furniture.

collar beam: A horizontal tie beam, in a roof truss, connecting two opposite rafters at a level considerably above the wall plate.

Colonial: A style of architecture used in America during Colonial times and sometimes used by builders as late as 1840; also, a type of furniture in vogue in early America before the American Revolution, and applied to this type of furniture as late as the nineteenth century.

column: A pillar usually round; a vertical shaft which receives pressure in the direction of its longitudinal axis; the parts of a column are: the *base* on which the shaft rests, the body, or *shaft,* and the head known as the *capital.*

column footings: Concrete footings, reinforced with steel rods; used as supports for columns which in turn carry the load of **I** beams which serve as supports for the superstructure of a building.

combination pliers: A pincerlike tool, with long, flat, roughened jaws adjustable for size of opening by means of a slip joint. The inner grip is notched for grasping and holding round objects, the outer grip is scored. The tool is used for cutting or bending wire.

combination square: A tool which combines in handy compact form the equivalent of several tools, including an inside try square, outside try square, mitre square, plumb, level. depth guage, marking guage, straight edge, bevel protractor, and center head in addition to square head.

common bond: In masonry, a form of bond in which every sixth course is a header course, and the intervening courses are stretcher courses. Sometimes varied, so a header bond is used every fourth or fifth course. See *typical bonds,* Fig. 11.

common brick: Any brick commonly used for construction purposes; pri-

marily made for building and not especially treated for texture or color, but including clinker and over-burned brick.

common lime: A material produced by the burning of limestone to the proper degree; used for making mortar for plastering and masonry work. Same as *quicklime.*

common rafter: A *rafter* which extends at right angles from the plate line to the *ridge* or *purlin* of a roof.

compass brick: In masonry, a curved or tapering brick for use in curved work, such as in arches.

compass plane: A cutting tool used for smoothing concave or convex surfaces; a plane with an adjustable sole

compass saw: A small handsaw of a special type, with a thin tapering blade designed for cutting a small circle or other small opening, such as a keyhole. Compass saws are often sold in sets called *nests.* See Fig. 33.

compo board: A trade name for a type of building board made from narrow strips of wood glued together to make a large sheet. Both sides are faced with heavy paper.

compound arch: An arch made up of a number of concentric archways placed successively within and behind each other.

concave: A curved recess; hollowed out like the inner curve of a circle or sphere; the interior of a curved surface or line; a bowl-shaped depression.

concave joint: In masonry, a mortar joint formed with a special tool or a bent iron rod. This type of mortar joint is weather resistive and inexpensive. See Fig. 32.

concentrated load: The weight localized on, and carried by, a beam, girder, or other supporting structural part.

concrete: In masonry, a mixture of cement, sand, and gravel, with water in varying proportions according to the use which is to be made of the finished product.

concrete-bent construction: A system of construction in which precast concrete-bent framing units are the basic load-bearing members. The principal advantages and problems are similar to those in *post and beam construction.*

concrete blocks: In masonry, precast, hollow, or solid blocks of concrete used in the construction of buildings.

concrete insert: A type of metal anchor used to secure structural wood parts to a concrete or masonry wall. See *anchors,* Fig. 1.

concrete paint: A specially prepared thin paint, consisting of a mixture of cement and water, applied to the surface of a concrete wall to give it a uniform finish, and to protect the joints against weathering by rain or snow.

concrete wall: In building construction, any wall made of reinforced concrete, such as a basement wall.

conduit: A natural or artificial channel for carrying fluids, as water pipes, canals, and aqueducts; a tube, or trough, for receiving and protecting electric wires.

console: In architecture, any bracket, or bracketlike support usually ornamented by a reverse scroll; an ornamental bracketlike support for a cornice or bust; any ornamented bracketlike architectural member used as a support.

construction: The process of assembling material and building a structure; also, that which is built; style of building, as of wood, iron, or steel *construction.*

consulting engineer: A person retained to give expert advice in regard to all engineering problems; supposedly an experienced engineer of high rating in his profession.

continuous beam: A timber that rests on more than two supporting members of a structure.

continuous header: The top plate is replaced by 2 x 6's turned on edge and running around the entire house. This header is strong enough to act as a lintel over all wall openings, eliminating some cutting and fitting of stud lengths and separate headers over openings. This development is especially important because of the new emphasis on one-story, open-planning houses.

contour: The outline of a figure, as the profile of a molding.

contractor: One who agrees to supply materials and perform certain types of work for a specified sum of money, as a *building contractor* who erects a structure according to a written agreement, or *contract.*

coped joint: The seam, or juncture, between molded pieces in which a portion of one piece is cut away to receive the molded part of the other piece.

coping: A covering or top for brick walls. Usually, the coping is made of glazed tile. The cap or top course of a wall. The coping frequently is projected out from the wall to afford a decorative as well as protective feature. See Fig. 25.

coping brick: In masonry, brick having special shapes for use in capping the exposed top of a wall. It is sometimes used with a creasing and sometimes without. In the latter case, the brick is wider than the wall, and has drips under its lower edges.

coping saw: A saw used for cutting curves and hollowing out moldings. The narrow blade of the *coping saw,* carried on pins set in a steel bow frame, is from $\frac{1}{16}''$ to $\frac{1}{8}''$ wide and $6\frac{1}{2}''$ long.

corbel: A short piece of wood or stone projecting from the face of a wall to form a support for a timber, or other weight; a bracketlike support; a stepping out of courses in a wall to form a ledge; any supporting projection of wood or stone on the face of a wall.

corbeled chimney: A chimney which is supported by a brickwork projection from a wall, forming a sort of bracket or corbel; also, a chimney erected on a bracket constructed of wood members.

corbel out: The building of one, or more, courses of masonry out from the face of a wall to form a support for timbers.

corbel table: A horizontal row of corbels supporting lintels or small arches; a projecting course, as of masonry, which is supported by a series of corbels; a cornice supported by corbels.

corbie stones: Stones used for covering the steps of a crow-stepped gable wall.

cord: Wood cut in four-feet lengths, usually for firewood. A pile of wood measuring four feet in width, four feet in height, and eight feet in length.

corner bead: A small projecting molding, or bead, built into plastered corners to prevent accidental breaking of the plaster; such a *bead* usually is of metal.

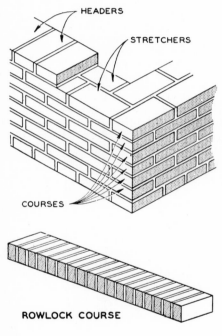

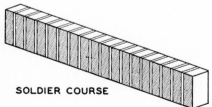

Fig. 19. Courses in Brickwork

corner bit brace: A specially designed *bit brace* for use in positions where it is difficult for a workman to operate the regular bit brace; a corner brace useful for tradesmen who have occasion to work close to perpendicular surfaces and in corners.

cornice: Projection at the top of a wall; a term applied to construction under the eaves, or where the roof and side walls meet; the top course, or courses, of a wall when treated as a crowning member. See Fig. 18.

corona: That part of a cornice supported by and projecting beyond the bed molding. The *corona* serves as a protection to the walls by throwing off rain water.

corridor: A passageway in a building into which several apartments open; a gallery, or passage, usually covered into which rooms open, as the *corridor* of a hotel, or of an art gallery.

counterbracing: Diagonal bracing which transmits a strain in an opposite direction from the main bracing; in a truss or girder, bracing used to give additional support to the beam and to relieve it of transverse stress.

counterclockwise: Motion in the direction opposite to the rotation of the hands of a clock.

countersink: To make a depression in wood or metal for the reception of a plate of iron, the head of a screw, or for a bolt, so that the plate, screw, or bolt will not project beyond the surface of the work; to form a flaring cavity around the top of a hole for receiving the head of a screw or bolt.

course: A continuous level range or row of brick or masonry throughout the face or faces of a building; to arrange in a row. A row of bricks, when laid in a wall, is called a *course*. See Fig. 19.

coursed ashlar: In masonry, a type of ashlar construction in which the various blocks of structural material have been arranged, according to height, to form regular courses in the face of walls. See Fig. 4.

coursed rubble masonry: Masonry composed of roughly shaped stones fitting approximately on level beds, and well bonded.

court: An open space surrounded partly or entirely by a building; an open area partly or wholly enclosed by buildings or walls.

cove: A concave molding; an architectural member, as a ceiling, which is curved or arched at its junction with the side walls: also, a large, hollow cornice; a niche.

cove bracketing: The lumber skeleton, or framing for a cove; a term applied chiefly to the *bracketing* of a cove ceiling.

cove ceiling: A ceiling which rises from the walls with a concave curve.

cove molding: A molding called the *cavetto;* a quarter round, or concave molding.

coving: The scotia inverted on a large scale; a concave molding often found in the base of a column.

cradling: Lumber work, or framing, for sustaining the lath and plaster of vaulted ceilings.

cramp: In masonry, a contrivance consisting of iron rods or bars with the ends bent to a right angle; used to hold blocks of stone together.

crawl space: In cases where houses have no basements, the space between the first floor and the ground is made large enough for a man to crawl through for repairs and installation of utilities.

cresting: An ornamental finish of the wall or ridge of a building. The *cresting* of shingle roofs is generally of sheet metal.

crib: A cratelike framing used as a support for a structure above; any of various frameworks, as of logs or timbers, used in construction work; the wooden lining on the inside of a shaft; openwork of horizontally, cross-piled squared timbers, or beams, used as a retaining wall.

cripple rafter: A rafter extending from a hip to a valley rafter.

crosscut saw: A saw made to cut transversely, as across the grain of wood.

cross grain: A section of wood cut at right angles to the longitudinal fiber.

crosslap: A joint where two pieces of timber cross each other. This type of joint is formed by cutting away half the thickness of each piece at the place of joining, so that one piece will fit into the other and both pieces will lie on the same plane. See Fig. 29.

cross section: A transverse section cut at right angles to the longitudinal axis of a piece of wood, drawing, or other work.

crotch veneer: A type of veneer cut from the crotch of a tree forming an unusual grain effect; also, veneer cut from wood of twin trees which have grown together, likewise forming an unusual grain effect.

crown molding: A molding at the top of the cornice and immediately beneath the roof.

cube root: A given number which taken three times as a factor produces a number called its *cube,* as $3 \times 3 \times 3$ equals 27, hence *3,* the given number, is the *cube root* of 27.

cubic content: In building construction, the number of cubic feet contained within the walls of a room or combination of rooms and used as a basis for estimating cost of materials and construction; cubic content is also important when estimating cost of installing heating, lighting, and ventilating systems.

cubic measure: The measurement of volume in cubic units, as follows:

1,728 cubic inches=1 cubic foot
27 cubic feet=1 cubic yard
231 cubic inches=1 gallon
128 cubic feet =1 cord

cup shake: A defect in wood where annual rings separate from each other, thus forming a semicircular flaw. Such flaws may occur between two or more concentric layers of wood. Because of their appearance, such defects are known as *cup shake,* but, since they are caused by the wind, they are also known as *windshake.* See Fig. 57.

curb edger: In masonry and cement work, a tool specially designed for shaping curved sections which must be finished smooth and true, such as the borders of driveways or pavements.

curb roof: The mansard roof which takes its name from the architect who designed it. This type of roof has a double slope on each side, with the lower slope almost vertical. Frequently the lower slope contains dormer windows, which make possible the addition of another story to the house.

curl: A spiral or curved marking in the grain of wood; a feather-form mark in wood.

curtain wall: A thin wall, supported by the structural steel or concrete frame of the building, independent of the wall below.

cushion head: In foundation construction, a capping to protect the head of a pile which is to be sunk into the ground with a *pile driver.* Such a cushion usually consists of a cast-iron cap.

cut nails: Iron nails cut by machines from sheet metal, as distinguished from the more common wire nails now in general use. See Fig. 37.

cutter: In masonry, a brick made soft enough to cut with a trowel to any shape desired, then rubbed to a smooth face. Sometimes called *rubbers.* The same as *seconds.*

cutting gauge: A gauge similar in construction to the regular marking gauges except that it has an adjustable blade for slitting thin stock, instead of the marking pin.

cutting pliers: A type of pliers which has a pair of nippers placed to one side for cutting wire, in addition to the flat jaws.

cyma: A molding in common use, with a simple waved line concave at one end and convex at the other end, similar in form to an italic *f.* When the concave part is uppermost the molding is called *cyma recta,* but if the convexity appears above and the concavity below the molding is known as *cyma reversa.*

D

dado: The vertical face of an insulated pedestal between the base and surbase, or between the base and cornice; a plain, flat surface at the base of a wall as in a room; such a surface is sometimes ornamented.

damper: A device used for regulating the draft in the flue of a furnace; also, a device for checking vibrations.

damp-proofing: The special preparation of a wall to prevent moisture from oozing through it; material used for this purpose must be impervious to moisture.

darby: A flat tool used by plasterers to level the surface of plaster, especially on ceilings. The *darby* is usually about three and one-half inches wide and forty-four inches long, with two handles on the back.

deadening: The use of insulating materials, made for the purpose, to prevent sounds passing through walls and floors.

dead level: An emphatic statement used to indicate an absolute level.

deal: A board of fir or pine cut to a specified size, or to one of several specified sizes.

deciduous: Pertaining to trees which shed their leaves annually.

decimal: A fractional part of a number, proceeding by tenths, each unit being ten times the unit next smaller.

decimal equivalent: The value of a fraction expressed as a decimal, as ¼ equals .25.

defect: In lumber, an irregularity occurring in or on wood that will tend to impair its strength, durability, or utility value.

deflection: A deviation, or turning aside, from a straight line; bending of a beam or any part of a structure under an applied load.

deformation: Act of deforming or changing the shape; alteration in form which a structure undergoes when subjected to the action of a weight, or load.

deformed bars: Reinforcing bars made in irregular shapes to produce a better bond between the bars and the concrete.

degree: One 360th part of a circumference of a circle, or of a round angle.

demarcation: In masonry, a fixed line for marking a boundary limit.

derrick: Any hoisting device used for lifting or moving heavy weights; also, a structure consisting of an upright or fixed framework, with a hinged arm which can be raised and lowered and usually swings around to different positions for handling loads.

design: A drawing showing the plan, elevations, sections, and other features necessary in the construction of a new building. As used by architects, the term *plan* is restricted to the horizontal projection, while *elevation* applies to the vertical, or exterior, views.

detail: A term in architecture applied to the small parts into which any structure or machine is divided. It is applied generally to moldings or other decorative features and to drawings showing a special feature of construction.

detail drawing: A separate drawing showing a small part of a machine or structure in detail; a drawing showing the separate parts of a machine or other object with complete tabular data, such as dimensions, materials used, number of pieces, and operations to be performed; also, a drawing showing the position of the parts of a machine or tool and the manner in which the various parts are placed in assembling them.

detailer: One who prepares small drawings for shop use; a draftsman who makes detailed drawings.

diagonal bond: In masonry, a form of bond sometimes used in unusually thick walls, or for strengthening the bond in footings carrying heavy loads. The bricks are laid diagonally across the wall, with successive courses crossing each other in respect to rake.

diagram: A figure which gives the outline or general features of an object; a line drawing, as a chart or graph used for scientific purposes; a graphic representation of some feature of a structure.

diameter: A straight line passing through the center of a circle or sphere and terminating in the circumference.

dimension shingles: Shingles cut to a uniform size as distinguished from *random shingles.*

distribution tile: Concrete or clay tile without bell mouths. These tile are laid with a little space at each joint, in lines which fan out from a septic tank distribution box.

dividers: Device for measuring or setting off distances, or dividing lines. Also known as *compasses.* Usually in plural only.

dogtooth: In architecture, a toothlike ornament or a molding cut into projecting teeth; a type of early architectural decoration in the form of a four-leafed flower, probably so named from its resemblance to a dogtoothed violet.

dome: An inverted cup on a building, as a cupola, especially one on a large scale; the vaulted roof of a rotunda.

door check: A device used to retard the movement of a closing door and to guard against its slamming, or banging, but also insures the closing of the door.

doorframe: The case which surrounds a door and into which the door closes and out of which it opens. The frame consists of two upright pieces called *jambs* and the *lintel* or horizontal piece over the opening for the door.

doorhead: The upper part of the frame of a door.

doorstone: The stone which forms the threshold of a door.

doorstop: A device used to hold a door open to any desired position; a device usually attached near the bottom of a door to hold it open and operated by the pressure of the foot. The *doorstop* may or may not be attached to the door. The strip against which a door closes on the inside face of a door frame is also known as a *doorstop.*

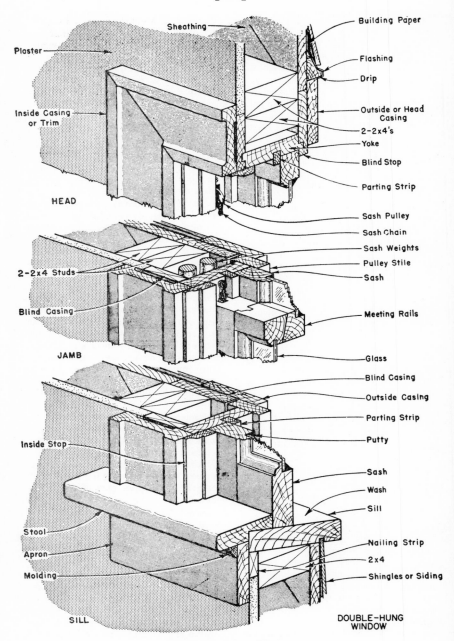

Plaster

Sheathing

Building Paper

Flashing

Drip

Inside Casing or Trim

Outside or Head Casing

2-2x4's

Yoke

Blind Stop

Parting Strip

HEAD

Sash Pulley

Sash Chain

Sash Weights

2-2x4 Studs

Pulley Stile

Sash

Blind Casing

Meeting Rails

JAMB

Glass

Blind Casing

Outside Casing

Parting Strip

Putty

Inside Stop

Sash

Wash

Sill

Stool

Apron

Nailing Strip

Molding

2x4

Shingles or Siding

SILL

DOUBLE-HUNG WINDOW

Fig. 20. Double-hung Window

dormer window: A vertical window in a projection built out from a sloping roof; a small window projecting from the slope of a roof.

dormitory: A large sleeping room, or a sleeping apartment containing several rooms; also, a building containing a number of sleeping rooms.

double-acting hinge: A hinge which permits motion in two directions, as on a swinging door, or on folding screens.

Double Flemish bond: A bond in which both the inner and outer faces of an exposed masonry wall are laid in *Flemish bond,* with all headers *true* or *full headers.* See Fig. 11.

double-hung window: A window with an upper and lower sash, each carried by sash cords and weights. See Fig. 20.

double-pitch skylight: A skylight designed to slope in two directions.

double-pole switch: A switch to connect or break two sides of an electric circuit.

dovetail: In carpentry, an interlocking joint; a joint made by cutting two boards or timbers to fit into each other. A common type of joint used in making boxes or cases. See Fig. 30.

dovetail cramps: A device, usually of iron bent at the ends, or of dovetail form, used to hold structural timbers or stone together.

dovetail cutter: A tool used for cutting the inner and outer dovetails for joints.

dovetail-halved joint: A joint which is halved by cuts narrowed at the heel, as in a dovetail joint.

dovetailing: A method of fastening boards or timbers together by fitting one piece into the other as with dovetail joints. See Fig. 30.

dovetail saw: A small saw similar to a backsaw, with smaller teeth and a different-shaped handle.

dowel: A pin of wood or metal used to hold or strengthen two pieces of timber where they join; a pin or tenon fitting into a corresponding hole and serving to fasten two pieces of wood together. See Fig. 29.

drive screw or **screw nail:** A type of screw

pieces of timber together by the use of dowels; butt joints are sometimes secured by the use of glue and dowel pins.

downspout: Any connector, such as a pipe, for carrying rain water from the roof of a building to the ground or to a sewer connection.

draftsman: One who draws plans or sketches; usually a term applied to one who uses mechanical aids or instruments for preparing drawings for tradesmen.

draftsman's scale: A measuring scale used by draftsmen, usually triangular in shape but sometimes flat. One edge is graduated in $\frac{1}{16}$, $\frac{1}{8}$, $\frac{1}{4}$, $\frac{1}{2}$ and so on, as on a standard scale. Other edges are divided into fractional parts to facilitate reducing measurements.

draft stop or fire stop: Any obstruction placed in air passages to block the passing of flames or air currents upward or across a building.

drag: In masonry, a tool which has steel teeth, used for dressing the surface of stone; also called a *comb.*

drawer pull: In woodworking, a handle placed on the front of a drawer so that it may be easily opened or pulled out.

drawer slip: A guide or strip on which a drawer moves when it is opened.

drawing: A sketch made with pen, pencil, or crayon representing by lines some figure or object.

drawknife: A woodworking tool with a blade and a handle at each end. The handles are at right angles to the blade which is long and narrow. It is used to smooth a surface by drawing the knife over it.

D & M: An abbreviation for the term *dressed and matched.*

D4S: A symbol used on building plans meaning *dressed on four sides.*

dressing: Any decorative finish, as molding around a door; also, in masonry, all those stone or brick parts distinguished from the plain wall of a building, such as ornamental columns, jambs, arches, entablatures, copings, quoins, and string courses. The process of smoothing and squaring lumber or stone for use in a building.

drip: A construction member, wood or metal, which projects to throw off rain water.

drip mold: A molding designed to prevent rain water from running down the face of a wall.

dripstone: In architecture, a stone drip placed over a window to throw off rain water; a label molding sometimes called a *weather molding.*

drive screw or **screw nail:** A type of screw which can be driven in with a hammer but is removed with a screw driver.

driving home: In shopwork, the placing of a part, a nail or screw, in its final position by driving it with the blows of a hammer or screw driver.

drop siding: A special type of weatherboarding used on the exterior surface of frame structures.

drop window: A type of window that is lowered into a pocket below the sill, usually seen on trolley cars, but also used in homes.

dry kiln: An ovenlike chamber in which wood is seasoned artificially, thus hastening the process of drying.

dry masonry: Any type of masonry work laid up without the use of mortar.

dry measure: A system of units of measure used in finding the volume of dry commodities, such as grain, fruit, and vegetables. The units of capacity are as follows:

2 pints (pts.) =1 quart (qt.)
8 quarts   =1 peck (pk.)
4 pecks   =1 bushel (bu.)
105 quarts   =1 barrel (bbl.)

dry mortar: In masonry, mortar which contains enough moisture to cause it to set properly, but is not wet enough to cause it to be sticky; also, mortar which still retains a granular consistency.

dry rot: Various types of decay in timber, all of which reduces the wood to a fine powder.

dry wood: Any timber from which the sap has been removed by seasoning.

dryer: A mechanical drying machine used to take moisture out of veneer.

duplex-headed nail: A specialized wood fastening, designed for use in temporary structures such as formwork for concrete and scaffolding, where ease of removal without damage to the wood is a prime factor. See Fig. 37.

Dutch arch: In masonry, a brick arch which is flat at both the top and bottom, constructed with ordinary brick which are not worked to a wedge shape but are laid so as to slope outward from the middle of the arch. See *French arch.*

Dutch bond: In masonry, a bond having the courses made up alternately of headers and stretchers. Same as *English cross bond.* See *typical bonds,* Fig. 11.

dutchman: An odd piece inserted to fill an opening or to cover a defect.

E

easement: In architecture, a curved member used to prevent abrupt changes in direction as in a baseboard or handrail. In stairway construction, a triangular piece to match the inside string and the wall base where these join at the bottom of the stairs.

eaves: That part of a roof which projects over the side wall; a margin, or lower part of a roof hanging over the wall; the edges of the roof which extend beyond the wall.

eaves trough: A gutter at the eaves of a roof for carrying off rain water.

economy brick: Modular brick related to every four-inch module in height, thickness, and length. *Economy brick* are always *cored brick.* Size 3½" x 3½" x 7½".

economy wall: In masonry, a brick wall four inches thick covered with a blanket of back mortaring. The wall is strengthened at intervals with vertical pilasters having brick corbeling which supports the floors and roof. This provides a four-inch outside reveal for windows and doors, with every window and door frame bricked in.

efflorescence: A whitish, loose powder which forms on the surface of a brick or stone wall.

egg-and-dart molding: A decorative molding with a design composed of an oval-shaped ornament alternating with another ornament in the form of a dart.

electric hand sander: Electrically powered hand sanders with interchangeable abrasive attachments for various on-the-job finishing purposes. See Fig. 21.

electric handsaw: Portable, electrically powered saws are available with interchangeable blades and other attachments, for various building jobs, including masonry cutting and tuck pointing, as well as wood cutting, trimming, etc. See Fig. 22.

electronic glue gun: An instantaneous curing glue gun, with its own electric heating unit, for synthetic thermo-setting of resin adhesives. The gun is light weight and portable, eliminates nailing and filling of nailheads and hammer marks on many jobs. Makes possible on-the-job gluing of

Fig. 21. Electric Hand Sander
Courtesy Skil Corporation

wall paneling, laminates for cabinets or counters, and hardwood flooring.

elevation: A geometrical drawing or projection on a vertical plane showing the external upright parts of a building.

Fig. 22. Electric Handsaw
Courtesy Skil Corporation

ell: An addition to a building at right angles to one end, or an extension of a building at right angles to the length of the main section.

ellipse: The path of a point the sum of whose distances from two fixed points is a constant; a conic section, the closed intersection of a plane with a right circular cone.

ellipsoid: A solid of which every plane section is an ellipse or a circle.

elliptical arch: An arch which is elliptical in form, described from three or more centers.

embossed: Ornamental designs raised above a surface; figures in relief, as a head on a coin; decorative protuberances.

emery: An impure corundum stone of a blackish or bluish gray color used as an abrasive. The stone is crushed and graded and made into emery paper, emery cloth, and emery wheels. *Emery* is mined in the eastern part of the United States but the best grade comes from Greece and Turkey.

emery cloth: A cloth used for removing file marks and for polishing metallic surfaces. It is prepared by sprinkling powdered emery over a thin cloth coated with glue.

emery wheel: A wheel composed mostly of emery and used for grinding or polishing purposes. It is revolved at high speed.

enameled brick: In masonry, brick with an enamel-like or glazed surface.

encased knot: A defect in a piece of wood, where the growth rings of the knot are not intergrown and homogeneous with the growth rings of the piece in which the knot is encased.

encaustic: Relating to the burning in of colors; applied to painting on glass, tiles, brick, and porcelain; any process by which colors are fixed by the application of heat.

end-grain: In woodworking, the face of a piece of timber which is exposed when the fibers are cut transversely.

end-lap joint: A joint formed at a corner where two boards lap. The boards are cut away to half their thickness so that they fit into each other. They are halved to a distance equal to their width, and, when fitted together, the outer surfaces are flush. See Fig. 29.

English bond: In brickwork, a form of bond in which one course is composed entirely of *headers* and the next course is composed entirely of *stretchers,* the header and stretcher courses alternating throughout the wall; a type of bond especially popular for use in a building intended for residential purposes. See *typical bonds,* Fig. 11.

English cross bond: A form of bond similar to Old English bond. It is used where strength and beauty are required. Same as *Dutch bond.* See *typical bonds,* Fig. 11.

engrailed: Indented with curved lines, or small concave scallops.

enrichment: Adornment; embellishing plain work by adding ornamental designs.

erecting: Raising and setting in an upright position, as the final putting together in perpendicular form the structural parts of a building.

escalator: A stairway consisting of a series of movable steps, or corresponding parts, joined in an endless belt and so operated that the steps or treads ascend or descend continuously. Commonly used in large department stores and railway stations.

escutcheon: In architecture, a metal shield placed around a keyhole to protect the wood; also a metal plate to which a door knocker is attached. Such plates are sometimes ornately decorated.

escutcheon pin: A decorative nail having a round head, used in fastening ornamental and/or protective metal plates to wood. See Fig. 37.

espagnolette: A kind of fastening for a French casement window, usually consisting of a long rod with hooks at the top and bottom of the sash, and turned by a handle. Also, a decorative feature on corners of Louis XIV furniture.

essex board measure: A method of rapid calculation for finding board feet; the essex board-measure table usually is

found on the framing square conveniently located for the carpenter's use.

estimating: A process of judging or calculating the amount of material required for a given piece of work, also the amount of labor necessary to do the work, and finally an approximate evaluation of the finished product.

excavation: A cavity or hole made by digging out of earth to provide room for engineering improvements.

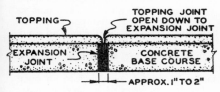

Fig. 23. Expansion Joint

expansion joint: In masonry, a bituminous fiber strip used to separate blocks or units of concrete to prevent cracking due to expansion as a result of temperature changes. See Fig. 23.

expletive: In masonry, a stone which is used to fill a cavity.

exposed joint: In masonry, a mortar joint on the face of a brick or stone wall, above the ground level.

exterior: The outer surface or part, as in building the *exterior* of the structure, or the *exterior* wall.

extrados: The exterior curve in an arch, or vault.

eyebolt: A bolt which is provided with an eye, or hole, instead of the ordinary head. The eye receives the pin, hook, or stud which takes the pull of the bolt.

F

facade: The entire exterior side of a building, especially the front; the face of a structure; the front elevation, or exterior face, of a building.

facebrick: The better quality of brick such as is used on exposed parts of a building, especially those parts which are prominent in view.

faced wall: A masonry wall in which

one or both sides is faced with a different material from the body of the wall, but with the facing and body so bonded that they will exert action as a unit under the weight of a load.

face hammer: A heavy hammer having flat faces, with one blunt end and one cutting end; used for rough dressing of blocks of quarried stone.

face joint: In masonry, a joint between the stones or brick in the face of a wall. Since it is visible, the joint is carefully struck or pointed.

face mark: In woodworking, a mark placed on the surface of a piece of wood to indicate that part as the face, according to which all other sides are dressed true.

face mix: In masonry, a mixture of stone dust and cement; sometimes used as a facing for concrete blocks in imitation of real stone.

face mold: In architectural drawings, the full-size diagram, scale drawing, or pattern of the curved portions of a sloping handrail. The true dimension and shape of the top of the handrail are given in the drawing.

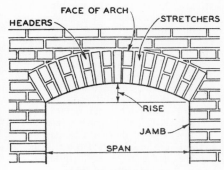

Fig. 24. Face of an Arch

face of arch: In building, the exposed vertical surface of an arch. See Fig. 24.

facing hammer: In masonry, a special type of stone hammer used for dressing the surface of stone or cast-concrete slabs.

faience: Glazed terra-cotta blocks used

as facing for buildings or fireplaces. Glazed plastic mosaic is known as *faience mosaic*, and is used for ornamental floors.

false header: In masonry, a half brick that is sometimes used in *Flemish bond;* in framing, a short piece of timber fitted between two floor joists.

false rafter: A short extension added to a main rafter over a cornice, especially where there is a change in the roof line.

falsework: Framework, usually temporary, such as bracing and supports used as an aid in construction but removed when the building is completed.

fastening tool: A tool which applies greater force and control to the insertion of fasteners than hand-hammer methods alone. Placing the fastener in a narrow channel or slot, open at one end of the tool, force produced in a larger area is concentrated on the fastener from the other end, thus driving the fastener into the desired surface with speed and accuracy, and leaving no hammer marks. Fastening tools may be activated by a hand-hammer blow, by release of a spring, and by pneumatic (compressed air) hammer action. One of these can be positioned for roof or floor nailing by means of a foot stirrup, thus eliminating all bending The above are usually called nailing machines and are used for fastening wood. More powerful tools for fastening steel and concrete are activated by exploding powder in a cartridge (as stud drivers); by gasoline (these are used for driving heavy spikes and can be self-contained); and, by electricity (as impact wrenches and electric hammers). Tackers of the hammer, gun, and air types operate on the same principles, using a bent wire staple instead of the usual nail or screw, to fasten thin construction material to walls or other surfaces. Many fastening devices have automatic, magnetic-fastener feed devices.

fat lime: A quicklime, made by burning a pure or nearly pure limestone, such as chalk; used especially for plastering and masonry work. Also called *rich lime.*

favus: A latin word meaning *honeycomb;* in architecture, a term applied to a square detail resembling the cells in a honeycomb.

featheredge brick: A brick which is used especially for arches, similar to a *compass brick.*

felt papers: Sheathing papers used on roofs and side walls of buildings as protection against dampness, also as insulation against heat, cold, and wind. *Felt papers* applied to roofs are often infused with tar, asphalt, or chemical compounds.

fender: A metal guard before an open fireplace to keep back the live coals; a rail in a farrowing pen to prevent the sow from crushing a pig when she lies down. Also called *guard rails.*

fender wall: A low brick wall supporting the hearthstone to a ground-floor fireplace.

fenestration: The arrangement of windows and doors in a building; in an architectural composition, the design and proportion of windows as a decorative feature.

ferroconcrete: Concrete work reinforced by steel bars or steel mesh, embedded in the material before it sets, to provide increased strength.

festoon: In architecture and furniture, a decorative feature of carved work representing a garland or wreath of flowers or leaves, or both.

fiberlic: A special type of building board; a trade name for a particular building-board product.

fibrotile: A corrugated tile, 4' long, 3' wide, and 10" thick, made of asbestos cement and used as a fire-retardant building material.

field tile: A type of porous tile which is placed around the outside of a foundation wall of a building, to absorb excess water and prevent seepage through the foundation.

figure: In carpentry, mottled, streaked, or wavy grain in wood.

file: A tool, with teeth, used principally

for finishing wood or metal surfaces. Common files are from 4 to 14 inches in length. The width and thickness are in proportion to the length. In cross section the *file* may be rectangular, round, square, half round, triangular, diamond shaped, or oval. Single-cut files have parallel lines of teeth running diagonally across the face of the file. The double-cut files have two sets of parallel lines crossing each other. Single-cut files have four graduations —rough, bastard, second cut, and smooth; double-cut files have an added finer cut known as *dead smooth.*

fillet: A narrow concave strip connecting two surfaces meeting at an angle. It adds strength and beauty of design by avoiding sharp angles.

fillister: A plane used for cutting grooves; also, a rabbet, or groove, as the groove on a window sash for holding the putty and glass; in mechanical work, the rounded head of a cap screw slotted to receive a screw driver.

finial: A decorative detail that adorns the uppermost extremity of a pinnacle, or gable. Any ornamental device capping a gable or spire.

finished string: In architecture and building, the end string of a stair fastened to the rough carriage. It is cut, mitered, dressed, and often finished with a molding or bead.

finishing: The final perfecting of workmanship on a building, as the adding of casings, baseboards, and ornamental moldings.

finishing tools: In masonry and cement work, tools designed especially for shaping curved section which must be made smooth and true.

Fink truss: A type of roof truss commonly used for short spans because of the shortness of its struts which makes it economical and prevents waste.

firebrick: Any brick which is especially made to withstand the effects of high heat without fusion; usually made of *fire clay* or other highly siliceous material.

fire clay: Clay which is capable of being subjected to high temperatures without fusing or softening perceptibly. It is used extensively for laying *firebrick.*

fire-division wall: A solid masonry wall for subdividing a building to prevent the spread of fire, but one not necessarily extending continuously from the foundation through all the stories and through the roof; also, a wall of reinforced concrete which is more or less fire-resistant, tending to restrict the spread of fire in a building.

fireproof: To build with incombustible materials in order to reduce fire hazards: to cover or treat with an incombustible material; anything constructed of a minimum amount of combustible material.

fire stops: Blocking, of incombustible material, used to fill air passages through which flames might travel in case the structure were to catch fire; any form of blocking of air passages to prevent the spread of fire through a building.

firmer tools: In woodworking, the tools commonly used on the workbench, such as the ordinary chisels and gouges.

fished joint: A joint commonly used when a structural piece must be lengthened. The joint is made by placing a second piece end to end with the first one, then covering the juncture with two additional pieces which are nailed or bolted on opposite sides of the joint. These pieces are called *fish plates,* and may be wood or metal. See *fished and keyed joint,* Fig. 29.

fish glue: A type of glue made from specially prepared parts of certain fish, usually the bladderlike portions of hake.

fitment: In carpentry and furniture making, any portion of a wall, room, or built-in furniture which is fitted into place, including chimney pieces, wall paneling, cabinets, and cupboards.

flagstone: A kind of stone that splits easily into flags, or slabs; also, a term applied to irregular pieces of such stone split into slabs from 1 to 3 inches thick and used for walks or terraces.

A pavement made of stone slabs is known as *flagging*.

flange: A projecting edge, or rib. Some types of insulation materials are provided with *flanges* for nailing purposes.

flank: In architecture, the side of an arch.

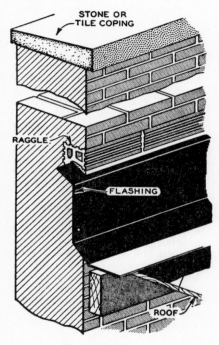

STONE OR TILE COPING

RAGGLE

FLASHING

ROOF

Fig. 25. Flashing

flashing: Piece of lead, tin, or sheet metal, either copper or galvanized iron, used around dormers, chimneys, or any rising projection, such as window heads, cornices, and angles between different members, or any place where there is danger of leakage from rain water or snow. These metal pieces are worked in with shingles of the roof or other construction materials used. See Fig. 25.

flat arch or jack arch: A type of construction in which both the outside of an arch and the underside of the arch are flat.

flat grain: Lumber sawn parallel with the pith of the log and approximately at right angles to the growth rings.

flat molding: A thin, flat molding used only for finishing work.

flat roof: A roof with just enough pitch to provide for drainage of rain water, or melting snow.

flat skylight: Any skylight which has only enough pitch to carry off rain water or water from melting snow.

flatting: In veneering, a process of flattening out buckled veneers; also, a finish given to painting which leaves no gloss.

fleam: A term used in woodworking to indicate the angle of bevel of the edge of a saw tooth with respect to the plane of the blade.

Flemish bond: A bond consisting of *headers* and *stretchers*, alternating in every course, so laid as always to break joints, each header being placed in the middle of the stretchers in courses above and below. See *typical bonds*, Fig. 11.

Flemish garden bond: In masonry, a bond consisting of three stretchers, alternating with a header, each header being placed in the center of the stretchers in the course above and below.

flier: Any single one of a flight of stairs whose treads are parallel to each other; a stair tread that is of uniform width throughout its length.

flight of stairs: A series of steps between floors of a building; a single flight of stairs may be broken into two flights by means of a landing.

flint-and-stone work: A system of external ornamentation of buildings used in eastern Europe during the fifteenth century, by means of which inscriptions were produced in stone on a ground of flint which had been split to expose a black surface. Sometimes the stones were sunk about two inches, and the flints were let into it.

flitch girder: A combination beam composed of two or more joists which have between them steel plates ¼ inch or more in thickness. Bolts are used to hold the joists and steel plates together.

float coat: In cement work, a term frequently applied to the mortar-setting bed which is put on with a float; also, a term applied to a coat of finishing cement, sometimes called *float finish,* which is also put on with a float.

floater: A tool used to smooth and finish cement work.

floating: The process of spreading plastering, stucco, or cement on the surface of walls to an equal thickness by the use of a board called a *float.*

floating foundation: In building construction, a special type of foundation made to carry the weight of a superstructure which is to be erected on swampy land, or on unstable soil. Such a foundation consists of a large raftlike slab composed of concrete, reinforced with steel rods or mesh.

floatstone: In masonry, a type of stone used by bricklayers to smooth gauged brickwork. See *rubbing stone.*

floor: In architecture and building, different stories of structure are frequently referred to as floors, for example, the *ground floor,* the *second floor,* and the *basement floor;* also, that portion of a building or room on which one walks.

floor chisel: An all-steel chisel with an edge measuring from 2 to 3 inches in width, used especially for removing floorboards.

floor drain: A plumbing fixture used to drain water from floors into the plumbing system. Such drains are usually located in the laundry and near the furnace and are fitted with a deep seal trap.

floor plan: An architectural drawing showing the length and breadth of a building and the location of the rooms which the building contains. Each floor has a separate plan.

flue: An enclosed passageway, such as a pipe, or chimney, for carrying off smoke, gases, or air.

flue lining: Fire clay or terra-cotta pipe, either round or square, usually obtainable in all ordinary flue sizes and in two-foot lengths. It is used for the inner lining of chimneys with brick or masonry work around the outside. Flue lining should run from the concrete footing to the top of the chimney cap.

flush: The continued surface of two contiguous masses in the same plane; that is, surfaces on the same level.

flush door: A door of any size, not paneled, having two flat faces, frequently of hollow core construction.

flush joint: In masonry, a mortar joint formed by cutting surplus mortar from the face of a wall. If a rough texture is desired, the surface of the joint may be tapped with the end of a rough piece of wood after the mortar has slightly stiffened. See Fig. 32.

flying bond: In bricklaying, a bond formed by inserting a header course at intervals of from four to seven courses of stretchers.

foaming agent: A chemical which, when foamed by a generator and measured into cement mix, controls the cellular density of the resulting aerated material.

foil: A rounded leaflike architectural ornamentation used especially for window decoration, sometimes consisting of three divisions, sometimes of four and known as *trefoil* and *quatrefoil.*

folding door or partition: Any door or partition in which panels are built to bend back on themselves when opened. It may fold vertically or horizontally toward top or sides of opening. Center-hung types operate on pivoted hangers attached to the center of the same edge of each panel, and running along a track set in the opening. These panels straddle the track when folded. Pair-operated panels operate from hangers placed at opposite corners on the same edge of each of two panels. The hangerless inner edges are usually hinged and project together on only one side of the track, when folded. Light metal collapsible gate frames, covered with fabric, are also hung from tracks and pushed into folds to open. Concealing recesses or passageways are often built to accommodate the folded panels and leave the opening free of obstructions. See *rolling partitions*. All of these may be operated by power or electronic devices for special purposes, as garage doors.

folding stair: A stairway which folds into the ceiling, used for access to areas of a building not in general use. Such a stairway uses only limited space while in use. It is fixed by means of hinges at its uppermost end, while the lower end is provided with any of various catches which fasten the stairway when folded. Quite often the underside of such stairways is finished so as to match the ceiling area into which they are folded.

foliated: To ornament with foils or foliage; that is, decorated with a leaf design.

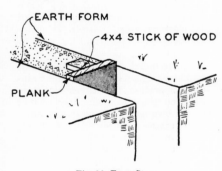

EARTH FORM
4x4 STICK OF WOOD
PLANK

Fig. 26. Form Stop

footing: A foundation as for a column; spreading courses under a foundation wall; an enlargement at the bottom of a wall to distribute the weight of the superstructure over a greater area and thus prevent settling. *Footings* are usually made of cement and are used under chimneys and columns as well as under foundation walls. See Fig. 10.

footing forms: Forms made of wood for shaping and holding concrete for footings of columns which support beams and girders.

footing stop: In concrete work, a term applied to a device consisting of a plank nailed to a 4 x 4, placed in the forms to hold the concrete at the close of a day's pouring. See Fig. 26.

footstone: A stone placed at the foot of a gable slope to receive and resist the outward thrust of the coping stone above it. A foundation stone.

fore plane: A bench plane 18 inches in length, intermediate between the jointer plane, which is larger, and the jack plane, which is smaller.

forming tool: A term frequently applied to any device which will facilitate a mechanical operation; a tool especially designed for a particular type of work with its cutting edge shaped like the form to be produced on the work.

forms: In building construction, an enclosure made of either boards or metal for holding green concrete to the desired shape until it has set and thoroughly dried.

form stop: In concrete work, a term applied to a device consisting of a plank nailed to a 4 x 4 placed in the forms at the end of a day's pouring. See Fig. 26.

foundation: The lowest division of a wall for a structure intended for permanent use; that part of a wall on which the building is erected; usually that part of a building which is below the surface of the ground and on which the superstructure rests.

foundation bolt: Any bolt or device used to anchor the structural parts of a building to the foundation on which it rests; any bolt used to hold machinery in position on its foundation.

four-way switch: A switch used in house wiring when a light (or lights) is to be turned on or off at more than two places. Thus, for three places, use two three-way and one four-way switches; for four places, use two three-way and two four-way switches—an additional four-way switch for each additional place of control.

fracture: In masonry, the breaking apart or separation of the continuous parts of a wall of brick or stone, caused by a sudden shock or excessive strain.

frame: In carpentry, the timber work supporting the various structural parts, such as windows, doors, floors, and roofs; the woodwork of doors, windows, and the entire lumber work supporting the floors, walls, roofs, and partitions.

frame high: In masonry, the level at which the lintel or arch of an opening is to be laid; also, the height of the top of window or door frames.

frame of a house: The framework of a house which includes the joists, studs, plates, sills, partitions, and roofing; that is, all parts which together make up the skeleton of the building.

framework: The frame of a building; the various supporting parts of a building fitted together into a skeleton form.

framing: The process of putting together the skeleton parts for a building; the rough lumber work on a house, such as flooring, roofing, and partitions.

framing square: An instrument having at least one right angle and two or more straight edges, used for testing and laying out work for trueness. A good *framing square* will have the following tables stamped on it for the use of the carpenter in laying out his work: *unit length rafter tables; essex board measure; brace measure; octagon scale;* and, a *twelfths scale.* Also called *square* or *steel square.*

free end: The end of a beam which is unsupported, as that end of a cantilever which is not fixed.

freemason: A term formerly applied to one of a class of skilled stone masons who worked in freestone as distinguished from an unskilled mason who worked only with rough stone.

free-standing vertical sunshades: A wall or fence standing a few feet from a house and placed so as to shade a wall or window opening to help keep the interior of the building cool during warm weather. When louvered or open in style, they do not block out breezes while providing neces-

sary shade. They are excellent against low sun, but can seldom be built high enough to shade walls during the middle of the day; most effective when painted in a light color and used in combination with tall green plants.

freestone: Any stone, as a sandstone, which can be freely worked or quarried; used for molding, tracery, and other work requiring to be executed with the chisel. Any stone which cuts well in all directions without splitting.

French arch: In masonry, a type of bonded arch which is flat at both top and bottom, having the bricks sloping outward from a common center. Same as *Dutch arch.*

French window: A long double-sash casement window with the sashes hinged at the sides and opening in the middle. The window extends down to the floor and serves as a door to a porch or terrace.

friction: Resistance to relative motion set up between particles of two moving surfaces in contact with each other.

friction catch: A device consisting of a spring and plunger contained in a casing, used on small doors or articles of furniture to keep them tightly closed but not locked.

frilled: An ornamental edging on furniture such as a *frilled* **C** scroll; a term used to refer to any scroll which has added decorative carving along its projecting edges.

frog: A depression, such as a groove or recess, in one or both of the larger sides of a brick or building block, thus providing a key for the mortar at the joints, and also effecting a saving in the weight of the material. A name also applied to a part of a carpenter's plane.

furred: The providing of air space between the walls and plastering or subfloor and finish floor by use of wood strips, such as lath or 1x2's nailed to the walls in a vertical position. Walls or floors prepared in this manner are said to be *furred.*

furring: The process of leveling up

part of a wall, ceiling, or floor by the use of wood strips; also, a term applied to the strips used to provide air space between a wall and the plastering. See Fig. 27.

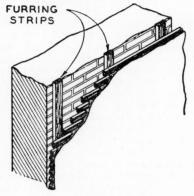

FURRING STRIPS

Fig. 27. Furring Strips

furring strips: Flat pieces of lumber used to build up an irregular framing to an even surface, either the leveling of a part of a wall or ceiling. The term *furring strips* or *furrings* is also applied to strips placed against a brick wall for nailing lath, to provide air space between the wall and plastering to avoid dampness. See Fig. 27.

G

gable: The end of a building as distinguished from the front or rear side; the triangular end of an exterior wall above the eaves; the end of a ridged roof which at its extremity is not returned on itself but is cut off in a vertical plane which above the eaves is triangular in shape due to the slope of the roof.

gable molding: The molding used as a finish for the gable end of a roof

gable roof: A ridged roof which terminates either at one end or both ends in a gable.

gain: The notch or mortise where a piece of wood is cut out to receive the end of another piece of wood.

gallery: An elevated floor, or platform equipped to increase the seating capacity of auditoriums in churches, theaters, and other large audience rooms. Projecting from the interior wall of a building, the *gallery* usually is supported by columns below, but sometimes it is hung on supports from above. In some cases supports are provided both above and below.

gallet: A splinter of stone chipped off by chiseling. Also called a *spall.*

galleting: In rubble work, a term applied to the process of filling in the coarse masonry joints of fresh mortar with small stone chips or gallets. Same as garreting.

gambrel roof: A type of roof which has its slope broken by an obtuse angle, so that the lower slope is steeper than the upper slope; a roof with two pitches.

ganister: In building, a material made of ground quartz and fire clay; used for fireproofing purposes, especially around the hearths of furnaces.

garden bond: A type of masonry construction consisting of three stretchers in each course followed by a header. However, this bond may have from two to five stretchers between headers.

gardenwall bond: In bricklaying, a bond formed by stretchers with headers inserted at intervals of several courses only; also called *flying bond.*

garderobe: A room for keeping articles of clothing, a wardrobe; also, a small private room, as a bedroom.

garnet paper: An abrasive paper used for polishing and finishing surfaces of woodwork. The paper is prepared by covering one side with glue and a reddish abrasive material.

gauge: A tool used by carpenters and other woodworkers to make a line parallel to the edge of a board.

gauged arch: In masonry, an arch constructed with special bricks which have been cut with a bricklayer's saw, then rubbed to the exact shape required for use in an arch where the joints radiate from a common center.

gauging: In masonry, cutting brick or

stone to make them uniform in size. In plastering, the mixing of plaster of Paris with mortar to effect quick setting.

geometrical stair: A winding stair which returns on itself with winders built around a well. The balustrade follows the curve without newel posts at the turns. It is also known as a *spiral stair*.

geometry: That branch of mathematical science which treats of the properties and relations of lines, surfaces, and solids.

German siding: A type of weatherboarding with the upper part of the exposed face finished with a concave curve and the lower portion of the back face rebated.

gingerbread work: A gaudy type of ornamentation in architecture, especially in the trim of a house.

girder: A large, supporting, built-up, horizontal member used to support walls or joists; a beam, either timber or steel, used for supporting a superstructure. See Fig. 7.

girt: The same as girth; the circumference of round timber.

girt strip: A board attached to studding to carry floor joists; a ledger board.

glass block: A hollow glass building brick having the advantage of admitting light with privacy, insulating against the passage of sound, but not safe to use in a load-bearing wall. Sometimes called *glass brick*.

glazed: Equipped with window panes; the process of placing glass in windows, doors, and mirrors is known as *glazing*.

glazed brick: Building brick prepared by fusing on the surface a glazing material; brick having a glassy surface.

glazed doors: Doors which have been fitted with glass and usually having a pattern or lattice of woodwork between the panes.

glazed tile: A type of masonry tile which has a glassy or glossy surface.

glazing: Placing glass in windows, doors, and mirrors; the filling up of interstices in the surface of a grindstone or emery wheel with minute abraded particles detached in grinding.

glyph: In architecture, an ornamental channel, or groove; a short, vertical groove.

gooseneck: Something curved like the neck of a goose, such as an iron hook, or other mechanical contrivance bent or shaped like a goose neck; the curved or bent section of the handrail on a stair.

Gothic arch: A type of arch usually high and narrow, coming to a point at the center at the top, especially one with a joint instead of a keystone at the apex.

gouge: A cutting chisel which has a concavo-convex cross section, or cutting surface.

grade: In building trades the term used when referring to the ground level around a building.

grading: Filling in around a building with rubble and earth, so the ground will slope downward from the foundation, at an angle sufficient to carry off rain water.

gradual load: The gradual application of a load to the supporting members of a structure, so as to provide the most favorable conditions possible for receiving the stress and strain which these members will be required to carry when the building is completed.

graduate: To mark with degrees of measurement, as the division marks of a scale; the regular dividing of parts into steps or grades.

graduation: The process of separating a unit of measure into equal parts; also, one of the division marks, or one of the equal divisions of a scale.

grain: In woodworking, a term applied to the arrangement of wood fibers; working a piece of wood longitudinally may be either with or against the grain; a cross-section, or transverse, cut of wood is spoken of as cross grain.

granite: An igneous rock composed chiefly of feldspar but containing also some quartz and mica, used extensively in construction work and for monuments. It is extremely hard and will take a high polish.

granulated slag: The product of rapid cooling of molten blast-furnace slag, resulting in a mass of friable, porous grains, most of which are under one-half inch in size. See *air-cooled slag.*

grating: A framework, or gratelike arrangement of bars either parallel or crossed, used to cover an opening.

gravel fill: Crushed rock, pebbles, or gravel, deposited in a layer of any desired thickness at the bottom of an excavation, the purpose of which is to insure adequate drainage of any water. See Fig. 10.

green brick: In masonry, a molded clay block before it has been burned in preparation for building purposes.

green mortar: A term sometimes applied to mortar before it has set firmly.

green wood: A term used by woodworkers when referring to timbers which still contain the moisture, or sap, of the tree from which the wood was cut. Lumber is said to be *seasoned* when the sap has been removed by natural processes of drying or by artificial drying in a kiln.

grille: A grating or openwork barrier, usually of metal but sometimes of wood, used to cover an opening, or as a protection over the glass of a window or door. A *grille* may be plain but often it is of an ornamental or decorative character.

grind: To reduce any substance to powder by friction or crushing; to wear down or sharpen a tool by use of an abrasive, such as a whetstone, emery wheel, or grindstone; to reduce in size by the removal of particles of material by contact with a rotating abrasive wheel.

grinder: Any device used to sharpen tools, or remove particles of material by any process of grinding.

grindstone: A flat rotating stone wheel used to sharpen tools or wear down materials by abrading, or grinding. *Grindstones* are natural sandstone.

grommet: A metal eyelet used principally in awnings or along the edges of sails.

groove: A channel, usually small, used in woodworking and building for different purposes which sometimes are practical but often merely decorative.

ground: One of the pieces of wood flush with the plastering of a room, to which moldings and other similar finish material are nailed. The *ground* acts as a straight edge and thickness gauge to which the plasterer works to insure a straight plaster surface of proper thickness.

ground course: A horizontal course, usually of masonry, next to the ground.

ground floor: Usually the main floor of a building; the floor of a house most nearly on a level with the ground; that is, the first floor above the ground level.

ground joist: A joist which is blocked up from the ground.

ground wall: In building, the foundation wall; the wall on which a super-structure rests.

grout: A mortar made so thin by the addition of water it will run into joints and cavities of masonry; a fluid cement mixture used to fill crevices.

Gunite: A construction material composed of cement, sand or crushed slag, and water mixed together and forced through a cement gun by pneumatic pressure. Sold under the trade-mark *Gunite.*

gusset: A brace or angle bracket used to stiffen a corner or angular piece of work.

gutter: A channel of wood or metal at the eaves or on the roof of a building for carrying off rain water and water from melting snow.

gypsum: A mineral, hydrous sulphate of calcium. In the pure state gypsum is colorless. When part of the water is removed by a slow heating process the product becomes what is known as *plaster of Paris,* used extensively for decorative purposes.

Gypsum blocks: A type of building material usually grayish white in color; because of its friable texture it is used only in nonload-bearing partition walls.

H

hack saw: A narrow, light-framed saw used for cutting metal; a fine-toothed, narrow-bladed saw stretched in a firm frame. It may be operated either by hand or by electric power.

haft: The handle of any thrusting or cutting tool, such as a dagger, knife, sword, or an awl.

half-back bench saw: A cutting tool in which a stiffening bar extends over only a portion of the blade length, combining the action of both the handsaw and the backsaw.

half bat: A term applied to one-half of a building brick.

half-lap joint: A jointing of two pieces by cutting away half the thickness of each piece so that the pieces fit together with the surfaces flush.

half-round file: A tool which is flat on one side and curved on the other; however, the convexity never equals a semicircle.

half story: An attic in a pitched-roof structure having a finished ceiling and floor and some side wall.

half-timbered: A term applied to any building constructed of a timber frame with the spaces filled in, either with masonry or with plaster on laths.

hammer: A tool used for driving nails, pounding metal, or for other purposes. Though there are various types of hammers, used for a variety of purposes, all hammers are similar in having a solid head set crosswise on a handle. See Fig. 17.

hand drill: A hand-operated tool used for drilling holes.

hand file: A tool used in finishing flat surfaces. See *file*.

handiwork: Any work done by the hands; usually refers to work requiring some special skill.

handrail: Any railing which serves as a guard; a rail which is intended to be grasped by the hand to serve as a support, as on a stair or along the edge of a gallery. See Fig. 50.

handrail wreath: The curved section of a stair rail. See *wreath*.

handsaw: Any ordinary saw operated with one hand; that is, a one-handled saw, either a ripsaw or a cross-

cut saw, used by woodworkers. See Fig. 28.

hand screw: A clamp with two parallel jaws and two screws used by woodworkers; the clamping action is provided by means of the screws, one operating through each jaw.

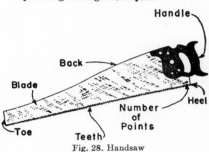

Fig. 28. Handsaw

hand tools: Any tools which are operated by and guided by hand.

hangar: A shelter or shed for housing aircraft.

hanger: A drop support, made of strap iron or steel, attached to the end of a joist or beam used to support another joist or beam. See *stirrup*.

hanger bolt: A bolt used for attaching hangers to woodwork; it consists of a lag screw at one end with a machine-bolt screw and nut at the other end.

hanging stile: That part of a door to which the hinges are attached; the vertical part of a door or casement window to which the hinges are fixed.

hardpan: A cemented or compacted layer in soils, often containing some proportion of clay, through which it is difficult to dig or excavate.

hardwood: The botanical group of broad-leaved trees, such as oak, maple, basswood, poplar, and others. The term has no reference to the actual hardness of the wood. *Angiosperms* is the botanical name for hardwoods.

hasp: A hinged-metal strap designed to pass over a staple and secured by a peg or padlock.

hatching: Parallel lines drawn closely together for the purpose of shading, or to indicate a section of an object shown in a drawing.

hatchway: An opening covered by a hatch, or trap door, to provide easy access to an attic or cellar; any opening in a floor, ceiling, or roof which makes it possible to pass from one story to another; the opening on ships for passage from one deck to another.

haunch: In architecture, either side of an arch between the crown, or vertex, and the impost where the arch rests on the top of a pier or wall; the shoulder of an arch.

H beam: An H-shaped steel beam.

header: In building, a brick or stone laid with the end toward the face of the wall.

header bond: A form of bond in which all courses are laid as headers; used for wall or partitions eight inches thick. See *typical bonds,* Fig. 11.

header-high: In masonry, when a portion of a wall has been laid up to the point where headers are necessary, the wall is said to be *header-high.*

header joist: In carpentry, the large beam or timber into which the common joists are fitted when framing around openings for stairs, chimneys, or any openings in a floor or roof; placed so as to fit between two long beams and support the ends of short timbers. See Fig. 12.

head joint: A vertical joint which joins brick at their ends. See Fig. 6.

head room: The vertical space in a doorway; also, the clear space in height between a stair tread and the ceiling or stairs above.

hearth: The floor of a fireplace; also the portion of the floor immediately in front of the fireplace.

heavy joist: In woodworking, a timber measuring between 4 and 6 inches in thickness and 8 inches or over in width.

heel: That part of a timber, beam, rafter, or joist which rests on the wall plate.

height: In reference to an arch, the perpendicular distance between the middle point of the chord and the intrados. Sometimes called the *rise.* See Fig. 24.

helve: The handle of a tool, such as a hammer, hatchet, or ax.

herringbone: In masonry, a pattern used in brickwork where the brick in alternate courses is laid obliquely in opposite directions forming a design similar in appearance to the spine of a herring; a zigzag pattern used in brickwork; in flooring, material arranged diagonally.

herringbone bond: In masonry, the arrangement of bricks in a course in a zigzag fashion, with the end of one brick laid at right angles against the side of a second brick.

hewing: Dealing cutting blows with an ax or other sharp instrument for the purpose of dressing a timber to a desired form or shape.

hexagon: A *polygon* with six sides.

hick joint: In masonry, a mortar joint finished flush with the surface of the wall.

hiearly cement: A contraction of the more generally used term *high early strength Portland cement or concrete.*

high early strength cement: A specially prepared Portland cement for giving quick strength to concrete work. It is frequently used when the temperature is below freezing.

hinge: A movable joint upon which a door turns; a mechanical device consisting primarily of a pin and two plates which may be attached to a door and the door frame to permit the opening and closing of the door. Hinges are used also on gates and other places where movable joints are desired.

hip rafters: Rafters which form the hip of a roof as distinguished from the common rafters. A *hip rafter* extends diagonally from the corner of the plate to the ridge, and is located at the apex of the outer angle formed by the meeting of two sloping sides of a roof whose wall plates meet at a right angle. See Fig. 47.

hip roof: A roof which rises by inclined planes from all four sides of a building.

hips: Those pieces of timber or lumber placed in an inclined position at the corners or angles of a hip roof. See Fig. 47.

hollow concrete blocks: A type of precast concrete building block having a hollow core.

hollow core door or wall: A faced door or wall with a space between the facings which is occupied by a structure consisting of air or insulation filled cells; made of wood, plastic, or other suitable material. Hollow core constructions have special fire, temperature, and sound insulating properties, as well as being light weight and strong.

hollow masonry unit: A masonry unit whose cross-sectional area in any given plane parallel to the bearing surface is less than 75 per cent of its gross cross-sectional area measured in the same plane.

hollow wall: In masonry, a wall constructed of brick, stone, or other materials, having an air space between the outside and inside faces of the wall. Also called *cavity wall*.

hollow tile: Tile made in a variety of forms and sizes; used extensively as a building material for both exterior walls and partitions. When used for outside walls the tiles usually are covered with stucco.

honeycomb: A cell-like structure. Concrete that is poorly mixed and not adequately puddled having voids or open spaces is known to be *honeycombed*.

honeycomb core: A structure of air cells, resembling a honeycomb, often made of paper, which is placed between plywood panels, sometimes replacing studs. This type of wall construction provides lighter prefabricated walls with excellent insulating properties. See *hollow core door or wall*.

horizontal: On a level; in a direction parallel to the horizon. For example, the surface of a still body of water is *horizontal*, or level.

horse: In building and woodworking, a trestle; one of the slanting supports of a set of steps to which the treads and risers of a stair are attached; a kind

of stool, usually a horizontal piece to which three or four legs are attached, used as a support for work; a braced framework of timbers used to carry a load.

housed string: A stair string with horizontal and vertical grooves cut on the inside to receive the ends of the risers and treads. Wedges covered with glue often are used to hold the risers and treads in place in the grooves.

Howe truss: A type of truss used both in roofs and in construction of bridges; a form of truss especially adapted to wood and steel construction.

hutch: A chest, box, or trough; a small dark room; a storage place; a pen for small animals, as rabbits; also a hut or cabin.

hydrated lime: The material which remains after a chemical reaction due to the contact of quicklime and water. The same as *slaked lime*.

hydraulic cement: A type of cement which hardens under water.

hydraulic jack: A lifting device operated by a lever from the outside, and put into action by means of a small force pump, through the use of a liquid, such as water or oil.

hydraulic lime: A lime which will harden under water.

hydraulic limestone: A limestone which contains some silica and alumina, yielding a quicklime that sets or hardens under water.

hydraulic mortar: In masonry, a mortar which will harden under water; used for foundations or any masonry construction under water.

hypotenuse: The side opposite the right angle of any right *triangle*.

I

I beam: A steel beam whose cross section resembles a letter I, used in structural work.

impost: The uppermost member of a column, pillar, pier, or wall upon which the end of an arch rests. See Fig. 34.

incinerator: A furnace, or a container, in

which waste material and rubbish is burned.

incise: To cut or carve; to cut marks as in the process of engraving.

inclined plane: A surface inclined to the plane of the horizon; the angle which it makes with the horizontal line is known as the *angle of inclination.*

indenture: A contract, or official paper, by means of which an apprentice is legally bound to his employer. Also, a deed, mortgage, or lease.

inglenook: A nook in a corner by a fire, such as a corner by a chimney or fireside.

inlay: To decorate with ornamental designs by setting in small pieces of material in the body of a piece of work which is made of different material from the inlaid pieces; also, the designs so made.

inscribe: To write or engrave in any form, especially in a way that will endure. Also, to draw one figure within another as in geometry.

inside calipers: In shopwork, a type of calipers having the points at the ends of the legs turned outward instead of inward so the tool can be used for gauging the inside diameters.

instant grab adhesives: Adhesives which hold their grip on contact without clamping. Plywood wall panels, with adhesived backs, contact studs and hold their position without bracing. These adhesives can be used, with anchor plates, for attaching furring strips, cutting down on nailing damage to masonry walls. Laminating plastics on the job is also possible because of the instant grab property of these glues.

insulated: Any part of a building separated from other parts of the structure, to prevent the transfer of heat or electricity, is said to be *insulated.*

insulation: Any material used in building construction for the reduction of fire hazard or for protection from heat or cold. Insulation also prevents transfer of electricity.

intake belt course: In building, a belt course with the molded face cut so

that it serves as an intake between the varying thicknesses of two walls.

interior finish: A term applied to the total effect produced by the inside finishing of a building, including not only the materials used but also the manner in which the trim and decorative features have been handled.

intersection: The point where two intersecting lines cross each other.

intrados or soffit: The under surface or interior curve of an arch.

inverted arch: In masonry, an arch where the keystone is located at the lowest point of the arch.

involute: A curve such as would be described by the unwinding of a string from a cylinder.

ironwork: A term applied to the use of iron for ornamental purposes. Elaborately designed ornamentation in ironwork was used for hinges, door knockers, and escutcheons in the architecture of the Middle Ages.

irregular-coursed: In masonry, rubble walls built up in courses of different heights.

J

jack: A portable machine used for lifting heavy loads through short distances with a minimum expenditure of effort or power.

jack arch: An arch which is flat instead of rounded. This type of arch is sometimes called a *French arch.*

jack plane: A bench plane, appropriately named for a beast of burden often called upon to do the hardest and roughest kind of work. The *jack plane,* likewise, is called upon to do the hardest and roughest work on a piece of timber as it first comes from the saw. This plane is the one used to true up the edges and rapidly prepare the rough surface of a board for the finer work of the smoothing planes.

jack rafter: A short rafter of which there are three kinds: (1) those between the plate and a hip rafter; (2) those between the hip and valley rafters; (3) those between the valley

[47]

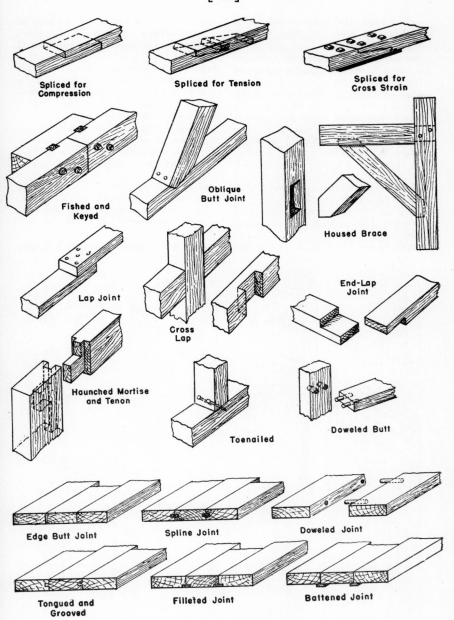

Fig. 29. Joinery of Boards

rafters and the ridge board. *Jack rafters* are used especially in hip roofs. See Fig. 47.

jackscrew: A mechanical device operated by a screw, used in lifting weights and for leveling work.

jamb: In building, the lining of an opening, such as the vertical side posts used in the framing of a doorway or window. See Fig. 43.

jambstone: In architecture, a stone which is set in an upright position at the edge of a wall opening, such as for a door or window, so one of the faces of the stone forms a part or all of a jamb.

jedding ax: In masonry, an ax having one flat face and one pointed peen. See *cavil.*

jig saw: In woodworking, a type of saw with a thin, narrow blade to which an up-and-down motion is imparted either by foot power or by mechanical means.

joggle: A projection, or shoulder, to receive the thrust of a brace; also, a key, or projecting pin, set in between two joining surfaces for the purpose of reinforcing the joint.

joggle joint: In masonry, or stonework, a joint in which a projection on one member fits into a recess in another member, to prevent lateral movement.

Johnson-Ackerman anchor: A concrete insert, provided with a lead shield, used to fasten wood parts to a concrete or masonry wall. See *anchors,* Fig. 1.

joiner: A craftsman in woodworking who

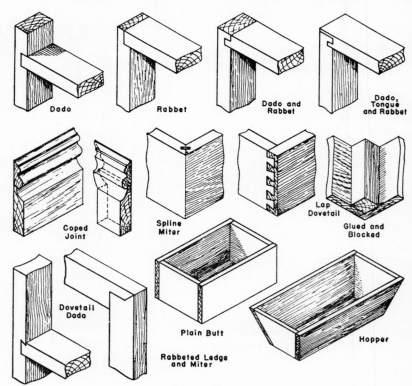

Fig. 30. Joints

Fig. 31. Jointers

constructs joints; usually a term applied to the workmen in shops who construct doors, windows, and other fitted parts of a house or ship.

joinery: A term used by woodworkers when referring to the various types of joints used in woodworking. Wood joints commonly used in timber framing, in edge joining of boards, and other forms of woodworking are shown in Fig. 29.

joint: In carpentry, the place where two or more surfaces meet; also, to form, or unite, two pieces into a *joint;* to provide with a *joint* by preparing the edges of two pieces so they will fit together properly when joined. Wood joints commonly used in cabinet construction and for interior trim are shown in Fig. 30.

jointer: In masonry, a flat steel tool used by bricklayers to form the various types of mortar joints between the courses of bricks upon the face of a wall in pointing, as the V, the concave, and weather joints. See Fig. 31.

jointer plane: A large bench plane used chiefly for long work and for final truing up of wood edges or surfaces for joining two pieces of wood; an iron or wood plane suitable for all kinds of plane work, and especially adaptable for truing large surfaces required in furniture making.

jointing: In masonry, the operation of making and finishing the exterior surface of mortar joints between courses of bricks or stones. See Fig. 32.

joist: A heavy piece of horizontal timber to which the boards of a floor, or the lath of a ceiling, are nailed. Joists are laid edgewise to form the floor support. See Fig. 7.

K

kellastone: In architecture, a stucco with crushed finish.

kerf: A cut made with a saw.

kerfing: The process of cutting grooves or kerfs across a board so as to make it flexible for bending. *Kerfs* are cut down to about two-thirds of the thickness of the piece to be bent. An example is found in the bullnose of a stair which frequently is bent by the process of kerfing.

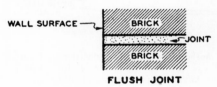

FLUSH JOINT

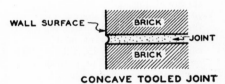

CONCAVE TOOLED JOINT

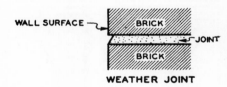

WEATHER JOINT

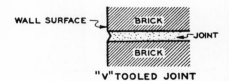

"V" TOOLED JOINT

Fig. 32. Jointing

kevel: A stonemason's hammer, used for breaking and dressing stone.

key: In building, a wedge for splitting a tenon in a mortise to tighten its hold; a strip of wood inserted in a piece of timber across the grain to prevent casting; also a wedge of metal used to make a dovetail joint in a stone; a hollow in a tile to hold mortar or cement; a groove made in cement footings for tying in the cement foundation of a structure. A footing key is shown in Fig. 54.

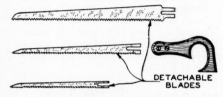

Fig. 33. Keyhole Saws

keyhole saw: A small cutting tool with a tapered blade used for cutting keyholes, fretwork, and other similar work. A nest of *keyhole saws* is shown in Fig. 33.

keystone: The wedge-shaped piece at the top of an arch which is regarded as the most important member because it binds, or locks, all the other members together. The position of a keystone is shown in Fig. 34.

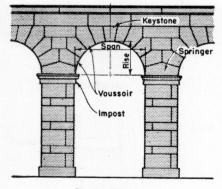

Fig. 34. Keystone

kick plate: A metal plate, or strip, placed along the lower edge of a door, to prevent the marring of the finish by shoe marks.

kiln: A large oven or heated chamber for the purpose of baking, drying, or hardening, as a *kiln* for drying lumber; a *kiln* for baking brick; a lime *kiln* for burning lime.

king closer: In masonry, a closer used to fill an opening in a course larger than a half brick. A *king closer* is about three-fourths the size of a regular-sized brick.

king post: In a roof truss, the central upright piece against which the rafters abut, and which supports the tie beam.

knee: A piece of lumber bent in an angular shape either naturally or artificially to receive and relieve the strain of a weight on another piece of timber.

kneeler: In masonry, a stone cut to provide a change in direction, as in the curve of an arch.

kraft paper: A type of strong brown paper used extensively for wrapping purposes, and as a building paper.

kyanize: The preparation of wood to prevent decay by a process of infusing the wood with mercuric chloride.

Kyan's process: In woodworking, a method of preserving wood by infusing the timber with bichloride of mercury.

L

label: A molding or dripstone over a door or window, especially one which extends horizontally across the top of the opening and vertically downward for a certain distance at the edges.

lacing course: In masonry, a course of brickwork built into a stone wall for bonding and leveling purposes.

La Farge cement: A cement produced as a by-product during the calcination of hydraulic lime. It is nonstaining and is imported. It develops almost as much strength as Portland cement.

lag screw: A heavy wood screw with a square head. Since there is no slot in the head, the screw must be tightened down with a wrench.

lally column: A cylindrically shaped steel member, sometimes filled with concrete, used as a support for girders or other beams.

laminate: In furniture making, the building up with layers of wood, each layer being a lamination or ply; also, the construction of plywood.

laminated construction: Any type of construction where the work is built up by thin layers to secure maximum strength with minimum weight. In pattern making this method is especially desirable since it eliminates cross-grain wood and provides strength, particularly on thin curved members.

landing: In stair construction, a platform introduced at some point to change the direction of the stairway, or to break the run.

landing newel: A post at the landing point of a stair supporting the handrail.

landing tread: In building, a term used when referring to the front end of a stair landing. The method of construction usually provides the front edge with a thickness and finish of a stair tread while the back has the same thickness as the flooring of the landing.

lap joint: The overlapping of two pieces of wood or metal. In woodworking, such a uniting of two pieces of board is produced by cutting away one-half the thickness of each piece. When joined, the two pieces fit into each other so that the outer faces are flush. See *end-lap* joint, Fig. 29.

large knot: In woodworking, any sound knot measuring more than 1½ inches in diameter. See *sound knot*.

lath: In building, a term applied to a strip of wood, usually measuring about 1½ inches in width, ⅜ of an inch in thickness, and 4 feet in length; used as a foundation for plaster. Rock lath is another type of plaster foundation.

lathe: In shopwork, a mechanical device used in the process of producing circular work, for wood or metal turning.

lathing: In architecture, the nailing of lath in position; also a term used for the material itself.

lattice: Any open work produced by interlacing of laths or other thin strips.

latticework: Any work in wood or metal made of lattice or a collection of lattices.

lead: In masonry, a part of a wall built as a guide for the laying of the balance of the wall.

leader: The same as a downspout.

lean-to roof: The sloping roof of a room having its rafters, or supports, pitched against and leaning on the adjoining wall of a building.

ledge: In architecture, any shelflike projection from a wall.

ledger board: In building, the same as a ribbon strip; a support attached to studding for carrying joists; horizontal member of a scaffold.

level: A device (also known as a *spirit level*) consisting of a glass tube nearly filled with alcohol or ether, leaving a movable air bubble. This device, protected by a metal or wood casing, is used for determining a point, or adjusting an object, in a line or plane perpendicular to the direction of the force of gravity. When centered, the bubble indicates the line of sight to be truly horizontal. A slight tilting of the *level* at either end will cause the bubble to move away from center, indicating a line which is not horizontal. An example of a *spirit-level* obtainable in either wood or metal is shown in Fig. 35.

Fig. 35. Level

leveling instrument: A leveling device consisting of a spirit level attached to a sighting tube and the whole mounted on a tripod; used for leveling a surface to a horizontal plane. When the bubble in the level is in the center the line of sight is horizontal.

leveling rod or leveling staff: A rod, or staff, with graduated marks for measuring heights, or vertical distances, between given points and the line of sight of a *leveling instrument*. The different types of leveling rods in common use are the *target rods* read only by the rodman and the *self-reading rods*, which are read directly by the men who do the leveling.

level man: The surveyor who has charge of the leveling instrument.

lewis: An iron dovetailed tenon, in sections, designed to fit into a dovetailed mortise in a heavy block of stone; used for attaching a derrick, or other hoisting apparatus, to the stone for lifting it to its proper position in a structure.

lewis bolt: An anchor bolt, with a ragged tapering tail, inserted in masonry and held in place by a lead casing.

light: A window pane; a section of a window sash for a single pane of glass.

lime: A caustic, highly infusible, white substance produced by the action of heat on limestone, shells, or other forms of calcium carbonate. The heat drives out the carbonic acid and moisture, leaving only the quicklime.

lime-burning: The process of producing lime by the burning of limestone. See *calcining*.

limestone: A type of stone used extensively for building purposes, especially in the better grade of structures. *Limestone* is composed largely of calcium carbonate originating usually from an accumulation of organic remains, such as shells, which yield lime when burned. Therefore, this stone is also used extensively as a source of lime.

limewash: Lime slaked in water and applied with a brush or as a spray. Salt is sometimes added to make it adhere better, and bluing may be added to give a white tone. It is used chiefly as a wall covering. See *whitewash*.

lineal foot: Pertaining to a line one foot in length as distinguished from a square foot or a cubic foot.

linear: Resembling a line, or thread; narrow and elongated; involving measurement in one direction; pertaining to length.

linear measure: A system of measurement in length; also known as *long measure:*

12 inches (in.)	=1 foot (ft.)
3 feet	=1 yard (yd.)
16½ feet	=1 rod (rd.)
320 rods	=1 mile (mi.)
5280 feet	=1 mile

lintel: A piece of wood, stone, or steel placed horizontally across the top of door and window openings to support the walls immediately above the openings.

lobby: In architecture, a hall or passage at the entrance to a building; in case of large buildings, the *lobby* is often used as a waiting room.

locking stile: The vertical section of a door to which the lock is fastened.

long-and-short work: In masonry, a method of forming angles of door and window jambs in rubble walls by laying stones horizontally alternating with stones set on end, the upright stones usually being longer than the horizontal stones.

longitudinal section: In shopwork and drawing, a lengthwise cut of any portion of a structure; also, pertaining to a measurement along the axis of a body.

lookouts: Short wooden brackets which support an overhanging portion of a roof (see Fig. 18); also, a place from which observations are made, as from a watchtower.

loose knot: In woodworking, a term applied to a knot which is not held in position firmly by the surrounding wood fibers; such a knot is a severe blemish in a piece of lumber making the board unfit for first-class work.

louver: An opening for ventilating closed attics or other used spaces; a lantern or turret on a roof for ventilating or lighting purposes, commonly used in medieval buildings; also, a louver board. A slatted opening for ventilation in which the slats are so placed as to exclude rain, light, or vision.

louver boards: In architecture, a series of overlapping sloping boards or slats in an opening so arranged as to admit air but keep out rain or snow.

louvered awning blinds: Adjustable louvers on slanted outside blinds control the amount of shade or sunlight entering windows.

lug sill: In building, a term applied to a window sill in a brick or stone wall, where the sill extends beyond the width of the window opening, with the ends of the sill set in the wall.

lumber: Any material, such as boards, planks, or beams cut from timber to a size and form suitable for marketing.

lump lime: Lime commonly known as *quicklime* produced by burning limestone in a kiln.

M

made ground: In building construction, a portion of land, or ground, formed by filling in natural or artificial pits with rubbish or other material.

magazine: In architecture, a warehouse, a storehouse for merchandise; also a protected building or room such as a depot for storage of military stores, especially explosives and munitions.

magnesite: Carbonate of magnesium obtained from natural deposits.

magnesite flooring: A composition flooring made of calcined *magnesite* and magnesium-chloride solution with a filler of sawdust, wood flour, ground silica, or quartz. It is used to cover concrete floors on which it is floated in a layer about 1½ inches in thickness.

mallet: A small maul, or hammer, usually made of wood used for driving another tool, such as a chisel.

malm: In brickmaking, an artificial marl produced by mixing clay and chalk in a wash mill. The product is used as clay in the manufacture of brick.

malm rubber: In brickwork, a soft form of malm brick which is capable of being worked by cutting or rubbing, into special shapes.

mansard roof: A roof with two slopes on all four sides, the lower slope very steep, the upper slope almost flat; frequently used as a convenient method of adding another story to a building.

mantel: The ornamental facing around a fireplace, including the shelf which is usually attached to the breast of the chimney above the fireplace.

marble: Any limestone capable of taking a high polish; used extensively for both interior and exterior finish of buildings; because of the wide range of colors from white to dark gray and brown, *marble* is much used in architectural work for decorative purposes.

marezzo marble: An artificial marble produced by mixing cement with fiber; specially designed for interior decoration.

margin draft: In ashlar work, a smooth surface surrounding a joint.

marine glue: In woodworking, an adhesive substance composed of crude rubber, pitch, and shellac; the proportions are: 1 part rubber, 2 parts shellac, and 3 parts pitch.

mason: A workman skilled in laying brick or stone, as a *bricklayer*, a *stonemason*.

masonry: A term applied to anything constructed of stone, brick, tiles, cement, concrete, and similar materials; also, the work done by a mason who works in stone, brick, cement, tiles, or concrete.

masonry arches: Arches, usually curved, thrown across openings in masonry walls for providing support for the superimposed structure. The arches may be constructed of such material as stone blocks or brick put together in a particular arrangement, so a completed masonry arch will resist the pressure of the load it carries by a balancing of certain thrusts and counterthrusts.

masonry nail: A hardened-steel nail of specialized design, used for fastening wood, etc., to masonry work. See Fig. 37.

masonry saw: Portable, electrically powered hand saw, similar to all-purpose *electric hand saw.* Designed specifically for cutting masonry, this saw has a variety of masonry blade choices, including diamond blades and abrasive blades.

masonry wall: Any wall constructed of such material as stone, brick, tile, cement blocks, or concrete, put in place by a mason.

matched boards: Boards which have been finished so as to hold a tongue-and-groove joint securely in place; also boards finished with a rebated edge for close fitting.

maul: A heavy hammer or club used for driving stakes or piles; also, a heavy mallet or mace; any of various types of heavy hammers used for driving wedges, piles, or stakes.

meager lime: In building, a lime in which the impurities are in excess of 6 per cent. See *poor lime.*

mechanic: Pertaining to a handicraft, or one skilled in some manual art; also, a skilled workman who makes repairs or assembles machines; a skilled worker with tools or machines.

mechanic arts: In school-shop training, a term applied to craftsmanship and the use of tools and machines.

meeting rail: The strip of wood or metal forming the horizontal bar which separates the upper and lower sash of a window. See *check rail,* Fig. 20.

mensuration: The process of measuring, especially that branch of mathematics which deals with the determining of length, area, and volume; that is, finding the length of a line, the area of a surface, and the volume of a solid.

metal-edged gypsum plank: A gypsum plank with tongue-and-groove metal edges. Its advantage over ordinary gypsum board is that it results in cleaner, better fitting joints when used for wall, floor, or ceiling construction.

metal strip: A term sometimes applied to metal flashing; used on water tables or around chimneys to prevent water seeping into the roof or walls. See *belt course,* Fig. 9.

metal ties: In masonry, a type of steel tie which is coated with Portland cement, and used to bond two separate wall sections together in cavity-type walls. Typical metal ties, commonly used, are shown in Fig. 36.

mezzanine: A low story between two higher stories, usually a gallerylike floor midway between the main floor and the next floor above it.

millwork: In woodworking, any work which has been finished, machined, and partly assembled at the mill.

millwright: A workman who designs and sets up mills or mill machinery; also, a mechanic who installs machinery in a mill or workshop.

mineral aggregate: In masonry work, an aggregate consisting of a mixture of broken stone, broken slag, crushed or uncrushed gravel, sand, stone, screenings, and mineral dust.

mineral wool: A type of material used for insulating buildings, produced by sending a blast of steam through molten slag or rock; common types now in use include: rock wool, glass wool, slag wool, and others.

minute of arc: A measure used by architects to find the proportion of a column; one sixtieth of a degree. See *module.*

miter: In carpentry, the ends of any two pieces of board of corresponding form, cut off at an angle and fitted together in an angular shape. See Fig. 30.

miter box: A device used by a carpenter for guiding a handsaw at the proper angle for cutting a miter joint in wood. The carpenter usually makes his own *miter box* on the job.

miter cut: In carpentry, a cut made at an angle for joining two pieces of board so cut that they will form an angle.

mitering: The joining of two pieces of board at an evenly divided angle;

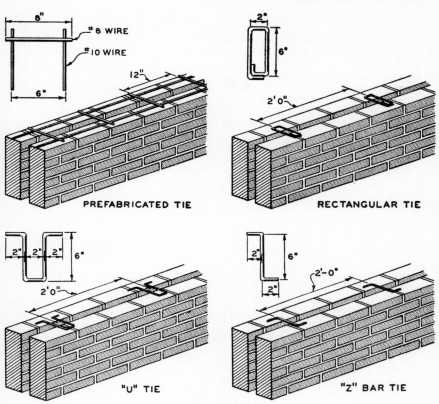

Fig. 36. Metal Ties

joining two boards by using a miter joint. See Fig. 30.

miter plane: A tool used for any type of utility work where a joint is made without overlapping of the boards, as in butt or miter joints.

miter-saw cut or **miter-sawing board:** A device used to guide a saw at a desired angle.

miter square: A square similar to the try square, but with one edge of the handle having a 45-degree angle, so it can be used for laying out miter joints.

modular brick: Brick which are designed for use in walls built in accordance with the modular dimensional standards. These brick include four basic sizes, known as *economy brick, oversize brick, standard brick,* and *twin brick.*

modular masonry: Masonry construction in which the size of the building material used, such as brick or tile, is based upon common units of measure, known as the *modular dimensional standards.*

module: A measure used by architects when designing columns; for example, taking the size of some part, as the semidiameter of a column at the base of the shaft, as a unit of measure for regulating the proportions of the entire column.

molded-intake belt course: In building, such a course usually is an elaboration of a plain-band course of masonry or cut-stone work located at a point where the thickness of the upper wall is less than the thickness of the wall below it.

molding: A strip of material, either plane or curved, formed into long regular channels or projections; used for finishing and decorative purposes. *Molding* can be bought in many different sizes and shapes.

molding plane: A small tool used in furniture making for cutting molding into various sizes, shapes, and widths.

Molly Expansion anchor: A type of metal fastener, consisting of a bolt encased in a shell which expands, wedging itself into a hole drilled to receive it; used principally for securing structural wood parts to a concrete or masonry wall. See *anchors*, Fig. 1.

monolithic: Pertaining to a hollow foundation piece constructed of masonry, with a number of open wells passing through it. The wells are finally filled with concrete to form a solid foundation; a term applied to any concrete structure made of a continuous mass of material or cast as a single piece.

mortar: In masonry, a pasty building material, composed of sand and lime, or cement mixed with water, which gradually hardens when exposed to the air. *Mortar* is used as a joining medium in brick and stone construction.

mortar bed: A thick layer of plastic mortar in which is seated any structural member, the purpose of which is to provide a sound, contour-formed base.

mortar board: In masonry, a small square board, with a handle underneath, on which a mason holds his mortar. Same as *hawk*.

mortar joints: Joints which represent a wide range of types in finishing the mortar in stone or brickwork. See *weathered joint, flush joint, exposed joint, struck joint, concave joint,* and **V** *joint*. See, also, Fig. 32.

mortar mixer: A machine which mixes mortar by means of paddles in a

rotating drum. These machines are usually power-driven, and sometimes a large one is mounted on the back of a truck. The truck-mounted machine mixes the mortar as it travels to the job, and also transports the mortar to various locations where needed on the job.

mortise: In woodworking, a cavity cut in a piece of wood, or timber, to receive a tenon, or tongue, projecting from another piece; for example, a mortise-and-tenon joint.

mortise chisel: A tool used in woodworking for cutting mortises; a heavy-bodied chisel with a narrow face.

mortise gauge: A carpenter's tool consisting of a head and bar containing two scratch pins which may be adjusted, for scribing parallel lines for cutting mortises to whatever width may be desired.

mortising machine: A carpenter's tool used for cutting mortises in wood, either by using a chisel or a circular cutting bit.

mosaic: A combination of small colored stones, glass, or other material so arranged as to form a decorative surface design. The various pieces are inlaid usually in a ground of cement or stucco.

mudsill: The lowest sill of a structure, as a foundation timber placed directly on the ground, or foundation.

mullion: The slender bars between the lights or panes of windows.

muntin: Small strips of wood, or metal, which separate the glass in a window frame; sometimes less correctly a *mullion*.

N

nail: A slender piece of metal pointed at one end for driving into wood, and flat or rounded at the other end for striking with a hammer; used as a wood fastener by carpenters and other construction workers. The sizes of nails are indicated by the term *penny*, which originally indicated the price per hundred, but now refers to the length. Although

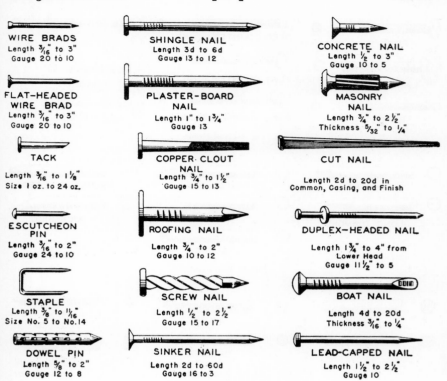

Fig. 37. Nails, Special

the sizes of nails may vary as much as ⅛″ to ¼″ from that indicated, the approximate lengths as sold on the market are:

4-penny nail = 1¼″
6-penny nail = 2″
8-penny nail = 2½″
10-penny nail = 3″
20-penny nail = 4″
60-penny nail = 6″

For different types of nails, nail-heads, nail points, and nail shanks, see Figs. 37, 38, 39, and 40.

nail-glued roof truss: A glued truss with plywood gusset plates that uses nails to hold it together only until the glue dries. A few hours after assembly, the strength of the truss bonds depend on the glue alone. Grade A casein glue is applied with

a specially designed spreader to members whose design specifications must be followed exactly to get proper stresses. This truss requires no special jointing or cutting, and is stronger than conventional truss designs, showing less deflection under test loads.

nail puller: Any small punch bar suitable for prying purposes, with a **V**-shaped, or forked, end which can be slipped under the head of a nail for prying it loose from the wood; also, a mechanical device provided with two jaws, one of which serves as a leverage heel for gripping a nail and prying it loose from a board.

nail set: A tool usually made from a solid bar of high-grade tool steel, measuring about 4 inches in length, used to set the heads of nails below the

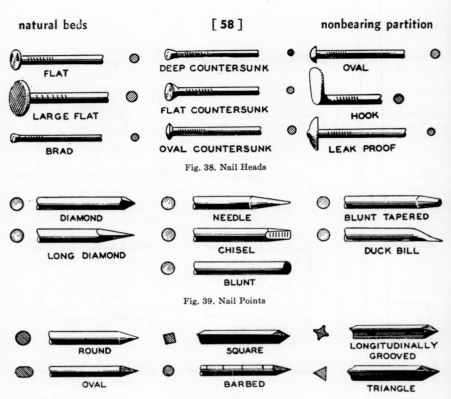

Fig. 38. Nail Heads

Fig. 39. Nail Points

Fig. 40. Nail Shanks

surface of wood. One end of the tool is drawn to a taper and the head is so shaped there is slight possibility of the device slipping off the head of a nail. Both ends are polished, body machine knurled.

natural beds: The surface of stone as it lies in the quarry. In stratified rocks, if the walls are not laid in their natural bed, the laminae, or scales, separate.

natural cement: A cement made from a natural earth requiring but little preparation; similar to hydraulic lime.

neat cement: In masonry, a pure cement uncut by a sand admixture.

neat work: In masonry, the brickwork above the footings.

nest of saws: A set of saw blades intended for use in the same handle, which is detachable. Such a collection of thin, narrow-bladed saws usually consists of one or more compass saws and a keyhole saw designed primarily for cutting out small holes, such as keyholes. See Fig. 33.

newel: In architecture, an upright post supporting the handrail at the top and bottom of a stairway, or at the turn on a landing; also, the main post about which a circular staircase winds; sometimes called the *newel post*. See Fig. 50.

nogging: In masonry, the filling-in with bricks of the spaces between timbers, such as studding in walls and partitions.

nonbearing partition: A term used in the building trade when referring to a dividing wall which merely separates space into rooms, but does not carry overhead partitions or floor joists.

nosing: The rounded edge of a stair tread projecting over the riser; also, the projecting part of a buttress. See Fig. 50.

O

obelisk: A four-sided shaft of stone, usually monolithic, tapering as it rises, and terminating in a pyramid at the apex.

octagon: A *polygon* with eight sides.

octagon scale: A scale which appears on the *tongue* of a *framing square;* used for laying out figures with eight equal sides.

odeum: In architecture, a small gallery, or hall, used for musical or dramatic performances.

offset: A term used in building when referring to a set-off, such as a sunken panel in a wall, or a recess of any kind; also, a horizontal ledge on a wall formed by the diminishing of the thickness of the wall at that point.

ogee: A molding with an S-shaped curve formed by the union of a concave and convex line; that is, a cyma recta or cyma reversa.

oilslip: A term used by woodworkers when referring to a small unmounted oilstone held in the hand while they sharpen the cutting edges of gouges.

oilstone: A fine-grained whetstone whose rubbing surface is moistened with oil, when used for sharpening the cutting edges of tools.

Old English bond: In masonry work, a bond consisting of alternating courses of stretchers and headers, with a *closer* laid next to the corner bricks in every course of headers. See *typical bonds,* Fig. 11.

oölitic limestone: A variety of rock formation composed of rounded concretions, usually carbonate of lime, resembling the roe of fish, cemented together.

open-corner fireplace: A fireplace of which two adjacent sides are open. Important factors which differ from conventional fireplace construction considerations are flue capacity and cross draft. A ¼" steel plate usually supports the corner overhang extending back beyond the corbeled abutment. Angle iron and plate rest on the cap of a steel column.

open planning millwork: Some millwork stock includes special profiles for use in large window area, and open modular planning constructions, where framing members are often used as finish members.

open-string stairs: In the building trade, a term applied to a stairway with a wall on one side and the other side open, so that a protective balustrade or handrail is necessary on the open side. The balustrade is supported at top and bottom by upright posts known as *newel posts.* The construction is such that the treads and risers are visible from the room or hallway into which the stairs lead. See Fig. 50.

openwork: Any type of construction which shows openings through the substance of which the surface is formed, especially ornamental designs of wood, metal, stone, or other materials.

oriel: In architecture, a window projecting from the outer face of a wall, especially an upper story, and supported by brackets or corbels.

orifice: A small opening as at the end of a vent pipe, or any similar mouthlike aperture.

ornament: In architecture and furniture making, any decorative detail added to enhance the beauty or elegance of the design.

ornamentation: In masonry, a design formed by the laying of stone, brick, or tile so as to produce a decorative effect.

orthography: In the building trade, a geometrical elevation of a structure which is represented as it actually exists and in perspective as it would appear to the observer.

outrigger: A projecting beam used in connection with overhanging roofs. A support for rafters in cases where roofs extend two or more feet beyond the walls of a house.

outside gouge: In woodworking, a type of gouge where the bevel is ground on the convex, or outside, face.

out of true: In shopworking and the building trade, a term used when there is a twist or any other irregularity in the alignment of a form; also, a varying from exactness in a structural part.

overhand work: In masonry, work performed on the outside of a wall from a scaffold constructed on the inside of the wall.

overhead door: A door which may either be mounted on a sliding track or a pivoted canopy frame, which moves upward to an overhead position when opened. Such doors may be manually operated, or may be impelled by a variety of power mechanisms, and are commonly used as garage doors. See *roll-up doors, tilt-up doors.*

oversize brick: Modular brick related to the 4-inch module, every 12 inches in height; size 2½″ x 3½″ x 7½″.

ovolo: A convex molding, forming or approximating in section a quarter of a circle; a quarter-round molding.

P

packing: In masonry, the process or operation of filling in a double or hollow wall; also, any material used in the operation of filling or closing up a hollow space, as in a wall. See *furring.*

pad saw: A small compass saw with a detachable handle, which also serves as a socket, or holder, for the narrow tapering blade when not in use.

pad stone: In building, a stone *template;* a stone placed in a wall under a girder or other beam to distribute the weight or pressure of the load above; also, a lintel of stone spanning a doorway and supporting joists. See *template.*

paint for concrete: Paints made of zinc oxide or barium sulphate, mixed with tung oil, are frequently used for the painting of concrete work.

pan: In half-timbered work, a panel of brickwork or lath and plaster; any large division of an exterior wall, such as the space between upright and horizontal timbers in a frame structure where the surface is to be filled with boards, brickwork, or lath and plaster; also, in carpentry, a recess bed for the leaf of a hinge.

panel: In architecture, a section, or portion, of a wall, ceiling, or other surface, either sunken or raised, enclosed by a framelike border; a term especially applied to woodwork.

panel saw: A carpenter's handsaw with fine teeth, making it especially suitable for cutting thin wood.

panel strip: A term used in the building trade when referring to a molded strip of wood or metal used to cover a joint between two sheathing boards forming a panel; also, a strip of any kind of material used in the framing of panels.

pantile: A type of roofing tile with straight lengthwise lines, but curved in cross section, laid so that the joint between two concave tiles is covered by a convex tile; also, a type of tile in which there is both a concave and convex portion; this tile is laid so that the convex portion overlaps the rim of the concave portion of an adjoining tile; also, a gutter tile.

parapet: In architecture, a protective railing or low wall along the edge of a roof, balcony, bridge, or terrace.

pargeting: A term used by architects when referring to the decoration of a room with plaster work, or stucco, in relief, such as raised ornamental figures; also, plastering on the inside of flues which gives a smooth surface and improves the draft.

parging: A thin coat of plastering applied to rough stone or brick walls for smoothing purposes. See Fig. 41.

paring: A term used by wood turners when referring to a method of wood turning which is opposed to the scraping method commonly employed by patternmakers.

paring chisel: A type of long chisel employed by patternmakers for slicing,

Face-Tier Stretchers

Brick Guide on Top of Last Course in Face Tier

Backing Tier

Parging or Back Plastering

Fig. 41. Parging

or paring, cuts in wood so as to make a smooth surface which is difficult to obtain when cutting directly across the grain.

paring gouge: A woodworker's bench tool with its cutting edge beveled on the inside, or concave face, of the blade.

parquetry: An inlaid pattern of various designs in wood, used especially for floors, and for decorative features in furniture.

parting strip: A thin strip of wood set into the pulley stile in a sash window for holding the sashes apart. See Fig. 20.

parting tool: A narrow-bladed turning tool used by woodworkers for cutting recesses, grooves, or channels.

partition: An interior wall separating one portion of a house from another; usually a permanent inside wall which divides a house into various rooms. In residences, partitions often are constructed of studding covered with lath and plaster; in factories, the partitions are made of more durable materials, such as concrete blocks, hollow tile, brick, or heavy glass.

partition plate: A term applied by builders to the horizontal member which serves as a cap for the partition studs, and also supports the joists, rafters, and studding.

party wall: In architecture, a term used

when referring to a wall on the line between adjoining buildings, in which each of the respective owners of the adjacent buildings share the rights and enjoyment of the common wall.

pavilion: A partially enclosed structure, usually roofed, for shelter purposes at the seaside, in parks, or other places where people gather for amusement or pleasure. A *pavilion* sometimes is adorned with ornamental designs intended to add a decorative feature to a landscaped park or garden.

Payne's process: A method of fireproofing wood by first treating it with an injection of sulphate of iron, then later infusing the wood with a solution of sulphate of lime or soda.

pebble dash: In the building trade, a term used for finishing the exterior walls of a structure by dashing pebbles against the plaster or cement.

peen hammer: A hammer of various designs, used especially by metal workers and by stonemasons. This hammer sometimes has two opposite cutting edges and is roughly toothed to facilitate the cutting of stone or the breaking of brick.

pegboard: A board with holes evenly spaced over its entire surface. May be cut to desired size and used to line closets or hang on walls. Hooks placed in the holes at convenient intervals provide facilities for hanging household objects of almost any size or shape, simplifying storage problems.

pent roof: A roof like that of a penthouse, attached to and sloping from a wall of a building in one direction only.

perch: A solid measure used for stone work, commonly 16½' x 1½' x 1', or 24¾ cu. ft. However, the measure for stone varies according to locality and custom, sometimes 16⅔ cu. ft. being used for solid work.

perpend: In masonry, a header brick or large stone extending through a wall so that one end appears on each side of the wall and acts as a binder.

perron: An architectural term referring to an out-of-door stairway leading to the first floor of a building; a name sometimes applied to the platform upon which an entrance door opens, together with the flight of steps leading up to it; also, a flight of stairs, as in a garden, leading to a terrace or upper story.

perspective drawing: The representation of an object on a plane surface, so presented as to have the same appearance as when seen from a particular viewpoint.

pew: A name commonly applied to long benches with backs used for seating the audience in a church.

picket: A stake, or narrow board, sharpened at the top used in making

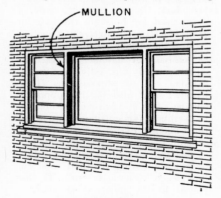

Fig. 42. Picture Window

fences; also, sometimes called a *pale.*

picture mold: A narrow molding, fastened to an interior wall, used for hanging pictures, which are suspended from the molding by means of fine wire and a metal hook.

picture window: A large window whose bottom ledge is not more than waist high, which includes a dominant fixed sash area, though movable sashes may also be enclosed by the frame. The fixed sash area is usually wider than it is high. See Fig. 42.

pier: One of the pillars supporting an arch; also, a supporting section of wall between two openings; a masonry structure used as an auxiliary to stiffen a wall.

pier glass: In building, a term applied to a large mirror between two windows.

pike pole: An implement, equipped with a sharp metal point, used for holding poles, such as telephone or telegraph poles, in an upright position while planting or removing them.

pilaster: A rectangular column attached to a wall or pier; structurally a pier, but treated architecturally as a column with a capital, shaft, and base.

pile: A large timber driven into the ground for the support of a structure or a vertical load. *Piles* are frequently made of the entire trunk of a tree.

pile driver: A machine for driving piles; usually a high vertical framework with appliances attached for raising a heavy mass of iron which, after being lifted to the top of the framework, is allowed to fall, by the force of gravity, on the head of the pile, thus driving it into the ground.

pillar: An upright shaft or column, of stone, marble, brick, or other materials, relatively slender in comparison to its height. Used principally for supporting superstructures but may stand alone as for a monument.

pin: In carpentry, a piece of wood used to hold structural parts together, as a small peg or wooden nail.

pincers: A jointed tool, with two handles and a pair of jaws used for gripping and holding an object.

pinchbar: A type of crowbar, or lever,

on one end of which a pointed projection serves as a kind of fulcrum; used especially for rolling heavy wheels. See *wrecking bar.*

pin knot: A term used by woodworkers when referring to a blemish in boards, consisting of a small knot of ½ inch or less in diameter.

pinnacle: In architecture, a tall, pointed, relatively slender, upright member usually terminating in a cone-shaped spire, used as a decorative feature on a buttress or in an angle of a pier; also, a slender ornament as on a parapet or any turretlike decoration.

pitch board: In building, a thin piece of board, cut in the shape of a right-angled triangle, used as a guide in forming work. When making cuts for stairs, the *pitch board* serves as a pattern for marking cuts; the shortest side is the height of the riser cut and the next longer side is the width of the tread.

pitch of a roof: The angle, or degree, of slope of a roof from the plate to the ridge. The pitch can be found by dividing the height, or rise, by the span, for example, if the height is 8 feet and the span 16 feet, the pitch is $\frac{8}{16}$ equals ½, then the angle of pitch is 45 degrees.

pith knot: In woodworking, a term used when referring to a blemish in boards, consisting of a small knot with a pith hole not more than ¼ inch in diameter.

pivoted casement: A casement window which has its upper and lower edges pivoted.

plain sawing: Cutting wood so the saw cuts are parallel to the squared side of a log. See *flat grain.*

plan: In architecture, a diagram showing a horizontal view of a building, such as floor plans and sectional plans.

plane: In woodworking, a flat surface where any line joining two points will lie entirely in the surface; also, a carpenter's tool used for smoothing boards or other wood surfaces.

planing mill: An establishment equipped with woodworking machinery for smoothing rough wood surfaces, cutting, fitting and matching boards with tongued-and-grooved joints; a woodworking mill.

plank: A long, flat, heavy piece of timber thicker than a board; a term commonly applied to a piece of construction material 6 inches or more in width and from 1½ to 6 inches or more in thickness.

plank truss: Any truss work constructed of heavy timbers such as planking in a roof truss or in a bridge truss.

plan shape: A plan shape is the basic pattern on which a house is laid out. Most commonly used plan shapes are the square, rectangular, T, L, H, U, and split-level patterns. T, L, H, and U plan shapes roughly follow the shape of the alphabet letter by which they are indicated. See *split-level.*

plaster: Any pasty material of a mortar-like consistency used for covering walls and ceilings of buildings. Formerly, a widely used type of plastering composed of a mixture of lime, sand, hair, and water. A more durable and popular plastering is now made of Portland cement mixed with sand and water.

plaster board: A rigid insulating board made of plastering material covered on both sides with heavy paper.

plaster lath: Thin, narrow strips of wood nailed to ceiling joists, studding, or rafters, as a groundwork for receiving plastering.

plastic wood: A manufactured product useful to the building industry. In making wood compounds, choice softwoods, such as white pine, spruce, and fir, which have been converted into sawdust, are employed. The sawdust, when ground into wood flour and mixed with the proper adhesives, forms a plastic material used extensively for filling cracks, defects in wood, and for other purposes. Since it dries quickly and hardens upon exposure to air, *plastic wood* can be painted almost immediately after being applied.

plate: A term usually applied to a 2 x 4 placed on top of studs in frame

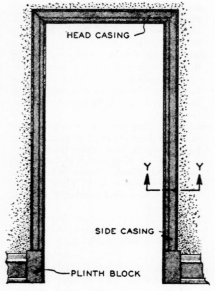

HEAD CASING

Y   Y

SIDE CASING

PLINTH BLOCK

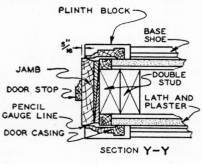

PLINTH BLOCK

BASE SHOE

5/16"

JAMB

DOUBLE STUD

DOOR STOP

LATH AND PLASTER

PENCIL GAUGE LINE

DOOR CASING

SECTION Y-Y

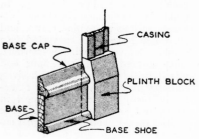

BASE CAP

CASING

PLINTH BLOCK

BASE

BASE SHOE

Fig. 43. Plinth Block

walls. It serves as the top horizontal timber upon which the attic joists and roof rafters rest, and to which these members are fastened. See Fig. 7. Also, a flat piece of steel used in conjunction with angle irons, channels, or **I** beams in the construction of lintels.

plate glass: A polished, high-grade glass cast in the form of a plate, or sheet, used principally in high-priced structures. A sheet of glass usually thicker and of a better quality than ordinary window glass, also with a smoother surface free from blemishes.

plate rail: A narrow railing usually placed at the edge of a drain for holding plates and other dishes; also, a narrow shelflike molding attached to the interior of a wall for supporting decorated pieces of chinaware, especially plates.

platform framing: A type of construction in which the floor platforms are framed independently; also, the second and third floors are supported by studs of only one story in height.

pliers: A small pincerlike tool having a pair of long, relatively broad jaws which are roughened for gripping and bending wire or for holding small objects. Pliers are sometimes made with nippers at the side of the jaws for cutting off wire. See *cutting pliers.*

plinth: The lowest square-shaped part of a column; a course of stones, as at the base of a wall. See *plinth block,* Fig. 43.

plinth block: A small block slightly thicker and wider than the casing for interior trim of a door. It is placed at the bottom of the door trim against which the baseboard or mopboard is butted. See Fig. 43.

plum: In masonry, a large, undressed stone which, together with other similar stones, is used in mass concrete to form footings for walls. When plum stones are used, less concrete is required.

plumb and level: A well-finished hardwood or metal case containing glass tube with bubble set lengthwise for testing accuracy of horizontal planes and lines, also containing a second glass tube with bubble set crosswise for testing accuracy of vertical lines and perpendicular walls.

plumb bob: A weight attached to a line for testing perpendicular surfaces for trueness; also, to test, or adjust, with a plumb line.

plumb cut: In roof framing, a cut made on a *rafter* parallel to the *ridge board*, at the point where the rafter and ridge board meet.

ply: One thickness of any material used for building up of several layers, as roofing felt or layers of wood, as in laminated woodwork.

pointed ashlar: In stonework, face markings on a stone made with a pointed tool.

pointing: A term used in masonry for finishing of joints in a brick or stone wall.

pointing trowel: A small hand instrument used by stone masons or bricklayers for pointing up joints, or for removing old mortar from the face of a wall.

polygon: A figure bounded by straight lines. The boundary lines are called sides and the sum of the sides is called the perimeter. *Polygons* are classified according to the number of sides they have.

poor lime: In building, a lime containing more than 15 per cent impurities; also called *meager lime*.

porch: A covered entrance to a building, projecting from the main wall with a separate roof; also, a type of veranda which often is partially enclosed.

portable: Anything which may be moved from place to place easily, as portable animal pens or portable houses for human beings.

portable electric drill: A portable, electrically operated drill with a wide variety of bits for various on-the-job drilling operations. Has bits for wood, metal, and masonry drilling. See Fig. 44.

portable electric generator: A portable

Fig. 44. Portable Electric Drill
Courtesy Skil Corporation

gasoline-powered generator of electricity, skid or trailer mounted, or provided with two-man handles, which can be carried from place to place, as electric power for various hand tools is needed.

portable electric plane: Electrically powered plane designed for on-the-job finishing purposes. Advantages include an ease of handling which results in highly accurate work. The

Fig. 45. Portable Electric Plane
Courtesy Skil Corporation

power plane turns out neat, well-finished work in appreciably less time than planes which depend upon manual power. See Fig. 45.

portal: An entranceway such as a door or gate, usually applied only to structures which are impressive in appearance or size as a massive church edifice.

portico: An open space covered with a roof supported by columns, often attached to a building as a porch but sometimes entirely detached from any structure.

Portland cement: A hydraulic cement, commonly used in the building trades, consisting of silica, lime, and alumina intimately mixed in the proper proportions, then burned in a kiln. The clinkers or vitrified product, when ground fine, form an extremely strong cement.

Portland cement paint: A specially prepared paint made by mixing cement and water; used on concrete walls as a finish, and to protect the joints against water from rain and snow.

post and beam construction: A system of construction currently used in one-story buildings in which post and beam-framing units are the basic load-bearing members. Fewer framing members are needed, leaving more open space for functional use, for easier installation of large windows, and more flexible placing of free standing walls and partitions. It is also adaptable for prefabricated modular panel installation. Wide roof overhangs, for sun protection, and outdoor living areas are simpler to construct when this framing system is used. Posts and beams may be of wood, structural steel or concrete. See *concrete bent construction.* Ceiling heights are higher for the same cubage, and it is reported that building is faster and cheaper. Roof deck can double as finished ceiling in the post, beam, and plank variation of the system. Problems include the necessity for extra insulation, difficulty in concealing wiring and duct work, and the necessity for extra care in the choice of materials and in planning.

post and pan: A term sometimes applied to half timbering formed of brickwork or of lath and plaster panels; the same as post and petrall.

power hammer: Portable electric, pneumatic, and self-contained gasoline-driven hammers, using a vibratory action principle. They accommodate such tools as chisels, frost wedges, solid drill steel, clay spades, tampers, diggers, asphalt cutters, ground rod drivers, offset trimming spades, plug and feathers, etc. They are used for removing defective brick from walls, hardened putty from steel sash, and mortar for repointing; for vibrating concrete wall forms, cutting wood, drilling holes in tile floors, digging holes for posts or sewers, and many other applications.

power troweler: A machine operated by one man, designed to do a complete job of concrete finishing. Generally gasoline powered, the power source, which is mounted vertically to the ground, turns troweling blades which are mounted radially on a central shaft. The pitch of the troweling blades is adjustable while the machine is in operation, allowing continual use on varying surfaces. Due to the circular swath of the troweler, hand finishing is generally necessary in corners and along walls.

Pratt truss: A special type of construction used in both roof and bridge building in which the vertical members are in compression and the diagonals are in tension.

prefabricated areawall: A corrugated steel wall which lines area space outside basement windows or crawl spaces. See Fig. 46.

prefabricated modular units: Units of construction which are prefabricated on a measurement variation base of 4 inches or its multiples, and can be fitted together on the job with a minimum of adjustments. Modular units include complete window walls, kitchen units complete with instal-

STRAIGHT TYPE   ROUND TYPE

Fig. 46. Prefabricated Areawall

lations, as well as masonry, wall panels, and most of the other components of a house. Units are usually designed in such a way that they will fit functionally into a variety of house sizes and plan types.

prefabricated skylight: A clear plastic bubble, set in an aluminum frame, often with built-in vent and exhaust fan, which can be set over a prepared opening.

pressed brick: A high-grade brick which is molded under pressure, as a result of which sharp edges are formed by the meeting of two surfaces and a smooth face, making it suitable for exposed surface work.

prestressed concrete: Prestressing is "the imposition of preliminary interval stresses in a structure before working loads are applied, in such a way as to lead to a more favorable state of stress when these loads come into action." Concrete is usually prestressed by means of high strength steel wire incorporated in it. If the wires are placed in tension, and held in this position before the concrete is placed, the process is called *pretensioning.* If the concrete is poured with pockets in it, where the wires can be placed and prestressed after the concrete is poured and cured, the process is called *post-tensioning.* In one type of construction, members are built up of units resembling concrete blocks, with adjacent faces ground smooth. Threaded reinforcing rods are placed

in side splines of the units and extend through washers. Tension is applied to the rods by hydraulic jacks. Pretensioning makes it possible to use much less steel than is needed for structural steel or reinforced concrete buildings. The concrete members can be less bulky. It is also used in making crackless tanks for storing liquids.

priming: The first coat of paint put on for sizing and preserving wood.

profile: An outline drawing of a section, especially a vertical section through a structural part; that is, a contour drawing.

projecting belt course: A masonry term used when referring to an elaboration of a plain band course or cut-stone work projecting beyond the face of a wall for several inches.

projection: In architecture, a jutting out of any part or member of a building, or other structure.

promenade tile: In masonry, unglazed machine-made tile; same as *quarry tile.*

puddle: A mixture of sand, clay, and water, worked while wet to form a substance impervious to water; to make loose dirt firm and solid by turning on water.

pugging: A coarse kind of mortar used for packing or covering, and laid between floor joists to prevent the passage of sound; mortar used to deaden sound; also called deadening.

pulley stile: In architecture, the upright pieces at the sides of a double-hung window frame on which the pulleys for the sash weights are fastened.

pulpit: A raised platform, as in a church, where the clergyman stands while preaching.

punch: A steel driving tool used principally for removing material of the same shape as the *punch*.

purlins: Horizontal timbers supporting the common rafters in roofs, the timbers spanning from truss to truss.

putlog: A crosspiece in a scaffolding, one end of which rests in a hole in a wall; also, horizontal pieces which support the flooring of scaffolding, one end being inserted into *putlog* holes; that is, short timbers on which the flooring of a scaffolding is laid.

puzzolano: A volcanic dust which has a hardening effect when mixed with mortar, producing a valuable hydraulic cement; first discovered at Pozzuoli, Italy.

Q

quadrangle: In architecture, an open court or space in the form of a parallelogram, usually rectangular in shape, partially or entirely surrounded by buildings, as on a college campus; also, the buildings surrounding the court.

quadrant: An instrument usually consisting of a graduated arc of 90 degrees, with an index or vernier; used primarily for measuring altitudes. Sometimes a spirit level or a plumb line is attached to the *quadrant* for determining the vertical or horizontal direction.

quarry-faced masonry: Squared stone as it comes from the quarry, with split face, only squared at joints; having the face left rough as when taken from the quarry, as building stone; masonry built of such stone.

quarry-stone bond: In masonry, a term applied to the arrangement of stones in rubble work.

quarry tile: In masonry, a name given to machine-made, unglazed tile. Also called *promenade tile*.

quarter bend: A bend, as of a pipe, through an arc of 90 degrees.

quarter sawing: The sawing of logs lengthwise into quarters, with the saw cuts parallel with the medullary rays, then cutting the quarters into boards, as in making quartered oak boards.

quatrefoil: In architecture, a single decorative feature consisting of an ornamental unit in the form of a four-leaved flower.

queen closure: A half brick made by cutting a whole brick in two lengthwise; also, a half brick used in a course of brick masonry to prevent vertical joints falling above one another. Sometimes spelled *closer*. See Fig. 11.

queen post: One of the two vertical tie posts in a roof truss, or any similar framed truss.

queen truss: A truss framed with queen posts, that is, two vertical tie posts, distinguished from the king truss which has only one tie post.

quicklime: The solid product remaining after limestone has been heated to a high temperature. The process of producing lime is known as *lime-burning*.

quirk: A small groove, or channel, separating a bead or other molding from the adjoining members; also, an acute angle between moldings or beads.

quirk bead: A bead molding separated from the surface on one side by a channel or groove. A *double quirk bead* refers to a molding with a channel on each side of the beads.

quirk molding: An architectural term usually applied to a molding which has a small groove, although sometimes the term is also used in reference to a molding with both a convex and a concave curve separated by a flat portion.

quoins: In architecture, large squared stones, such as buttresses, set at the angles of a building.

R

rabbet: In woodworking, a term used in referring to a groove cut in the surface, or along the edge, of a board, plank, or other timber, so as to receive another board or piece similarly cut. See Fig. 30.

rabbet joint: A joint which is formed by the fitting together of two pieces of timber which have been rabbeted. See Fig. 30.

radial bar: A device made by attaching a point and pencil to a wooden bar which is then used for striking large curves.

radiating brick: In masonry, a brick which tapers in at least one direction, so as to be especially useful for curved work, as in building arches. Sometimes called *radius brick*. See *compass brick*.

radius tool: In masonry and cement work, a finishing tool used for shaping curved sections which must be smooth and true.

rafters: The sloping members of a roof, as the ribs which extend from the ridge or from the hip of a roof to the eaves; used to support the shingles and roof boards.

raggle: In masonry, a manufactured building unit provided with a groove into which metal flashing is fitted. *Raggle* is used especially around parapet walls, or in connection with water tables, to prevent leaking where flashing is applied to a masonry wall. Also, a term applied to a groove made in a stone to receive adjoining material. See Fig. 25.

rag work: In masonry, a term applied to any kind of rubble work made of small, thin stones.

rail: A horizontal bar of wood or metal used as a guard, as the top member of a balustrade; also, the horizontal member of a door or window. See Fig. 50.

raked joint: In brick masonry, a type of joint which has the mortar raked out to a specified depth while the mortar is still green.

rake molding: A gable molding with a longer face than that of the eaves molding. The face of the *rake molding* is worked out so that it will line up with the eaves molding.

rake or raking bond: In masonry, a

method of laying the courses of brick in an angular or zigzag fashion, as is often seen in the end walls of Colonial houses. See *herringbone bond.*

rake out: In masonry, the removal of loose mortar by scraping, in preparation for pointing of the joints.

raking course: In masonry, a course of bricks laid diagonally between the face courses of a specially thick wall for the purpose of adding strength to the wall.

rammer: In building construction, a term applied to an instrument which is used for driving anything by force, as stones or piles, or for compacting earth; in concrete work, a kind of "stomper," used to pack concrete by removing the air bubbles.

ramp: A sloping roadway or passageway; also, a term used in architecture when referring to a short bend, slope, or curve usually in the vertical plane where a handrail, coping, or the like changes direction.

ramp and twist: In masonry, a term used when referring to work in which a surface both twisting and rising has to be, or is produced.

random ashlar: In masonry, a type of ashlar construction where the building blocks are laid apparently at random, but actually are placed in a definite pattern which is repeated again and again. See *ashlar*, Fig. 4.

random shingles: Shingles of different widths banded together; these often vary from 2½ inches to 12 inches or more in width.

random work: Any type of work done in irregular order, as a wall built up of odd-sized stones.

ranged rubble: Masonry built of rough fragments of broken stone or unsquared or rudely dressed stones, irregular in size and shape. See *rubble work.*

ranger: A horizontal bracing member used in form construction. Also called a *whaler* or *waler*. See Fig. 56.

rangework: Squared stone laid in horizontal courses of even height; same as *coursed ashlar;* also known as ranged masonry.

ratchet bit brace: A carpenter's tool consisting of a bit brace with a ratchet attachment which permits operation of the tool in close quarters.

ratchet drill: A hand drill which is rotated by a ratchet wheel moved by a pawl and lever.

ratchet wheel: A wheel with angular teeth on the edge, into which a pawl drops or catches, to prevent a reversal of motion.

ratio: The relation between two similar magnitudes in respect to the number of times the first contains the second, either integrally or fractionally, as the *ratio* of 3 to 4 may be written 3:4 or 3/4.

rat stop: A type of construction for a masonry wall which provides protection against rats by stopping them when they attempt to burrow down along the outside of the foundation.

Rawlplug: A fastener or holding device used in wood, glass, masonry, plaster, tile, brick, concrete, metal, or other materials. These devices are made of longitudinal strands of tough jute fiber compressed into a tubular form. See Fig. 1.

rebate: A woodworking term used when referring to a recess in or near the edge of one piece of timber to receive the edge of another piece cut to fit it; that is, a rabbet groove.

recess: An indention in the surface of a room as an alcove or bay window.

reeding: A general architectural term applied to various kinds of ornamental molding; for example, a small convex or semicylindrical molding resembling a reed; also, a set of such moldings as on a column; any ornamentation consisting of such moldings.

reflective insulation: Foil-surfaced insulation whose insulating power is determined by the number of its reflective surfaces, and which must be used in connection with an air space. This type of insulation also acts as a vapor barrier.

reinforced: To strengthen by the addition of new material, or extra material, for the reinforcement of concrete, iron or steel rods are embedded to give additional strength.

reinforced concrete: Concrete which has been strengthened by iron or steel bars embedded in it.

reinforced concrete construction: A type of building in which the principal structural members, such as floors, columns, and beams, are made of concrete, which is poured around isolated steel bars, or steel meshwork, in such a way that the two materials act together in resisting force.

reinforcing steel: Steel bars used in concrete construction for giving added strength; such bars are of various sizes and shapes.

rendering: A term used in perspective drawing meaning to finish with ink or color to bring out the effect of the design.

reticulated: In masonry, work in which the courses are arranged like the meshes of a net; work constructed or faced with diamond-shaped stones, or of stones arranged diagonally.

return nosing: In the building of stairs, the mitered, overhanging end of a tread outside the balusters. See Fig. 50.

reveal: In architecture, that part of a jamb or vertical face of an opening for a window or doorway, between the frame and the outside surface of a wall; also, a term sometimes applied to the entire jamb or vertical face of an opening.

revolving door: A type of door commonly used in entrances to department stores or public buildings; a door with four vanes operating in a curved frame and mounted on a central vertical axis about which it revolves.

revolving shelf: Sometimes called a *Lazy Susan,* this shelf revolves to provide easy access to the total shelf area. It is often placed in a closet, especially in the ordinarily unusable corners where two cabinets meet each other at right angles.

ribbon strip: A term used in building for a board which is nailed to studding for carrying floor joists.

ribbon windows: Two or more adjacent windows, each longer than it is high; usually placed with sills five feet or more above floor level.

rich lime: A quicklime which is free from impurities; used especially for plastering and for masonry work. Also called *fat lime.*

ridge: The intersection of two surfaces forming an outward projecting angle, as at the top of a roof where two slopes meet. The highest point of a roof composed of sloping sides. See Fig. 47.

ridge capping: The covering of wood or metal which tops the ridge of a roof.

ridge pole: The horizontal member, or timber, at the top of a roof, which receives the upper ends of the rafters.

ridge roof: A roof whose end view is a gable and whose rafters meet in an apex.

ridge tiles: Tiles used to cap the ridge of a roof.

ridge ventilator: A raised section on a roof ridge, provided with vents which admit air currents.

right angle: An angle formed by two lines which are perpendicular to each other; that is, the lines represent two radii that intercept a quarter of a circle, hence, is a 90-degree angle.

right line: The shortest distance between two points; that is, a straight line.

ring shake: A separation of the wood between the annual growth rings of a tree. See *annual growth rings,* Fig. 2.

ripping: In woodworking, the sawing or splitting of wood lengthwise of the grain or fiber.

riprap: In masonry construction, broken stones or other similar material, thrown together loosely and without definite order, for a sustaining bed where a foundation wall is to be formed on soft earth or under deep water.

ripsaw: A saw having coarse, chisel-shaped teeth used in cutting wood in the direction of the grain.

rise: The distance through which anything rises, as the *rise* of a stair, the *rise* of a roof. Also, the vertical distance between the springing of an arch and the highest point of the *intrados.* See Fig. 24.

rise and run: A term used by carpenters to indicate the degree of incline.

riser: A vertical board under the tread of a stair step; that is, a board set on edge for connecting the treads of a stairway. See Fig. 50.

rod: A polelike stick of timber used by carpenters as a measuring device for determining the exact height of risers in a flight of stairs; sometimes called a *story rod.*

rolling partitions: This type of partition is made up of narrow slats, tongue-and-grooved with one another along the edges, which roll up on a shaft when passage is desired. They may be set either horizontally or vertically. See *folding door or partition.*

roll-up door: Constructed in horizontally hinged sections, and usually made of wood, these doors are equipped with springs, tracks, counterbalancers, and other hardware which pull the sections into an overhead position, clear of the opening. They are often motor-operated with manual, radio, or magnetic driver controls, and are commonly used on garages. See *tilt-up doors.*

roll-up screen: A type of metal or plastic window screen installed on the inside of a window frame, which may be rolled up on tracks along the window's sides for full daylight and view. It can be left in place all year round.

roman brick: A *solid masonry unit* whose nominal dimensions are 2″ x 4″ x 12″. The nominal dimensions vary from the specified dimensions by the addition of the thickness of the mortar joint with which the unit is designed to be laid, but not more than ½ inch. The specified dimensions of Roman Brick are 1⅝″ x 3¾″ x 11¾″. Roman brick is sometimes made 16 inches or more in length to suit various construction needs.

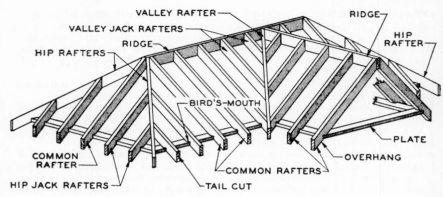

VALLEY RAFTER

VALLEY JACK RAFTERS

RIDGE

HIP RAFTERS

RIDGE

HIP RAFTER

BIRD'S-MOUTH

PLATE

OVERHANG

COMMON RAFTER

COMMON RAFTERS

HIP JACK RAFTERS

TAIL CUT

Fig. 47. Roof Members

roof members: In building construction, the various parts or members which compose a roof, as the framing members. The names of important *roof members* are given in Fig. 47.

roof truss: The structural support for a roof, consisting of braced timbers or structural iron fastened together for strengthening and stiffening this portion of a building.

room divider: A temporary curtain wall such as a *folding partition,* or permanent partition, which may or may not reach from floor to ceiling, as a bookcase or cabinet with *planter box.* These partitions serve to block off activity areas in a room, for various needs, while providing for flexibility of function.

rose window: A circular window decorated with ornamental designs similar to those found in the head of a Gothic window or in some ornate styles of vaulting; also, an ornamental circular window adorned with roselike tracery or mullions radiating from the center.

rosette: In architecture, any rounded ornament resembling a rose in the arrangement of its parts; any circular roselike unit of ornamentation with mullions or tracery radiating from the center; also, a decorative unit similar to a roundel filled with leaflike ornaments.

rostrum: A platform or stage on which a public speaker stands, such as a pulpit.

rotunda: A round-shaped building, or circular room, covered by a cupola or dome.

roughcast: A term used in the building trade for a kind of plastering, made of lime mixed with shells or pebbles, applied to the outside of buildings.

rough rubble: In masonry, a wall composed of unsquared field stones laid without regularity of coursing, but well bonded.

rout: A term in woodworking for cutting or gouging out material with a tool called a *router,* which is a special type of smoothing plane.

router: A two-handled woodworking tool used for smoothing the face of depressed surfaces, such as the bottom of grooves or any other depressions parallel with the surface of a piece of work.

routing: The cutting away of any unnecessary parts that would interfere with the usefulness or mar the appearance of a piece of millwork.

rowlock: In masonry, a term applied to a course of bricks laid on edge. Also, the end of a brick showing on the face of a brick wall in a vertical position. See Fig. 19.

rowlock-back wall: In masonry, a wall whose external face is formed of bricks laid flat in the ordinary manner, while the backing is formed of bricks laid on edge.

rubbing stone: In masonry, a stone used by bricklayers to smooth bricks which are designed for some particular purpose in a structure, as in a *gauged arch.*

rubble: Rough broken stones or bricks used to fill in courses of walls, or for other filling; also, rough broken stone direct from the quarry.

rubble concrete: In masonry work, a form of concrete reinforced by broken stones, especially that used in massive construction, such as solid masonry dams; also, masonry construction composed of large stone blocks set about six inches apart in fine cement concrete, and faced with squared rubble or ashlar.

rubble masonry: Masonry walls built of unsquared or rudely squared stones, irregular in size and shape; also, uncut stone used for rough work, such as for backing of unfinished masonry walls.

ruberoid roofing: A covering for roofs and exterior side walls. It is a manufactured material, patented and sold under the trade name of *ruberoid,* by the Ruberoid Company.

rubrication: The coloring, especially in red, of a background by use of enamel or paint.

rule joint: In woodworking, a pivoted joint where two flat strips are joined end to end so that each strip will turn or fold only in one direction; an example is the ordinary two-foot folding rule used by carpenters and other woodworkers.

running bond: In masonry, a form of bond used largely for internal partition walls in which every brick is laid as a stretcher, with each vertical joint lying between the centers of the stretchers above and below, making angle closers unnecessary. Same as *stretcher* or *stretching bond.* See, also, *chimney bond.*

run of stairs: A term used when referring to the horizontal part of a stair step, without the nosing; that is, the horizontal distance between the faces of two risers, or the horizontal distance of a flight of stairs. This is found by multiplying the number of steps by the width of the treads. If there are 14 steps each 10 inches wide, then 14×10 equals 140 inches or 11 feet 8 inches, which is the *run of the stairs.*

run of work: A term used in reference to a steady run of jobs following one another in rapid succession; also, applied to a type of job which calls for the repeated production of a quantity of the same kind of article.

rustication: In building and masonry, the use of squared or hewn stone blocks with roughened surfaces and edges deeply beveled or grooved to make the joints conspicuous.

rustic beveled work: Masonry in which the face of the stones are smooth and parallel to the face of the wall. The angles are beveled to an angle of 135°, with the face of the stone so that, when two stones come together on the wall, the beveling forms an internal right angle.

rustic joint: In masonry, a sunken joint between building stones.

rustics: In masonry, bricks which have a rough-textured surface, often multicolored.

S

safe carrying capacity: In the building industry, a term used with reference to construction of any piece or part so it will carry the weight, or load, it is designed to support, without breaking down.

sag: To droop or settle downward, especially in the middle, because of weight or pressure; also, the departure from original shape, a dragging down by its own weight, as a sagging door.

salon: A large, more or less elegant reception room where guests are entertained; also, more commonly, in the United States, an exhibit room where various works of art are displayed.

sandpaper: An abrasive paper, made by coating a heavy paper with fine sand or other abrasives held in place by some adhesive such as glue, used for polishing surfaces and finishing work.

sandstone: A building stone, usually quartz, composed of fine grains of sand cemented together with silica, oxide of iron, or carbonate of lime. *Grindstones* are made of sandstone in its natural state.

Sanitas: A wall covering somewhat similar to lightweight oilcloth, manufactured and sold under the trade name of *Sanitas.*

sap: In woody plants, the watery circulating fluid which is necessary to their growth.

sap streaks: Streaks showing through a finished wood surface which contains sapwood. Such streaks must be *toned out* in order to secure a uniform finish.

sapwood: The wood just beneath the bark of a tree, that is, the young soft wood consisting of living tissues outside the heartwood.

sash: A framework in which window panes are set. See Fig 20.

sash bars: In building, the strips which separate the panes of glass in a window sash.

sash chain: In a double-hung window sash, the chain which carries the weights; used especially on heavy sash. Same as *sash cord.*

sashless window: Panes of glass which slide along parallel tracks in the window frame toward one another, to leave openings at the sides, are used as windows; also fixed pane sashless windows are often used for picture and clerestory windows as well as other purposes. Sliding panes lift out for cleaning; panes, tracks, and frame are designed for moisture proofing and scratchless sliding.

sash pin: A heavy gauge barbed headless nail or pin used to fasten the mortise-and-tenon joints of window sash and doors.

sash pulley: In a window frame, the small pulley over which the sash cord or chain runs. See Fig. 20.

sash weight: An iron bar or cylinder attached to a window sash as a counterweight or balance, which holds the

window in position when it is raised or lowered. See Fig. 20.

saw arbor: The spindle, or shaft, on which a circular saw is mounted.

saw bench: A table or framework for carrying a circular saw.

saw gullet: The throat at the bottom of the teeth of a circular saw.

saw gumming: Shaping the teeth of a circular saw. Usually a grinding process.

sawhorse: A rack, or frame, for holding wood while it is being sawed; also, the ordinary trestle on which wood or boards are laid by carpenters for sawing by hand.

saw set: An instrument used for giving set to saw teeth.

saw-toothed skylight: In architecture, a term applied to a skylight roof with its profile shaped like the teeth of a saw.

saw trimmer: A machine used for sawing and trimming metal plates.

sawyer: One whose occupation is that of sawing wood or other material; sometimes used in a restricted sense meaning one who operates one of several saws.

scabble: The dressing down of the roughest irregularities and projections of stone which is to be used for rubble masonry. A stone ax or scabbling hammer is used for this work.

scaffold: An elevated, and usually temporary, platform for supporting workmen, their tools, and material while working on a building.

scagliola: An imitation of ornamental marble, consisting of a base of finely ground gypsum, mixed with an adhesive such as a hard cement, and variegated on the surface while in a plastic condition, with chips of marble or with colored graphite dust. When this mixture is hardened, it is finished with a high polish and used for floors, columns, and other interior work.

scale: An instrument with graduated spaces for measuring; also, a term applied to the outside covering, or coating, of a casing. In lumbering, estimating the amount of standing timber.

scaled drawing: A plan made according

to a scale, smaller than the work which it represents but to a specified proportion which should be indicated on the drawing.

scantling: A piece of timber of comparatively small dimensions, as a 2x3 or 2x4, used for studding.

scarf joint: The joining of two pieces of timber, by notching and lapping the ends, then fastening them with straps or bolts.

scissors truss: In architecture, a type of truss used in roof framing; so named from its resemblance to a pair of scissors. It is often used for supporting roofs over hallways and in construction of church roofs.

sconce: A decorative bracket projecting from a wall for holding candles.

scoring: To mark with lines, scratches, and grooves across the grain of a piece of wood with any kind of steel instrument, for the purpose of making the surface rough enough to make it a firmer joint when glued.

scotch: In masonry, a tool resembling a small pick with a flat cutting edge, used for trimming brick to a particular shape. Same as *scutch*.

scotia: A concave molding as at the base of a pillar or column; so called because of the dark shadow it casts. From the Greek word *skotia* meaning *darkness*.

scratch awl: A tool used by shopworkers for marking on metal or wood. It is made from a sharp-pointed piece of steel.

scratch coat: The first coat of plastering applied to a wall.

"SCR brick": A *solid masonry unit* whose greater thickness permits the use of a single wythe in construction. Its nominal dimensions, which vary from the specified dimensions by the addition of the thickness of the mortar joint with which the unit is designed to be laid (but not more than ½ inch), are 6″ x 2⅔″ x 12″. See Fig. 48.

screeds: Narrow strips of plaster put on a wall as guides for the workmen. The strips usually are about 8 inches wide with a thickness of two coats of plaster, serving also as thickness guides when applying the remainder of the plastering; also a strip of wood to act as a guide for plaster or concrete work.

screenings: In masonry, when mixing

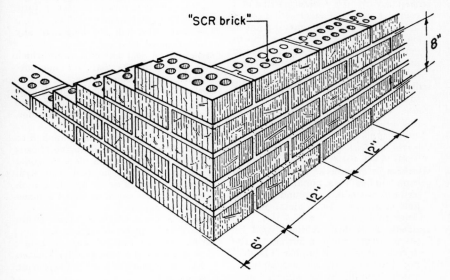

"SCR brick"

8″

12″

12″

6″

Fig. 48. SCR Brick

screw anchor [76] settlement

mortar, the coarse part of the sand, such as pebbles, which does not run through the screen.

screw anchor: A metal shell much like that used with an *expansion bolt,* which expands and wedges itself into the hole drilled for it. Also, like the expansion bolt, it is used to fasten light work to masonry construction. See *Rawlplug anchor,* Fig. 1.

screw chuck: A contrivance for holding work in a wood-turning lathe, with a projecting screw as live center.

screw clamp: A woodworker's clamp consisting of two parallel jaws and two screws; the clamping action is obtained by means of the screws, one operating through each jaw.

screw driver: A woodworker's tool used for driving in or removing screws by turning them. The tool is made of a well-tempered steel bar or rod flattened at one end to fit into the slots of screw heads. The steel bar is then fitted into a handle made of tough wood reinforced to prevent splitting.

screw eye: A screw with the head shaped into a completely closed ring or circle, forming a loop or eye.

scriber: A carpentry tool, consisting of a compass of pressed steel with a pencil in one leg or end and a metal point in the other leg; used to draw a line to mark the irregularities of a surface in fitting cabinets or other trim members to the wall or floor.

scribing: Marking and fitting woodwork to an irregular surface.

scutch: In masonry, a bricklayer's cutting tool used for dressing and trimming brick to special shapes. It resembles a small pick and is sometimes called a *scotch.*

scutcheon or **escutcheon:** In carpentry, a term applied to a metal shield used to protect wood, as around the keyhole of a door; also, a metal plate of a decorative character.

seasoning of lumber: A term used by woodworkers when referring to the drying out of green lumber. The drying process may be accomplished either naturally by allowing the lumber to dry in the air while sheltered from the weather under a shed, or the wood may be dried artificially in an oven, or kiln, specially prepared for that purpose.

seconds: In masonry, bricks which are similar to cutters, but having a slightly uneven color. See *cutters.*

sectional view: A drawing that shows the internal detail of a building, but supposes the building to be cut through in sections to exhibit certain features, such as wall thicknesses, sizes and designs of interior doors, fittings, and thickness of floors or other parts.

segment: Any portion of a whole which is divided into parts, as when an apple is cut into quarters each quarter is a *segment.* In geometry, a term specially applied to the portion of a circular plane bounded by a chord and an arc; for example, the diameter of a circular plane divides the plane into two equal segments.

segmental arch: A type of masonry construction where the curve of an arch though an arc, or segment, or a circle is always less than a semicircle.

self-faced: In masonry, a term applied to stone, such as flagstone, which splits along natural cleavage planes and does not require dressing.

semichord: One-half the length of any chord of an arc.

semicircle: A segment of a circle which is bound by the diameter and one-half of the circumference.

semicircular arch: In architecture, a type of masonry construction where the curve of an arch, that is the intrados, forms a half circle.

set: In woodworking, a term applied to a small tool used for setting nail heads below the surface of a piece of work; also, a term used in connection with the adjusting of some part of a tool, as to *set* saw teeth, or to *set* a plane bit. See *nail set.*

set-off: A horizontal line shown where a wall is reduced in thickness.

settle: A long wooden seat, or bench with arms and a high solid back, often having an enclosed foundation serving as a chest.

settlement: A term used in the building

industry for an unequal sinking or lowering of any part of a structure, which may be caused by the use of unseasoned lumber, by skimping in material, by the weakness of the foundation, or settlement of earth.

serration: A formation resembling the toothed edge of a saw.

shake: A defect in timber such as a fissure or split, causing a separation of the wood between the annual growth rings. See *windshake*, Fig. 57.

shakes: In the building industry, a term applied to a type of handmade shingles.

sheathing: In construction work, a term usually applied to wide boards nailed to studding or roofing rafters, as a foundation for the covering of the outer surface of the side walls or roof of a house. See Fig. 7.

shed: A one-story structure for shelter or storage, often open on one side. It may be attached to another building but frequently stands apart from other structures.

sheeting: In construction work, a term synonymous with *sheathing*.

shell construction: Construction in which the structure and enclosure are one, instead of consisting of a framework to carry a load, and a covering to keep out the weather. It may be built of steel, tile, wood, or other material, but reinforced concrete is most often used. A structure of this type derives its strength from the calculated distribution of tension, compression, and shear stresses over the entire thickness of the shell through shapes and balance. This method of load calculation cuts down or completely eliminates extra supports and bending of elements, as found in other construction, permitting the shell itself to be much thinner. Shells have a great capacity for carrying unbalanced loads, great reserve strength when damaged, and provide great economy in use of materials. They are particularly well adapted for roofs, which may be of different shapes. Some of the shapes used are: long barrels; short barrels; domes; umbrella in tension; and, umbrella in compression. Related types of construction are geodesic, box frame, and *post and beam*.

shingles: Thin pieces of wood, or other material, oblong in shape and thinner at one end, used for covering roofs or walls. The standard thicknesses of wood shingles are described as 4/2, 5/2¼, and 5/2, meaning, respectively, 4 shingles to 2 inches of butt thickness, 5 shingles to 2¼ inches of butt thickness, and 5 shingles to 2 inches of butt thickness. Lengths may be 16, 18, or 24 inches. Wood shingles may be bought in random widths or dimensioned.

shiplap: In carpentry, a term applied to lumber that is edge dressed to make a close rabbeted or lapped joint.

shopwork: Any type of work performed mechanically in a shop.

shore: A piece of lumber placed in an oblique direction to support a building temporarily; also, to support as with a prop of stout timber.

shoring: The use of timbers to prevent the sliding of earth adjoining an excavation; also, the timbers used as bracing against a wall for temporary support.

short length: A term used by woodworkers when referring to lumber which measures less than 8 feet in length.

show rafter: An architectural term applied to a short rafter which may be seen below the cornice; often an ornamental rafter.

side cut: Both *hip* and *valley rafters* must have an angle cut, called a *side cut*, to fit against the *ridge* or *common rafter* at the top.

siding: In the building industry, a term applied to boards used for forming the outside walls of frame buildings. See *bevel*, also *drop siding*.

sieve: In masonry, a screen or open container with a mesh bottom; used for removing stones and large particles from sand.

silica brick: In building, a refractory material made from quartzite bonded with milk of lime; used where resistance to high temperature is desired.

sill: The lowest member beneath an opening, such as a window or door; also, the horizontal timbers which form the lowest members of a frame supporting the superstructure of a house, bridge, or other structure. See Fig. 7.

sill anchor: In building construction, a bolt embedded in the concrete or masonry foundation for the purpose of anchoring the sill to the foundation; sometimes called a *plate anchor*. See *anchor bolt*, Fig. 12.

sill high: The distance from the ground level to the window sill. In masonry, the height from floor to sill.

single-pole switch: An electric device for making or breaking one side of an electric current.

site: The local position of a house or town in relation to its environment.

skewback: A sloping surface against which the end of an arch rests; that is, the course of masonry against which the end of the arch abuts.

skewback saw: A curved-back handsaw made to lessen its weight without sacrificing stiffness.

skew chisel: A woodworking tool with a straight cutting edge, sharpened at an angle, used in wood turning.

skew nailing: A carpentry term referring to the driving of nails on a slant, or obliquely. See *toenailing*.

skintled brickwork: In masonry, an irregular arrangement of bricks with respect to the normal face of a wall. The bricks are set in and out so as to produce an uneven effect on the surface of the wall; also, a rough effect caused by mortar being squeezed out of the joints.

skirting: The same as baseboard, that is, a finishing board which covers the plastering where it meets the floor of a room.

skylight: An opening in a roof or ceiling for admitting daylight; also, the window fitted into such an opening.

slab: A relatively thin slice of any material, such as stone, marble, or concrete; also, a term applied to the outside piece cut from a log.

slag cement: An artificial cement made by first chilling slag from blast furnaces in water, then mixing and grinding the granulated slag with lime, a process which produces a cement with hydraulic properties.

slag concrete: A concrete in which blast-furnace slag is used as an aggregate. Relatively light in weight, *slag concrete* is used in almost every type of construction, and is also valued because of its fire-resistant properties, as well as for its insulating qualities against cold and sound.

slag sand: Any fine slag product, carefully graded, used as fine aggregate in mortar or concrete.

slag wool: A material made by blowing steam through fluid slag. The final product is similar to asbestos in appearance and is used for insulating purposes.

slaked lime: A crumbly mass of lime formed when quicklime is treated with water Same as *hydrated lime*.

slamming stile: A term used in carpentry when referring to the upright strip, at the side of a door opening, against which the door slams, or against which it abuts when closed; also, the strip into which the bolt on the door slips when the lock is turned.

sledge: A heavy hammer having a long handle, usually wielded with both hands and used for driving posts or other large stakes.

sleeper: A heavy beam or piece of timber laid on, or near, the ground for receiving floor joists and to support the superstructure; also, strips of wood, usually 2x2, laid over a rough concrete floor, to which the finished wood floor is nailed.

sleeper clips: Sheet-metal strips used to anchor wood flooring to concrete. See *anchors*, Fig. 1.

sliding doors: Doors hung from an overhead track on which the panels are wheeled into a special recess at the sides to clear the opening. A related construction operates on a scissors type suspension attached to the narrow strip of wall at the inner end of the recess, and to that edge of the door which first enters the recess when it is pushed.

slip joint: In masonry, especially in brickwork, a type of joint made where a new wall is joined to an old wall by cutting a channel or groove in the old wall to receive the brick of the new wall. This method of joining the two walls forms a kind of telescopic, nonleaking joint.

slip sill: In the building trade, a term applied to a simple sill consisting of a stone slab just as long as the window is wide, and fitting into the walls between the window jambs. The *slip sill* differs from the *lug sill,* which is longer than the width of the window opening and is *let in* to the wall on each side. See *lug sill.*

slip stone: An oilstone used in wood turning and wood patternmaking for sharpening gouges. The small wedge-shaped stone has rounded edges and can be conveniently held in one hand while whetting a tool.

sloyd knife: A type of woodworker's knife used in the sloyd system of manual training. A special feature of this system, which originated in Sweden, is the use of wood carving as a means of acquiring skill in the use of woodworking tools. The Swedish sloyd system was a forerunner of the American manual-training system.

smoothing plane: A small woodworking plane, usually not more than 9 inches in length, with a varying iron width measuring from 1¼ inches to 2¼ inches. It is used principally for smoothing and finishing surfaces.

sneck: A small stone used to fill in between larger stones, as in rubblework masonry; also, a term sometimes applied to the laying of a rubble-work wall, or snecked wall.

snecked masonry: A term applied to rubble walls in which the stones are roughly squared but of irregular sizes, and not arranged in courses.

socket chisel: A woodworker's tool of great strength and with sharp cutting edges on each side. Usually the upper

end of the shank terminates in a socket into which the handle is driven. In the best quality tools of this type, the blade and socket are forged in one piece with no welded socket.

socle: An architectural term applied to a projecting member at the base of a supporting wall or pier, or at the bottom of a pedestal or column.

soffit: The underside of any subordinate member of a building, such as the under surface of an arch, cornice, or stairway.

soffit vent: An opening in the underside of a roof overhang which acts as a passageway into the house for air currents.

soil stack: In a plumbing system, the main vertical pipe which receives waste material from all fixtures.

soldier course: In masonry, a term applied to a course of bricks where they are laid so that they are all standing on end. See Fig. 19.

sole: In carpentry, a term applied to a horizontal foot piece on the bottom of a wall to which the studs are nailed.

solid masonry unit: A masonry unit whose cross-sectional area in every plane parallel to the bearing surface is 75 per cent or more of its gross cross-sectional area measured in the same plane.

soot pocket: In chimney construction, an extension of a flue opening to a depth of 8 or 10 inches below the smoke-pipe entrance. The pocket thus formed prevents soot from collecting in the smoke pipe.

sound knot: A term used in woodworking when referring to any knot so firmly fixed in a piece of lumber that it will continue to hold its position even when the piece is worked; also, is solid across its face and hard as the wood encircling it.

spall: A fragment or chip of stone or brick, especially bad or broken brick; in masonry, to reduce an irregular stone block to approximately the desired size by chipping with a stone hammer. Also spelled *spawl.* See *gallet.*

span: The distance between the abut-

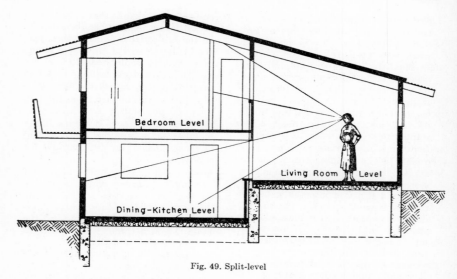

Fig. 49. Split-level

ments of an arch or the space between two adjoining arches (Fig. 34); also, the distance between the wall, or rafter, plates of a building.

spandrel: The space between the exterior curve of an arch and the enclosing right angle; or the triangular space between either half of the extrados of an arch and the rectangular molding enclosing the arch.

spike: In the building trade, a term commonly applied to a large-sized nail usually made of iron or steel, used as a fastener for heavy lumber.

spike knot: In woodworking, a knot sawed lengthwise.

spire: In architecture, a tapering tower or roof; any elongated structural mass shaped like a cone or pyramid; also, the topmost feature of a steeple.

spirit level: An instrument used for testing horizontal or vertical accuracy of the position of any structural part of a building. The correct position is indicated by the movement of an air bubble in alcohol. See *level,* Fig. 35.

splash block: A small masonry block laid with the top close to the ground surface, to receive drainage of rain water from the roof and carry it away from the building.

splay: An inclined surface, as the slope or bevel at the sides of a door or window; also, to make a beveled surface, or to spread out, or make oblique.

splayed brick: A purpose-made brick having one side beveled off.

splay end: The end of a brick which is opposite the end laid squarely by rule.

split-level: A house in which two or more floors are usually located directly above one another, and one or more additional floors, adjacent to them, are placed at a different level. See Fig. 49.

spokeshave: A cutting tool, or plane, with a transverse blade set between two handles. This device is especially suitable for dressing rounded pieces of wood of small diameter, such as spokes or other similarly curved work.

spread footing: A footing whose sides slope gradually outward from the foundation to the base.

sprig: In woodworking, a term applied to a small brad with no head; also, one of the small triangular-shaped pieces of tin or zinc used for holding a pane of glass in a window sash.

springer: In architecture, a stone or other solid piece of masonry forming the impost of an arch; that is, the topmost member of a pillar or pier upon which the weight of the arch rests. See Fig. 34.

spring hinge: A joint with a spring built into it, used for self-closing doors, such as screen doors.

sprung molding: In carpentry, a term applied to a curved molding.

spar: A sharp-pointed carpenter's tool used for cutting veneer.

spur center: A term used by woodworkers when referring to the center used in the headstock of a woodturning lathe.

square: The multiplying of a number by itself; also, a plane figure of four equal sides, with opposite sides parallel, and all angles, right angles. Shingles for the trade are put up in bundles so packed that 4 bundles of 16- or 18-inch shingles, when laid 5 inches to the weather, will cover a *square* 10 by 10, or 100 square feet, and three bundles of 24-inch shingles will also cover a *square.* An instrument for measuring and laying out work is called a *framing square.* See also *steel square.*

square measure: The measure of areas in square units.

144 square inches= 1 square foot
(sq. in.) (sq. ft.)
9 square feet = 1 square yard
(sq. yd.)
30¼ square yards = 1 square rod (sq. rd.)
160 square rods = 1 acre (A.)
640 acres = 1 square mile (sq. mi.)
36 square miles = 1 township (twp.)

square root: A quantity of which the given quantity is the square, as 4 is the *square root* of 16, the given quantity.

squinch: A small arch built across an interior corner of a room for carrying the weight of a superimposed mass, such as the spire of a tower.

squint brick: In masonry, a brick which has been shaped or molded to a specially desired form; a purpose-made brick.

stabbing: In masonry a term used when referring to the process of making a brick surface rough in order to provide a key for plasterwork.

stack: In architecture, a large chimney usually of brick, stone, or sheet metal for carrying off smoke or fumes from a furnace, often a group of flues or

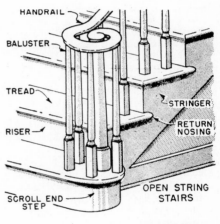

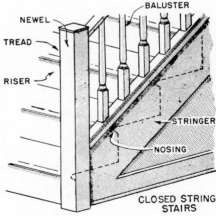

Fig. 50. Open and Closed String Stairs

chimneys embodied in one structure rising above a roof.

staff bead: In the building trades, a term applied to a strip of molding inserted between the masonry of a wall and a window frame, for protection against the weather.

staggered screeds: Wood screeds (2" x 4"), imbedded in mastic, are staggered below flooring, instead of sub-flooring, to provide nailing surface for floor boards. This method has been approved by the F.H.A. for oak flooring.

staging: In building construction, the same as scaffolding, that is, a temporary structure of posts and boards on which the workmen stand when their work is too high to be reached from the ground.

stair: One step in a flight of stairs. Also called a stairstep. See Fig. 50.

staircase: A flight of steps leading from one floor or story to another above. The term includes landings, newel posts, handrails, and balustrades. See Fig. 50.

stairs: In building, a term applied to a complete flight of steps between two floors. *Straight run stairs* lead directly from one floor to another without a turn; *close string stairs* have a wall on each side; *open string stairs* have one side opening on a hallway or room; *doglegged* or *platform stairs* have a landing near the top or bottom, introduced to change direction.

stair treads: The upper horizontal boards of a flight of steps. See Fig. 50.

stair well: A compartment extending vertically through a building, and in which stairs are placed.

staking out: A term used for the laying out of a building plan by driving stakes into the ground showing the location of the foundation. To insure a clean edge when excavating, the stakes are connected with strong cord indicating the building lines. See *batter boards,* Fig. 8.

standard brick: In masonry, common brick, size 2¼" x 3¾" x 8". Permissi-

ble variables are, plus or minus, 1/16" in depth, 1/8" in width, and 1/4" in length.

standard modular brick: A brick, size 2⅛" x 3½" x 7½", related to the 4-inch module, every 8 inches in height, if the mortar joint is ½ inch. Thus, 3 bricks, plus 3 one-half-inch joints, add up to an even 8 inches.

star drill: A tool with a star-shaped point used for drilling in stone or masonry.

Star Dryvin anchor: A type of *expansion anchor* used for securing wood structural parts to a masonry or concrete wall. See *anchors,* Fig. 1.

star expansion bolt: A bolt or screw having a shield of two semicircular parts which spread apart as the bolt is driven into the shield. Used for securing structural wood parts to a masonry wall.

starling: A protection about a bridge or pier made by driving piles close together to form an enclosure.

starting board: In form building, the first board nailed in position at the bottom of a foundation form.

starting newel: A post at the bottom of a staircase for supporting the balustrade. See Fig. 50.

starting step: The first step at the bottom of a flight of stairs. See Fig. 50.

steel forms: Removable pieces of steel which hold wet concrete in desired shapes for casting foundations, footings, and window frames on the spot. Some foundation formwork comes with interlocking modular hardware. Steel forms are said to last indefinitely, produce a clean, accurate face, and to be easier to set up and clean than wooden forms.

steel square: An instrument having at least one right angle and two or more straight edges, used for testing and laying out work for trueness. A term frequently applied to the large framing square used by carpenters.

steel wool: A mass of fine steel threads matted together and used principally for polishing and cleaning surfaces of wood or metal.

stepped footings: If a house is built on sloping ground, all the footings cannot be at the same depth, hence they are stepped.

stile: In carpentry, one of the vertical members in a door or sash, into which secondary members are fitted.

stilt house: A house which is constructed on stilts above the ground; used mostly in hot, moist regions and on very uneven ground level sites; provides breeze passage underneath, protection from insects, and space for car.

stirrup or **hanger:** In building trades, a term applied to any stirruplike drop support attached to a wall to carry the end of a beam or timber, such as the end of a joist. *Stirrups* or *hangers* may also be suspended from a girder as well as from a wall. See *hanger*.

stonecutter's chisel: A stonemason's tool used for dressing soft stone. Also called *tooth chisel*.

stonemason: In building, one who builds foundations and walls of stone.

stool: In architecture, a term applied to the base or support of wood at the bottom of a window, as the shelflike piece inside and extending across the lower part of a window opening. See Fig. 20.

stoop: A raised entrance platform, with steps leading up to it, at the door of a building; sometimes the term is applied to a porch or veranda.

stop: In building, any device which will limit motion beyond a certain point, as a doorstop in a building, usually attached near the bottom of a door and operated by pressure from the foot. See *doorstop*.

storm door: An extra outside, or additional, door for protection against inclement winter weather. Such a door also serves the purpose of lessening the chill of the interior of a building, making it easier to heat, and also helps to avoid the effects of wind and rain at the entrance doorway during milder seasons.

storm sash: An additional sash placed at the outside of a window for protection against the severe weather of winter.

story rod: A rod or pole cut to the proposed clear height between finished floor and ceiling. The *story rod* is often marked with minor dimensions, as for door trims.

stove bolt: A special type of bolt with a nut. Formerly such bolts were provided with a coarser thread pitch than a machine bolt; however, the only difference now is, that without a nut a stove bolt is called a *machine screw*.

straightedge: A bar of wood or metal with the edges true and parallel, used for testing straight lines and surfaces; that is, gauging the accuracy of work.

stretcher: In masonry construction, a term applied to a course in which brick or stone lies lengthwise; that is, a brick or stone is laid with its length parallel to the face of the wall.

stretcher bond: In masonry, a bond which consists entirely of stretchers, with each vertical joint lying between the centers of the stretchers above and below, so that angle closers are not required. This type of bond is used extensively for internal partition walls which have a thickness of a single tier of brick. See Fig. 11.

string: In building trades, a term applied to the inclined member which supports the treads and risers of a stair. Also called a *stringer*. See Fig. 50.

stringcourse or **sailing course:** In building, a horizontal band forming a part of the design, consisting of a course of brick or stone, projecting from a wall, for decorative purposes, or to break the plain effect of a large expanse of wall surface.

stringer: A long, heavy, horizontal timber which connects upright posts in a structure and supports a floor; also, the inclined member which supports the treads and risers of a stair. See Fig. 50.

strip: In the building trades, a term applied to a narrow piece of wood, relatively long, and usually of a uniform width; also, used when referring to the breaking, tearing, or stripping off the threads of a bolt or nut.

struck joint: In masonry, a mortar joint which is formed with a recess at the bottom of the joint. It is the reverse of the *weathered joint* shown in Fig. 32. The *struck joint* is used extensively, but chiefly for interior-wall surfaces, since it is inferior for outside joints because of its lack of weather-resisting qualities. The recess at the bottom allows water from rain or snow to seep into the wall.

structural clay tile: A term applied to various sizes and kinds of hollow and practically solid building units; molded from surface clay, shale, fire clay, or a mixture of these materials, and laid by masons. See *clay tile.*

structural glass: A vitreous finishing material used as a covering for masonry walls. It is available in rectangular plates which are held in position by a specially prepared mastic in which the plates are embedded.

strut tenon: A term applied to a piece of wood or iron, or some other member of a structure, designed to resist pressure or weight in the direction of its length; used on a diagonal piece, usually on heavy timbers, as a timber extending obliquely from a rafter to a king post. See *king post.*

stucco: Any of various plasters used as covering for walls; a coating for exterior walls in which cement is largely used; any material used for covering walls which is put on wet, but when dry becomes exceedingly hard and durable.

stud: In building, an upright member, usually a piece of dimension lumber, 2 x 4 or 2 x 6, used in the framework of a wall. On an inside wall the lath are nailed to the studs. On the outside of a frame wall, the sheathing boards are nailed to the studs. The height of a ceiling is determined by the length or height of the studs. See Figs. 7 and 12.

subbase: In architecture, the lowest part of a structural base, which consists of two or more horizontal members, as the base of a column; also, a *baseboard.*

subfloor: In carpentry, a term applied to a flooring of rough boards laid directly on the joists and serving the purpose of a floor during the process of construction on the building. When all rough construction work is completed, the finish floor is laid over the subfloor. See Figs. 7 and 12.

subrail: In building a closed string stair, a molded member called a *subrail* or *shoe* is placed on the top edge of the stair string to receive and carry the lower end of the balusters. See Fig. 50.

substructure: The lower portion of a structure forming the foundation which supports the superstructure of a building.

summer: In building, a large horizontal timber or stone; the lintel of a door or window; a stone forming the cap of a pier or column to support an arch; a girder; the principal timber, or beam, which carries the weight of a floor or partition.

sump: A pit or depression in a building where water is allowed to accumulate; for example, in a basement floor to collect seepage or a depression in the roof of a building for receiving rain water and delivering it to the downspout. A device used for removing water from such a depression is known as a *sump pump.*

sunk panels: A term used in the building trade, when referring to panels recessed below the surrounding surface.

supplement of an angle: An angle which is equal to the difference between the given angle and 180 degrees. If the given angle is 165 degrees its supplement is 15 degrees.

surbase: In architecture, a molding above a base, as that immediately above the baseboard of a room; also, a molding, or series of moldings, which crown the base of a pedestal.

S4S: An abbreviation for the term *surfaced on four sides.*

surfacing of lumber: In woodworking, symbols are used to indicate how lumber has been surfaced, as *S1E,* surfaced on one edge; *S1S,* surfaced on one side; *S2S,* surfaced on two sides, and so on.

surveying: That branch of applied mathematics dealing with the science of measuring land, the unit of measure being the surveyor's chain, with 80 chains equal to 1 mile.

swing saw: A woodworker's tool, consisting of a circular saw mounted on a hinged frame suspended from above. When needed, the saw is pulled to the work which remains stationary.

symmetrical: Pertaining to any plane or solid body or figure which is well-proportioned, with corresponding parts properly balanced and harmonious in all details; anything which exhibits symmetry in size, form, and arrangement of its parts.

T

table: In carpentry, the insertion of one timber into another by alternate projections or scores from the middle; same as a coak. In architecture, a flat surface of a wall, usually raised, as a *stringcourse,* especially a projecting band of stone or brick where an offset is required. See *water table,* Fig. 55.

tabling: In masonry, the forming of a type of horizontal joint by arranging various stones in a course so they will run into the next course, hence preventing them from slipping; in carpentry, the shaping of a projection on a piece of timber, so it will fit into a recess prepared to receive it in another timber.

tackle: A construction of blocks and ropes, chains, or cables used for hoisting purposes in heavy construction work. Often spoken of as *block and tackle.*

tail beam or tail joist: Any timber or joist which fits against the header joist.

tailing: In building construction, any projecting part of a stone or brick inserted in a wall.

tail joist: Any building joist with one end fitted against a header joist.

take-up: In shopworking, any equipment or device provided to tighten or take up slack, or to remove looseness in parts due to wear or other causes.

tamp: To pound down, with repeated light strokes, the loose soil thrown in as filling around a wall.

tape: Any flexible narrow strip of linen, cotton, or steel marked off with measuring lines similar to the scale on a carpenter's rule. Usually the tape is contained in a circular case into which it can easily be rewound after using.

tarpaulin: Any heavy material, usually canvas, waterproofed with tar or paint and used for covering purposes, such as hatches of ships or boats, or anything exposed to the weather.

taut: Anything tightly drawn until it is tense and tight, with all sag eliminated, as a rope, wire, or cord pulled *taut.*

T bevel: A woodworker's tool used for testing the accuracy of work cut at an angle such as a beveled edge. See Fig. 51.

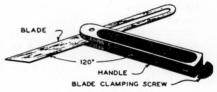

BLADE

120°

HANDLE

BLADE CLAMPING SCREW

Fig. 51. T Bevel

temperature stress rods: Steel rods placed horizontally in concrete slabs for prevention of cracks, due to temperature changes, drying, etc., parallel to the reinforcing rods. The rods are the same physically as reinforcing rods, and are usually laid at right angles to, and almost in, the same plane as reinforcing rods.

template: A gauge, commonly a thin board or light frame, used as a guide for forming work to be done.

tenon: In carpentry, a piece of lumber or timber cut with a projection, or tongue, on the end for fitting into a mortise. The joint formed by inserting a tenon into a mortise constitutes a so-called *mortise-and-tenon joint.*

tenon saw: In woodworking, any small backsaw used on the bench for cutting tenons.

terminal: In carpentry, the extremity of any structural part, especially the finish of a newel post, or standard; also, a carving used for decorative purposes at the end of some structural member, such as a pedestal.

termite shield: A protective shield made of noncorrosive metal, placed in or on a foundation wall, or other mass of masonry, or around pipes entering a building, to prevent passage of termites into the structure.

terrace: An elevated level surface of earth supported on one or more faces by a masonry wall, or by a sloping bank covered with turf.

terra cotta: A clay product used for ornamental work on the exterior of buildings; also, used extensively in making vases, and for decorations in statuettes. It is made of hard-baked clay in variable colors with a fine glazed surface.

terrazzo: A type of Venetian marble mosaic in which Portland cement is used as a matrix. Though used in buildings for centuries, *terrazzo* is a modern floor finish, used also for bases, borders, and wainscoting, as well as on stair treads, partitions, and other wall surfaces

terrazzo flooring: A term used in the building trades for a type of flooring made of small fragments of colored stone, or marble, embedded irregularly in cement. Finally, the surface is given a high polish.

tessellated: Formed of cubes of stone, marble, glass, or other suitable material (*tessera*), arranged in a checkered pattern, as in mosaic floors and pavements.

tessera: Any one of the small square pieces of marble, stone, tile, or glass used in mosaic work, such as in floors or pavements.

thermal unit: Any unit chosen for the calculation of quantities of heat; that is, a unit of measurement used as a standard of comparison of other

quantities of heat, such as *B.t.u.* (British thermal unit).

thermostat: An automatic device for regulating the temperature of a room by opening or closing the damper of a heating furnace.

T hinge: A type of joint with an abutting piece set at right angles to a strap, thus forming a **T**-shaped hinge, used mainly on outside work, such as barn doors and gates.

three-ply: Anything composed of three distinct layers or thicknesses, as plywood used in building construction or in furniture making, in which the material used consists of three separate plies or layers.

three-way switch: A switch used in house wiring when a light (or lights) is to be turned on or off from two places. A three-way switch must be used at each place.

threshold: In building construction, a term applied to the piece of timber, plank, or stone under a door.

through shake: A separation of wood between annual growth rings, extending between two faces of timber; similar to a *windshake*. See Fig. 57.

through stone: In stone masonry, a term applied to a stone which extends through a wall forming a bond.

thumb plane: In woodworking, a term sometimes applied to a small plane not more than 4 or 5 inches in length with a bit about 1 inch in width.

thumbscrew: A screw with its head so constructed that it can be turned easily with the thumb and finger.

tie: In architecture, anything used to hold two parts together, as a post, rod, or beam.

tie beam: A timber used for tying structural parts together, as in the roof of a building. Any beam which ties together or prevents the spreading apart of the lower ends of the rafters of a roof.

tile: A building material made of fired clay, stone, cement, or glass used for floors, roofing, and drains; also made in varied ornamental designs for decorative work.

tile hanging: A term applied to the

hanging of tile on a vertical surface, such as a wall, to protect the wall against dampness. See *weather tiling.*

tile setting adhesives: Specially formulated glues or mastics, used instead of mortarbed, for tile setting. They are said to be clean, waterproof, less expensive, and faster.

tile shell: A construction tile unit consisting of a number of hollow cells separated by webs.

tilt-up construction: A method of constructing walls, and sometimes floors, by pouring concrete, or putting wooden walls together in flat panels, and, when completed, moving them to the building site where they are tilted into permanent place.

tilt-up doors: Usually consisting of a rigid panel of sheet steel, aluminum, or wood, these doors are equipped with springs, tracks, counterbalances, and other hardware, which pull the door clear of the opening to an overhead position. They are often motor-operated, with manual, radio, or magnetic driver controls, and are commonly used on garages. See *roll-up doors.*

tin snips: A cutting instrument, such as the ordinary hand shears, used by sheet-metal workers.

toeing: In carpentry, the driving of nails or brads obliquely; also, to clinch nails so driven. See Fig. 29.

toenailing: The driving of a nail, spike, or brad slantingly to the end of a piece of lumber to attach it to another piece, especially as, in laying a floor, to avoid having the heads of the nails show above the surface. See Fig. 29.

tongue: A projecting rib cut along the edge of a piece of timber so it can be fitted into a groove cut in another piece. See Fig. 30. Also, the shorter of the two extending arms of the *framing square,* usually 16 inches long and 1½ inches wide. The *blade* of the square forms a right angle with the *tongue.* The *octagon scale* and the *brace measure scale* appear on the faces of the tongue.

tooled joints: In masonry, mortar joints which are specially prepared by compressing and spreading the mortar after it has set slightly. *Tooled joints* present the best weathering properties, and include the *weathered joint,* V *joint,* and *concave joint.* See Fig. 32.

tooth chisel: A chisel especially designed for cutting stone; same as *stonecutter's chisel.*

toothing: In masonry construction, the allowing of alternate courses of brick to project toothlike to provide for a good bond with any adjoining brickwork which may follow.

topping: A mixture of cement, sand, and water, used in creating the finished surface of concrete work such as walks and floors. See Fig. 23.

topping joint: In concrete finishing, a space or break of about ⅛" made at regular intervals, particularly over expansion joints, to allow for contraction and expansion in the topping layer of sidewalks, driveways, and similar structures. See Fig. 23.

torus: In architecture, a type of molding with a convex portion which is nearly semicircular in form, used extensively as a base molding.

tower: A structure whose height is proportionally much greater than its width, often surmounting a large building, such as a cathedral or church, usually less tapering than a steeple. A *tower* may stand alone entirely apart from any other building.

T plate: A T-shaped metal plate commonly used as a splice; also used for stiffening a joint where the end of one beam abuts against the side of another.

tracery: An architectural term applied to any delicate ornamental work consisting of interlacing lines such as the decorative designs carved on panels or screens; also, the intersecting of ribs and bars, as in rose windows, and the upper part of Gothic windows; any decorative design suggestive of network.

trammel: An instrument used for drawing arcs or radii too great for the capacity of the ordinary compass; a *beam compass* with adjustable points attached to the end of a bar of wood or metal used by draftsmen and shopworkers for describing unusually large circles or arcs.

transit: An instrument, commonly used by surveyors, consisting of four principal parts: (1) a telescope for sighting; (2) a spirit level; (3) a vernier or graduated arc for measuring vertical or horizontal angles; and (4) a tripod with leveling screws for adjusting the instrument.

transite: A fireproofing material used in walls, roofs, and for lining ovens. It is composed of asbestos and Portland cement molded under high pressure and is sold under the trade name of *transite.*

transom: A term used in building for any small window over a door or another window.

transom bar: A crossbar of wood or stone which divides an opening horizontally into two parts.

trap door: A covering for an opening in a floor, ceiling, or roof; usually such a door is level, or practically so, with the surface of the opening which it covers.

trass: In plastering, a type of gray, yellow, or whitish earth common in volcanic districts, resembling puzzolano; used to give additional strength to lime mortars and plasters; also used in the making of hydraulic cement.

trass mortar: In masonry, a mortar made of lime, sand, and *trass* or brick dust; or a mortar composed of lime and *trass* without sand. The *trass* makes the mortar more suitable for use in structures exposed to water.

tread: In building, the upper horizontal part of a stair step; that portion of a step on which the foot is placed when mounting the stairs. See Fig. 50.

trefoil: In architecture, an ornamental three-lobed unit resembling in form the foliage of an herb whose leaf is divided into three distinct parts, such as the common varieties of clover.

treillage: A latticework erected for supporting vines, as in a vine arbor.

trellis: An ornamental structure of latticework over which vines are trained, such as a summerhouse, usually made of narrow strips of wood which cross each other at regular intervals.

trestle: A braced framework, usually consisting of a horizontal beam supported at each end by a pair of spreading legs which serve as braces.

trestle table: A large drawing board supported by trestles.

triangle: A *polygon* enclosed by three straight lines called sides.

triangular scale: A draftsman's three-faced measuring device having six graduated edges. On one edge is shown a scale of full-size measurements, while on the other edges are shown various reductions in scale.

triangular truss: A popular type of truss used for short spans, especially for roof supports.

trim: In carpentry, a term applied to the visible finishing work of the interior of a building, including any ornamental parts of either wood or metal used for covering joints between jambs and plaster around windows and doors. The term may include also the locks, knobs, and hinges on doors.

trimmer: The beam or floor joist into which a header is framed.

trimmer arch: A comparatively flat arch, such as may be used in the construction of a fireplace.

trimmer beam: Usually two joists spiked together around a fireplace opening in floor framing.

trimming joist: A timber, or beam, which supports a header.

triple brick: A *solid masonry unit* whose nominal dimensions, which include allowance for the mortar joint described for use with it, are 4″ x 5⅓″ x 12″.

trowel: A flat, steel tool used to spread and smooth mortar or plaster. Typical *trowels* are shown in Fig. 52.

truss: A combination of members, such as beams, bars, and ties, usually arranged in triangular units to form a rigid framework for supporting loads over a long span, as in bridges or massive roof construction.

trussed beam: An architectural term applied to a beam stiffened by a truss rod.

try square: A tool used for laying out right angles and for testing work for squareness.

T square: A tool used by draftsmen. It consists of a ruler usually from 2 to 3 inches in width and from 1 to 5 feet in length, with a crosspiece attached to one end of the ruler or blade. The crosspiece, or head, is at least twice as thick as the blade.

tubular scaffolds: Scaffolds for interior and exterior construction work, made of tube steel. These scaffolds are lightweight, offer low wind resistance, and are easily dismantled. They are obtainable in several strengths for varying heights and types of work.

tuck pointing: In masonry, the finishing of joints along the center lines, with a narrow parallel ridge of fine putty or fine lime mortar.

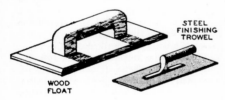

STEEL FINISHING TROWEL

WOOD FLOAT

Fig. 52. Trowels

turnbuckle: A type of coupling between the ends of two rods, used primarily for adjusting or regulating the tension in the rods which it connects. It consists of loop or sleeve with a screw thread on one end and a swivel at the other, or with an internal screw thread at each end.

turning gouge: In woodworking, a tool used for roughing down woodwork in a lathe. The widths of gouges vary from ¼ to 1½ inches.

turrets: Small towers, often merely ornamental features at an angle of a large building. Turrets frequently begin at some distance above the

ground, although they may rise from the ground or be built on corbels.

twelfth scale: A scale which divides the inch into 12 parts instead of 16; found usually on the back of the *framing square* along the outside edge. In this scale, one inch equals one foot. The *twelfth scale* makes it possible to reduce layouts to $\frac{1}{12}$ of their regular size and to solve basic right triangle problems.

twin brick: Modular brick related to the 4-inch module, every 12 inches in height. Size 2½″ x 7½″ x 7½″ A double-sized brick.

twist bit: In woodwork, a tool used for boring holes in wood for screws. A tool similar to the twist drill used for drilling holes in metal, except that the cutting edge of the *twist bit* is ground at a greater angle.

twist drill: A drilling tool having helical grooves extending from the point to the smooth portion of the shank. This type of drill is made of round stock with a shank that may be either straight or tapering. It is used for drilling holes in metal. A similar drill used for wood is known as a *twist bit.*

T wrench: A tool for tightening a nut on a bolt. The **T** wrench consists of a handle, or lever, with a **T**-shaped socket which fits over and completely encircles a nut or bolthead. It may or may not have a ratchet but it sometimes has an extension to permit working in places not easily accessible.

U

U bolt: An iron bar bent into a **U**-shaped bolt, with screw threads and nuts on each end. Often called a clip, as a spring clip on an automobile.

umbrella house: A house with a parasol roof, which may be lattice work, covering the main structure and terraces. There is space for the passage of air currents between the covering roof and the house structure.

unit length rafter table: A table which appears on the *blade* of the *framing square.* It gives unit lengths of *common rafters* for seventeen different rises, ranging from 2 to 18 inches. It also gives the unit lengths for *hip* or *valley rafters,* difference in lengths of *jack rafters* set 16 inches on center, jack rafters set 24 inches on center, and the *side cuts* for jack and hip rafters.

unsound knot: A term used by woodworkers when referring to a *knot* which is not as solid as the wood in the board surrounding it.

upright: In building, a term applied to a piece of timber which stands upright or in a vertical position, as the vertical pieces at the sides of a doorway or window frame.

V

valley: In architecture, a term applied to a depressed angle formed by the meeting at the bottom of two inclined sides of a roof, as a gutter; also, the space, when viewed from above, between vault ridges.

valley rafter: A rafter disposed in the internal angle of a roof to form a *valley* or depression in the roof. See Fig. 47.

vane: Any flat piece of metal attached to an axis and placed in an elevated position where it can be readily moved by the force of the wind, such as a weathercock on a barn or steeple, indicating the direction of the wind.

vault: In architecture, an arched structure of masonry usually forming a ceiling or roof; also, an arched passageway under ground, or any room or space covered by arches.

vaulting course: A course formed by the springers of a vault which usually are set with horizontal beds, either corbeled out or in projection.

veneer: Thin pieces of wood, or other material, used for finishing purposes to cover an inferior piece of material, thus giving a superior effect and greater strength with reduced cost.

veneer wall: A wall with a masonry facing which is not bonded, but is attached to a wall so as to form an integral part of the wall for purposes of load bearing and stability.

ventilating brick: A brick which has been cored to provide an air passage for ventilating purposes.

ventilation: The free circulation of air in a room or building; a process of changing the air in a room by either natural or artificial means; any provision made for removing contaminated air or gases from a room and replacing the foul air by fresh air.

vent pipe: A flue, or pipe, connecting any interior space in a building with the outer air for purposes of ventilation; any small pipe extending from any of the various plumbing fixtures in a structure to the vent stack.

vent stack: A vertical pipe connected with all vent pipes carrying off foul air or gases from a building. It extends through the roof and provides an outlet for gases and contaminated air, and also aids in maintaining a water seal in the trap.

veranda: An open portico, usually roofed, attached to the exterior of a building. In the United States commonly called a *porch.*

verge: The edge of tiling, slate, or shingles projecting over the gable of a roof, that on the horizontal portion being called the *eaves.*

verge board: The board under the verge of a gable, sometimes molded. During the latter part of the nineteenth century, *verge boards* were often richly adorned with decorative carving, perforations, and cusps, frequently having pendants at the apex. The term *verge board* is often corrupted into *bargeboard.*

vermiculated: Pertaining to stone or other material with designs worked on the surface, giving it the appearance of being worm-eaten.

vertical: Pertaining to anything, such as a structural member, which is upright in position, perpendicular to a horizontal member, and exactly plumb.

vestibule: A small entrance room at the outer door of a building; an anteroom sometimes used as a waiting room.

V & C V: An abbreviation for the term meaning **V** *grooved* and *center* **V** *grooved;* that is, the board is **V**

grooved along the edge and also center **V** grooved, on the surface.

viaduct: Any elevated roadway, especially a bridge of narrow arches of masonry, or reinforced concrete, supporting high piers which carry a roadway or railroad tracks over a ravine or gorge. In the United States, viaducts are sometimes of steel construction consisting of short spans carried on high steel towers.

vista: A view, especially one seen through a long narrow passage as between rows of houses facing on an avenue.

vitrified tile: In building construction, pipes made of clay, baked hard and then glazed, so they are impervious to water; used especially for underground drainage.

volute with easement: The spiral portion of a handrail which sometimes supplants a newel post in stair building. See Fig. 50.

voussoir: In architecture, any one of the wedge-shaped pieces, or stones, used in forming an arch. See Fig. 34. The middle one is called the *keystone*.

voussoir brick: Building brick made especially for constructing arches. Such brick are so formed that the face joints radiate from a common center.

V tooled joint: In masonry, a mortar joint formed with a special tool similar to that shown in Fig. 31. After excess mortar has been removed, the tool is run along the joint. See Fig. 32.

W

wainscot: The wooden lining of the lower part of an interior wall. Originally, only a superior quality of oak was used for this purpose, but now the term includes other materials.

wainscoting: The materials used in lining the interior of walls; also, the process of applying such materials to walls.

wainscoting cap: A molding at the top of a wainscoting.

waler: Timbers used in form construc-

tion to which the ties are fastened, or against which the end of the braces are butted; timbers used for holding forms in line. Same as *whaler*. See Fig. 56.

wall beam: In masonry, a metal member or type of anchor fastened to a floor joist to tie the wall firmly to the floor. The anchor extends into the masonry wall and, at the end of the anchor, there is some kind of bolt or wall hook, which may be either L-shaped or T-shaped, for holding the anchor in the wall.

wall bed: In building, any one of the various types of beds which fold or swing into a wall or closet when not in use. A type of bed commonly used where the conserving of space is important, such as in city apartment buildings.

wallboard: An artificially prepared sheet material, or board, used for covering walls and ceilings as a substitute for wooden boards or plaster. There are many different types of *wallboard* on the market.

wall coping: The covering course on top of a brick or stone wall; also referred to as capping. Where porches or other similar spaces are enclosed with solid walls to the height of the porch railing, the material which is used as a finish is called *coping*.

wall cornice: A kind of coping with a cornicelike finish at the top of a masonry wall; also, a finish for the top of a wall.

wall plates: Horizontal pieces of timber placed on the top of a brick or stone wall under the ends of girders, joists, and other timbers to distribute the weight of the load or pressure of the superstructure, especially the roof.

wall spacers: In concrete work, a type of tie for holding the forms in position while the concrete is being poured, and until it has set. For typical *wall spacers,* see Fig. 53.

wall tie: A device, in any of various shapes, formed of ¼″ diameter steel wire, the purpose of which is to bind together the tiers of a masonry wall, particularly those in hollow wall

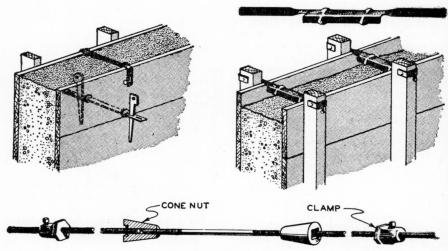

CONE NUT   CLAMP

Fig. 53. Wall Spacers

construction. See Fig. 36. Also, a contrivance, usually a metal strip, employed to attach or secure a brick veneer wall to a frame building.

wane: Bark, or lack of bark or wood, from any cause, on edge or corner of a piece of lumber.

warped: In woodworking, a term applied to any piece of timber which has been twisted out of shape and permanently distorted during the process of seasoning.

water bar: A strip of material inserted in a joint between wood and stone of a window sill, to prevent or bar the passage of water from rain or snow.

water joint: In stone work, a joint protected from rain and snow by sloping the surface of the stone away from the wall, so it will shed water easily.

water lime: A lime or cement which will harden under water; hydraulic cement.

waterproofing walls: In concrete work, the making of walls impervious to water, or dampness, by mixing a compound with concrete, or by applying a compound to the surface of the wall. A method of waterproofing the foundations of walls is shown in Fig. 54.

water putty: In woodworking, a powder which, when mixed with water, makes an excellent filler for cracks and nail holes. It is not suitable for glazing purposes.

water table: A ledge or slight projection of the masonry or wood construction on the outside of a foundation wall, or just above, to protect the foundation from rain by throwing the water away from the wall. See Figs. 9 and 55.

weatherboards: Boards shaped so as to be specially adaptable for overlapping at the joints to prevent rain or other moisture from passing through the wall. Also, called *siding*.

weathered: In masonry, stonework which has been cut with sloped surfaces so it will shed water from rain or snow. See *water joint*. In carpentry, a term applied to lumber which has been seasoned in the open air.

weathered joint: In masonry, a mortar joint formed as a plain cut joint, finished with the trowel after the mortar has slightly stiffened. A water-shedding, low-cost joint. See Fig. 32.

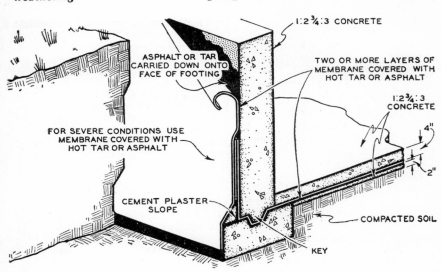

Fig. 54. Waterproofing Foundation

weathering: A slope given to the top of cornices, window sills, and various moldings to throw off rain water.

weather strip: A piece of metal, wood, or other material used to cover joints around doors and windows to prevent drafts, and to keep out rain and snow.

weather tiling: Tiles hung on battens to form a weatherproof covering for a vertical surface such as a wall. See *tile hanging.*

wellhole: An open space such as a shaft or well in a building, as for a staircase; also, the open space about which a circular stairs turns.

wet rot: A term used by woodworkers for decay of lumber or wood, due particularly to moisture and warmth.

whaler or waler: A horizontal bracing member used in form construction. Also known as a *ranger.* See Fig. 56.

white cement: When a white surface is required, a cement which has been specially burned to make it white is used. This cement has the same qualities as Portland cement.

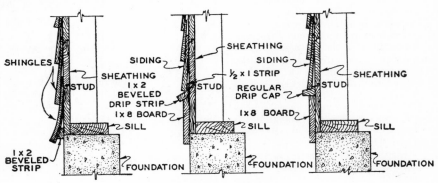

Fig. 55. Water Tables

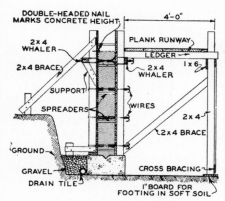

Fig. 56. Whaler or Waler

white oak: An American oak of the eastern part of the United States. It is the hardest of American oaks, characterized by its heavy, close grain. Used extensively where strength and durability are required.

wicket: A small door set within a larger door; also, a window or similar opening closed by a grating through which communication takes place, as a cashier's window.

winders: Treads of steps used in a winding staircase, or where stairs are carried around curves or angles. *Winders* are cut wider at one end than at the other so they can be arranged in a circular form.

winding stair: A circular staircase which changes directions by means of winders or a landing and winders. The wellhole is relatively wide and the balustrade follows the curve with only a newel post at the bottom.

windlass: A device for hoisting weights, consisting usually of a horizontal cylinder turned by a lever or crank. A cable, attached to the weight to be lifted, winds around the cylinder as the crank is turned, thus raising the load to whatever position is desired.

window: An opening in an outside wall, other than a door, which provides for natural light and ventilation. Such an opening is covered by transparent material inserted in a frame conveniently located for admitting sunlight and constructed so that it can be opened to admit air.

window head: In architecture, a term applied to the upper portion of a window frame.

window jack: A portable platform which fits over a window sill projecting outward beyond the sill; used principally by painters.

window seat: A seat built in the recess of a window, or in front of a window.

window wall: An outside wall, of which a large portion is glass. Glass area may consist of one or more windows. A window wall may be made up entirely of windows.

windshake: A defect in wood, so-called because of the belief that it is caused by wrenching of the growing tree by the wind. Since there is a separation of the annual rings from each other around the trunk of the tree, this defect is cuplike in appearance and is sometimes known as *cupshake*. See Fig. 57

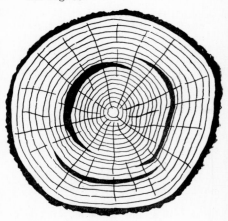

Fig. 57. Windshake

wing: In building, a term applied to a section, or addition, extending out from the main part of a structure.

wire-cut brick: Brick formed by forcing plastic clay through a rectangular opening designed for the purpose, and shaping clay into bars. Before burning, wires pressed through the plastic mass cut the bars into uniform brick lengths.

wire glass: In building construction, a type of window glass in which wire with a coarse mesh is embedded to prevent shattering of the glass in case it is broken; also, to protect a building against intruders. *Wire glass* is used principally in windows of buildings where valuables are kept, such as a United States mint; also used as a safety measure in case of fire.

wire ties: Short lengths of wire in various shapes and gauges for reinforcing the bond between two members. They may be embedded in mortar; nailed; twisted around and between masonry, wood, or metal. Wire ties are usually of cement-coated steel or galvanized metal.

withe: In architecture, a term applied to the portion between flues in the same chimney.

wood brick: A wooden block, the size and shape of a brick; built into brickwork to provide a hold for nailing finish material. A nailing block.

wood screws: Wood fasteners of various types and sizes, ranging from No. 0 to 30, and in length from ¼ inch to 6 inches. Length is measured from largest bearing diameter of head to the point of the screw. Threads extend for seven-tenths of the length, beginning at the point. Screws are made in oval-, round-, and flat-headed types, while gimlet points are standard.

wood turning: The process of shaping pieces of wood or blocks into various forms and fashions by means of a lathe.

woodwork: Interior fittings of wood, such as moldings and staircases; also, work done in or with wood, objects or parts made of wood.

working drawing: In architecture, a drawing or sketch which contains all dimensions and instructions necessary for carrying a job through to a successful completion.

wreath: The curved section of a stair rail, curved in both the vertical and horizontal planes; used to join the side of a newel post to the ascending run of the handrail.

wreath piece: In stair building, the curved section of the handrail string of a curved or winding stair. Any ornamental design intertwined into a circular form.

wrecking bar: A steel bar about ¾ of an inch in diameter and 24 to 30 inches in length, used for prying and pulling nails. One end of the bar is slightly bent with a chisel-shaped tip and the other end **U**-shaped with a claw tip for pulling nails.

wythe: In masonry, the partition wall between flues in the same chimney stack. Also spelled *withe*.

Y

year ring: One of the clearly defined rings in a cross section of a tree trunk, showing the amount of annual growth of the tree. Each ring represents one year of growth; also called *growth ring* and *annual ring*. The rings are made up of cells or tubes which convey sap through the tree. Year rings are shown in Fig. 2.

yoke: In architecture, a term applied to the horizontal top member of a window frame. See Fig. 20.

Z

Z bar: A heavy wire fabrication shaped in the form of the letter **Z**, usually about 4″ x 6″ in size. See Fig. 36. Such ties are used to bind together the two separate sections of a cavity wall, the ends of each tie being embedded in the horizontal mortar joint of both tiers at intervals of 24″.

zeprex: A lightweight mineral composed of siliceous material, cement, chemicals, and water; can be used for roof decking, walls, ceilings, and floors. Stronger than concrete of similar density, this material can be nailed, drilled, and hand-sawed. It is incombustible, termite proof, has minimum shrinkage and swelling, and high thermal insulation value.

zoning: A term applied to the division of a certain political subdivision into districts which may have different types of regulation. Such a condition is brought about by local ordinance under the police power of a state, granted by specific legislation commonly called an *enabling act*. Zoning laws pertain to the use of land in a particular area.

zonolite concrete: A form of concrete which acts as insulation; used as parts of floor slabs for houses without basements.

INDEX

BOOKS OF THE BUILDING TRADE SERIES

Published by the American Technical Society

DATE DUE